About the Author

Joe Average was born in County Antrim, Northern Ireland/North of Ireland. He has lived most of his life, through the troubles, and all of life's average, everyday problems and celebrations. He now lives in Scotland with his wife and daughters.

L of a Life

Joe Average

L of a Life

Olympia Publishers
London

www.olympiapublishers.com
OLYMPIA PAPERBACK EDITION

A CIP catalogue record for this title is
available from the British Library.

ISBN: 978-1-80074-966-5

.

First Published in 2023

Olympia Publishers
Tallis House
2 Tallis Street
London
EC4Y 0AB

Printed in Great Britain

Dedication

I dedicate this book to my most important thing in life – family. To those who brought me into this world and brought me up in it. To my ever-loved and loving wife, who has and continues to make my soul whole, and always will. Finally, to our beautiful, special daughters who make my world sing and dance, and who will forever be my sunshines, no matter what life's weather.

Acknowledgements

Just to thank the team at Olympia publishers for all their help and for taking a chance on a novice author like me.

Last Word

Sometimes people go straight to the last pages of a book, being too impatient, or too curious, or simply out of laziness, or trying to cheat. They want to see if the hero and heroine survive, with the added bonus of romance, or to make sure there is a happy ending, or to find out who the murderer was. Murders, many, many of them, are a morbid and brutal fact of life. As this book is about Joe Average's experiences of growing up mostly through Ulster's 'Troubles' and troubled peace, it means there are unavoidable references to smoking guns and bombs ending lives and killing hopes and dreams. These very sadly loom large in some of the following chapters, where no killer is ever found. Only killer puns, jokes and lines are the deadliest things you will find. Life and death go hand in hand; that is just the way things are. This book is not about the end, focusing on the everyday small and large adventures in the beginning and the middle. It does not focus on the last breath but instead on every breath we take to make us feel the joy of being alive.

This book is not some murder mystery, and Joe Average does not even try to be some moustached Belgian sleuth or tweed-wearing elderly lady detective. Sure, the book touches on death, but it is about life which, perhaps ironically, death is also part of, being the final chapter for every single one of us. That is in no way morbid, or depressing, just a basic fact. If anything, that should act as an inspiration to jump in at the deep end of all life's possibilities and opportunities, soaking and swimming for all we are worth, while we are here to make the most of it.

Joe Average does not even try to attempt to solve the eternal mystery of life, nor does he worry too much about death. He just tries to survive it and to lead as happy an average life he can. Whether he succeeds in achieving a happy ending is entirely your decision, so going to the end of the book will not help in any way. This is because, like life, it is all arbitrary, all conjecture; one person's junk is another person's treasure and so on.

Having the last word, where the foreword section should be, is just a way of looking at things a bit differently, and that is what this book is all about! How we all live our lives so personally. How each of our unique experiences, good and bad, shapes us, in our so-called, but not-so-ordinary lives. These all make us who we were in the past, are now and will be in the future. Not one of us knows when we will say our last words and what those might be. 'Bollocks', 'Not now!' or 'Is that it?' might spring to many peoples' minds! What about saying nothing and just sighing contentedly at a life well lived instead? Sure, every life is full of bollocks. Joe's is no exception, with him sometimes having to check he has not grown an extra testicle or two to accommodate all the bollocks in his life! These are all the things that cause stress, unhappiness and hurt. Joe does sometimes manage to cough at these, usually when his hands are full of the tiny, special memories that are so important to each of us. The ones that make us smile or laugh every time we think of them, even the times we balls up big-time. Joe eventually learns to appreciate these little life treasures, along with the big ones. These should be your last thoughts and words, shouldn't they? That is a happy ending, surely?

Everything ends and many times that is a blessing. Wars and pain all have a conclusion and sometimes death is the only, and sometimes welcome, escape. That is a rather sad but very real fact. Happiness is finite, too. Acceptance of this, as Joe discovers, is hard. He blames himself a lot, as we all do, overthinking what he could have done differently to have better, more positive outcomes for himself and his family. Those, to Joe, are never ending questions. However, as you will see from these brief and random snapshots of his life, no matter how much he mentally tears himself to pieces he can never change what has gone before. What happened yesterday, last week, last year, last decade are all concreted in the past, that no amount of chipping at will hammer out or bolster any change.

The chances of Joe's life, depicted in these chapters, being used as a history textbook are as remote as the furthest star in the sky. At best it will only ever achieve a miniscule footnote in the grand scheme of things. Joe's entire life will probably be the same, just another name with statistics on government paperwork or a genealogy website. Fame is not his aim. He has no ambition to be some great leader, promising and often failing to take humankind to some real or imaginary utopia. He feels he cannot shape the messed-up national or global politics and economics that make society as unfair as it is. He can, however, and does, change things – sometimes for the better, sometimes not – in his own life and for those close to him. These are what make him who he is, in his own average way, and they do alter the course of his and others' lives. He, as we all do, often forgets to allow some pride and back-slapping for those achievements.

There are races in life when it is actually fantastic to finish last, but most of the time being in the middle is the best place to be. Joe often feels hindered and frustrated by being average by name. He realises he is often average by nature too. At times that truly annoys and drags him down to places which are the last places he wants to go. Life's rollercoaster never stays for long down in such dips, nor on the slow, reluctant climb up to scary heights. There are the terrifying, in a good way, thrills of the freefall feelings that Joe only feels partly, mostly not at all, in control of. These are the moments when life is experienced to the full. Then, they are over all too briefly, leaving hearts still racing and the squeals of delight only as recent memories. Then the climb of uncertainty begins again from the low point, none of us knowing when the ride of a lifetime will come to an end.

I sincerely hope you enjoy this book. You may not, and probably will not, agree with the views and opinions shared in this book, which is great! We are all entitled to and should have our personal viewpoints and stances, after all. The opinions, attitudes and decisions Joe has and makes are based on his life experiences, gut reactions, emotional responses and everything else that influences us all. Sometimes he gets things right, but, not surprisingly, things go wrong as well. Sometimes it is his fault, sometimes not, sometimes it is just luck, fate, divine will or whatever you wish to call it, and sometimes just being in the right or wrong place at the right or wrong time. It is written simply to make us all think about real life issues, even the so called 'normal' (whatever that is?) ones, to form our own opinions and, ultimately, focus on what matters in our own life. These are the important things that should never be taken for granted. These things are never average but especially personal.

It has been fun to write this series of books, and who knows where Joe's twisty and turny, but average, mayhem of a life will go. Please enjoy reading it, and thank you. If there is one thing to take away from these chapters, it is to encourage you and us all to please just keep living an ordinary life; it is much more exciting than you realise.

Late

"It's not a bus timetable!" she mock-scolded with a smile on her tea-wet lips. He nodded with an acknowledging look that only partially hid his frustration, twirling his mug of lukewarm tea on the table in front of him. Looking up into her bright blue but tired eyes, he slowly reached across and gently grasped her delicate hand, completely engulfing it in his large, calloused palm. Her eyes held his stare as she gently shrugged her shoulders. "Nature has its own timetable and we just have to go with it!" she continued smiling meekly.

"Yeah, but Joanne was early! I thought wee Joseph would be early, too! Averages are always good timekeepers," he answered, his face betraying that being an Average and being on time were not, in fact, one and the same thing. She knew that too well and let out a little laugh.

"So, you're sure it's a boy, then?" she teased tentatively.

"Definitely! Has to be! No doubt about it! I just know it is!" he stated with over-confidence. His bright-eyed, broad-smiling face, he knew, did not provide the complete mask of definitive belief he hoped for.

"But what if it is not? What if it is another daughter? Would you be disappointed?" she questioned quietly. There was seriousness in her voice that revealed a not-so-well-hidden and genuine concern. Her lips moved again, as if to speak, but she did not dare mention that he had said almost the exact same words before Joanne became their firstborn. That would have probably been too much of a challenge for him to cope with. It would remind him of his failure to predict before, which he could take as a snipe at his credibility. She left all that unsaid and still contained within her, dashing about between her emotions, not being sure which one this affected the most.

"Don't be daft, woman!" he replied dismissively, a flash of regret at possibly rudeness in his tone passing across his anxious face. "I would love her just the same as Joanne. Maybe even more, if she sleeps better and has less teething problems?" He laughed once at that. She took her hand out from under his and slapped the back of it in jest, before returning it to the warmth underneath his. He snorted another laugh. "Seriously, as long as you and our wee baby is healthy, when it does eventually decide to arrive, that is all that matters to me."

His eyes were fixed on hers, providing the reassurance both he and she needed. He felt relieved that he had managed to hide his deepest wish that it was a son. He had to do that a lot in the many conversations they had, discussing these same possible scenarios. Realistically, he had absolutely no say in the outcome and truthfully admitted he, with frustrating reluctance, would gratefully accept whatever they were blessed with. He could still wish and hope, though!

They both went silent, paused and looked towards the stairs in the hallway. They had heard a garbled murmur and shuffling coming from upstairs in the silent stillness of the house. Joanne must have been dreaming and rustling about in her cot. Her bedroom door was wide open so any noise travelled easily down to their ears. She had already started to attempt a few escape bids, but her legs were still a little too short and her arms not strong enough yet to pull her up and out. Both knew it would not be long before that would be another parenting hurdle they would have to deal with. Joanne would eventually and successfully jump the bars of her comfy cage. A welcome silence returned and they looked at each other again.

"How much longer do we have to wait before they will tell you to go to the hospital?" he asked with a tinge of frustration. "I have a big job on for the next wheen of days. There's a pile to do and they are really busting our balls to get it done quick. The boss knows you are almost due, but he is a bit funny about me needing to take a day off to take you to the hospital. He really pisses me off, when he talks to me. The other lads on site think the same. He talks like he is God Almighty himself! I have been really close a few times to telling him to stick it up his arse, if it was long enough!" A flash of anger crossed his face as he spoke.

"Joseph!" she tutted, half serious, half in jest. "Don't be so crude! Not in front of the baby!" She patted her expanded belly with her free hand before reaching across and gripping his hand hard on the table with both of hers. "Don't do anything to upset yer man. Please don't do or say anything risky. Please! We really, really need the money. Especially now with this wee one on the way!" Her eyes grew wider as she spoke, tugging at his parental responsibility heartstrings so much that he could only look into her eyes for a short time.

"Nah! Nah! Don't worry. He is a first-class prick, though!... But I know." He grinned, slightly reluctantly. "I know!" he added quietly for reinforcement, and again averted his gaze from her almost begging eyes. He looked back at her. "It's just tough going. That one really needs to be told a few home truths to bring him back into the real world! He has all of us running about like headless chickens trying to get the work done. All of us are getting seriously fucked off with him..." He stopped as she held his hand tighter to squeeze the neck of his bottled anger. She gave an understanding look that reminded him gently of there being no need for bad language. He sighed deeply then carried on. "It's just... It's just we are flat out at work, and I am sick of being late home. Especially now it is so close to seeing wee Joseph." She saw the hurt and frustration in his eyes, smiled gently but remained silent.

She shuffled on the creaky kitchen chair, something she was doing more and more often, no matter how she sat, to try to ease the discomfort. Her lips parted into a broad grin. "So, if, and I mean if, it is a boy, we are calling him Joseph, then?" she asked with a teasing look on her face. He nodded vigorously. "No other names then?" she added cockily.

He stared at her, perplexed, wondering how serious she was. "I am Joseph. My da was Joseph and his da before him. So, it has to be Joseph. He can call himself Joe, or Joey, even J if he wants, but it will be Joseph on his birth certificate. He can, as we agreed before, have any middle name you want, but he will be another Joseph Average." He nodded seriously, knowing she was mocking him, having had this conversation many times before.

"So, what about middle names, then? What do you think he should have?" she said, waiting to see what he said before she forwarded her wish again, to make sure it was agreed. She was planting the same seed she had done numerous times before, trying to make sure she knew what would grow. He shrugged his shoulders and pouted as if that was not important at all, slightly annoyed at ploughing this same field again and knowing what would be harvested.

"I really like the name Oliver," she uttered again firmly and hopefully, as she had done before.

His eyes flicked around their small kitchen, to make it appear as if he was giving this some thought. "Yeah, that would do!" he answered, knowing he had given his approval before and irked at having to do it again.

"That would do!" she said with a little anger in her voice that he was not sure was real or not. "A name is a really important decision!"

His brow furrowed, thinking he should have phrased that better. "Yeah! Yeah! I really do still like Oliver as his middle name." He lifted his mug and drained the last of the now cold tea, coughing slightly as it trickled down his throat.

"That's good," she said, "as I really like it, too." She reached over, lifted her empty cup and set it back down again. "And when our daughter arrives…" she paused and stared at him smugly.

He glared jokingly back, his mind saying *please don't go there,* but his words came out, "If! And it is a big if! If it is a wee girl we will decide when we have a look at her."

"You cannot just leave it until the baby arrives to decide that!" she scolded with sincerity.

"Loads of people do!" he replied matter-of-factly.

"But we have to have some ideas. Some options, at least!" she continued scolding, showing annoyance.

"Okay!" he sighed, yet again having this same conversation. "But we already have our shortlist."

"It's not really a 'short' list, is it?" she answered abruptly. She reached into the small, disorganised pile of papers in the middle of the table, between the salt cellar and brown sauce bottle. An old, opened and written-on envelope was tugged out. She laid it flat on the table and began smoothing it out one-handed, like it was some precious ancient scroll. He let out a long sigh, *not again!* flashing across his mind. She sensed this from him but remained silent.

He placed his large hand over the paper, his other squeezing her hand. "Look! We have this list. Any one of these names would suit our wee daughter. But you are carrying our son. I just know you are. I have had dreams that it will be a boy. I had one last night…"

"That means you will be disappointed if it is a girl!" she interrupted, her voice stressing 'will' as much as she was stressing, her bubbling frustration having now boiled over a little.

"Nah! Nah! I have already said I would love her as much as you and Joanne. I just know it's a boy. I just know it is," he stated quietly and lightly to take away the tension thickening the air. Having said it, he knew how pathetic his boy-belief sounded, but he was just being honest about his feelings.

"But it is still a fifty-fifty chance. In fact, because we have already had Joanne, it means the chances of having a girl are probably higher," she responded, a little shocked at his face's inability to hide his lack of comprehension of the reality of that fact. He took his hand away from hers and rubbed it through his thick, still cement-dusty hair. This was an attempt to provide him with a moment to think how to ease the building agitation. They had been through this before, several times. Too many times! Perhaps he was deluding himself, he had to confess. He was scared to stop thinking it was a boy, just in case even the smallest particle of doubt in his mind would mean it did not happen.

She sighed and shuffled again in her hard seat. Moving her hips again, she felt the discomfort increase. Heartburn rose and burned hotly in the back of her throat. She tried to dismiss this as a response to having this stressful conversation, yet again. More stomach acid rose up, coming onto the back of her tongue and stinging slightly as she swallowed. She moved yet again in her seat and found no relief. Rising up from the table, she stepped left and right, hands on her hips and realising that she was breathing fast and deep. A little, sharp pain shot across her stomach. This had happened before, and was happening more and more over the past days, so she ignored it. Another one quickly followed and she walked back and forth some more, waiting for it to pass. He just sat there watching her, concern growing on his expression. Another elephant-sized suck in of air did nothing to ease the strange feelings spiralling across her expanded trunk.

She shot a glance of worry towards him. He jumped up immediately, but just stood statue-like, waiting on instructions from her. Breathing hard again, as more indescribable soreness surged across her body, her slightly fearful eyes met the growing concern in his. He looked intently at her, wishing, willing and wanting her to say something, to tell him what to do or say as his mind was completely blank. The awkward, fearfully expectant silence continued for a few seconds more. Then it was over.

She stood up straight, relief coursing over her body. The discomfort was gone as quickly as it had arrived. The heartburn was gone. The tension between them was gone. With a small laugh she returned to her seat, lifted her empty cup and set it back down again. He sat down suddenly as well, arms resting on the table, hands gripped together tightly, and confusion all over his face.

"I think we need to wait another wee while yet," was all she said, tittering with small laughs. He nodded, a little disappointed, caught up in a flurry of his own thoughts. A little cry came down the stairs, followed quickly by a louder one. He rose slowly from his seat, stepped over to her and kissed her on the cheek. He touched her stomach tenderly and looked deep into her eyes with kindness. Turning towards the kitchen door, he strode over and up the stairs as loud wailing began.

She rose, cup in hand and moved tentatively towards the kettle. A huge spasm of pain shot across her stomach and she white knuckle-gripped the edge of the wooden cabinet. She immediately guldered, "Joseph!" This knocked him off his stride. He half-fell on the stairs, missing a step, and looked anxiously through the stair railings towards her.

"Which Joseph are you shouting at?" he asked, rubbing his knee as the crying from the cot increased in its heart-wrenching volume.

"Both," she answered cryptically and urgently.

Language

I could not say it, like the many, many, many other ones. I could not transfer things from my brain to make understandable sounds from my mouth. The words may not have been coming but all I was thinking, more and more, was how absolutely scunnered I was becoming with all this. I wanted to shout that out loud but only incomprehensible, to my parents, wails came when I tried. Yet I could not escape it. It was constant, or rather, she was constantly persistent in doing it. When I tried to wander off to do something, anything else, as an escape from it, she stopped me, picking me up and setting me back down beside her again. When I became bored and distracted, she gently prodded me to bring my attention back to her face. That face was so special to me but was becoming tarnished as I associated it more and more with forcing my speaking. If I could only speak my mind perhaps she would understand. Despite her excellent acting, I knew the still mostly gurgles and squeals I was only able to make did not have any subtitles to help her know what I meant.

I was allowed to bang my little red tractors about on the floor during these sessions but still had to keep my attention on her. Being with her, staring at her, cuddling her were what I loved doing and always had, as long as I could remember and even long before. I knew instinctively I always would. Now, though, from all this bombardment of vocabulary, even these pleasurable experiences were becoming sullied by these consistent attempts at making me repeat, and repeat, and repeat what was coming out of her ever-smiling mouth. Again and again and again she would say the same thing, alternating between slowly pronouncing every syllable and then quickly, as an example of the final version of what she wanted me to achieve. She did not seem to realise that what she was achieving was creating a level of annoyance within me I could not find the words to describe.

"Good boy!" she repeated so often it lost its proud praise intention. I tried to copy uttering this, trying to end the monotony of this increasingly boring game. So far I only had achieved 'guh buh!', yet still she encouragingly said it as my reward. Thus far these two words had been my only payment for when I worked and made the effort to mimic her. Maybe she was saving other incentives for later on when I did really word well, I hopefully thought, but was beginning to doubt this. She may have stopped me monkeying around, but when I made such aping attempts the, whether real or pretence, happiness expressed on her face moved up a notch. Her eyes twinkled even more and the look in those loving eyes and smile-curled mouth bordered on looking a bit manic with delight. It was this prize that motivated me more. When I heard her and Dada saying, 'good boy!' to old Rex the dog, this reduced the feel-good factor rewarding of these two words in me considerably more.

At times I regretted starting this whole thing off. Or was it me who really had or not? Maybe it was just my misunderstanding of what I had been asked to do. Mama and Dada were playing a game, or so I thought, with me at the centre of it. Mama would, along with all the other words she spoke to me in our, as of then, one-way conversations, always include a little round of 'Mama. Mama. Mama…' Although I had absolutely no idea how to count, she would say this one word a dozen or more times in quick succession. Conversations with Dada were likewise one way, with him saying the words and me responding to him. My replies were the same as for Mama. To them, for the time being, at least, all they heard were incoherent noises, which sometimes had spittle flying out of my mouth.

Dada's words, although being no mathematician at fourteen months old, were probably only half or even a quarter of Mama's. Dada was much more into wrestling about, throwing me in the air and making the same 'brrmm brrmm' noises I made as we drove my two hand-me-down, battered toy tractors around and around on the faded, green carpet. He was not there most of the time, away at a thing called 'work', which I still could not say and did not like the sound of. When he was at home, he too would include a session of reciting, "Dada. Dada. Dada…" almost as many times as Mama repeated 'Mama' to me. I vividly remember the look on work-weary, home-coming Dada's face when he was pounced on by an over-excited Mama to tell him what I had done. She actually squealed to him that I had for the first time clearly said 'Mama'. He beamed with pride as he lifted and hugged me, but I could see specks of disappointment in his tired eyes.

I had just said 'Mama' to her as a last resort, really, an attempt to stop her being stuck on that same record that was needling me more and more. I was with her an awful lot more than Dada, which had meant the ever-recurring 'Mama' increased the only awful part of being with her. This was probably the reason I wanted to end her sustained attrition sooner than Dada's, as it was wearing me down. Yet I remember feeling a strange little sadness for him as it was clear Mama had won their game. Dada had still smiled when he begrudgingly and briefly congratulated Mama, saying then how she had won the same game with my older sister Joanne, or 'Ohhahh', as I called her. I remember Mama looking a little shocked when Dada said, in a minutely-barbed, joking way, "Maybe I will have better luck with the next one!" My clearly saying 'Dada' to him a day or two later, when we were on our own, was rewarded with a happy and excited tossing me about in the air. Dada proudly told Mama when she came back into the room. Perhaps that made their little game a draw instead, which made me happy for a reason I could not explain.

That was the turning point. After my saying 'Mama' and 'Dada', both of them, but Mama especially, pressed the 'on' button for making me repeat more words. She had left it on ever since. I could not even find it, to turn it off or even twiddle its intensity down a bit, to provide some rest from its incessant constancy. Even in my sleep, my brain still was chanting words. The old system had worked so well, I thought, where I just pointed at, or reached for, or made my own unique noise associated with certain things. Mama, Dada and even Ohhahh and Nan knew what I meant. Mama had obviously decided that was no longer good enough. Now, I was reluctantly being forced to understand; I had to call things by the same name as everyone else. I was not given a reason why, which irked me slightly. *What about individuality and not having to conform?* I asked in my thoughts. I could have argued this point if I had been sharp enough to find the right words.

Time with Mama became like a mantra of attempts to memorise shopping lists, as things were pointed at or shown to me with me supposed to repeat what she had said. As I began, over the next while, to comply, the correct sounds began to come. It never ended, though! Once I mastered speaking the name of one thing, then another and another, more and more and more names were verbally berated at me. No matter how many words I seemed to formulate and get right, more came. I began to wonder if this would ever end. How many words were there? I knew I could not count at all, but wondered if I could ever count that far.

Although no wordsmith and my mood blackening at times, I steelily forged ahead and added almost daily to endlessly hammering out naming lists. Being a little older meant I was even starting to put two words together, rather than just saying the same ones on their own. One day, however, I made an unexpected discovery. After all those previous months of persistently having to say words, I found out that there were words Mama and Dada did not want me to say.

Two of our teenage cousins came to visit with their mama and dada. Their mama and dada were crowded in the kitchen, with my mama and dada. My exuberant sister Joanne was in there too, all of them gathered around at the dinner table. She was opening her two-days-late birthday present she had just been gifted with by our kind but disorganised uncle and aunt. I was in the living room with my two tractors as usual. The two large lads I was related to knelt beside me messing about with the few plastic farm animals I had, putting bulls on their hind legs and cows underneath. I could not understand why they chuckled. Immediately on their arrival, they could not have avoided overhearing Mama's excited telling of how good I was getting at talking now, poking and goading me tenderly until I forced a few names of things out of my mouth. Our uncle and aunt genuinely showed, or feigned really well, their amazement at my new abilities. They congratulated me with 'he's a big boy now' and similar comments after my performance as they were warmly welcomed over our threshold.

As my cousins quickly became bored with my limited and childish toys, they decided that they too would help with my words. "Joe!" they said quietly to get my attention, which they did as we squatted on the floor. I looked up at them a little unsure. I would have described it as apprehensively if I had known that big word. "Joe!" one said quietly again to make sure I was listening, which I was. "Can you say, 'shit'?"

I stared and frowned a little as I could not remember if I had heard this word before or not. They repeated the 's' word on its own, individually and then in unison in hushed voices. As my brain processed this, I recollected Mama saying this word before when the oven had started smoking, and when she had dropped a plate onto the tiled floor, and when she had opened letters sometimes. Dada had said it too, I thought I remembered, but could not place when. He preferred a word with an 'f' sound when he was cross, surprised or in pain. What I did remember was after either of the 's' or 'f' words had been said, Mama and Dada had both talked to me a lot more about random things. They knew they could not bring the words back into their mouths. Their tactic was to try to fill my head with so many other words that the ones they had just said would be forgotten. The fact that I remembered them proved that theory wrong.

"Shit! Joe! Can you say 'shit'!" they repeated again softly as they both started sniggering more. I sat quietly and did not say anything at all. "Oh, come on, Joe! You can do it. Say it, Joe. Shit! Say 'shit', Joe." I started to feel a little anxious, not entirely sure why, but this did not feel right, somehow. They were forcing me to do something that I could sense they both knew was wrong. I remained quiet, just staring up at them with a toy tractor in each hand. This must have frustrated the both of them as they became more insistent, their voices becoming a little louder as their annoyance grew. As they were not going to stop, I decided to give it a try. Just as I had started with 'Sss…' a big scuffle and furore happened before me in our living room.

All four grownups had just come in from the kitchen to where we were, Joanne following close behind holding her new plastic doll by its short, blonde hair. The two lads, sat either side of me, had not noticed as the parents briefly loomed like storm clouds over them. They had been too set on, now a little loudly, repeating and badgering me with this 's' word. They most definitely were made very aware when their Dada, like lightning, smacked them both around the head, raining down on them with the palm of his hand several times. He let fly with a whole flock of words that appeared to hurt the lads almost as much as the slaps. Somewhat ironically, I was sure I heard a few 's' and 'f' words mixed in with the angry tirade. Then he slapped them some more around their shoulders as the lads rapidly rose to their feet to try to escape, holding their hands and forearms up before them ineffectively defensively. The lads' Mama was busy machine gunning 'sorry', 'I'm so embarrassed', 'I can't believe it' in a verbal loop to my Mama and Dada. This seemed to be doing absolutely nothing to either ease her embarrassment or quell the rising anger in both my parents.

The lads' Dada turned to my Dada with a face so black and fiery it should have been in the fireplace. All he said was, "I am sorry about this, Joseph, but I will sort these two out when we get home. I'll talk to you later. Come on, let's go!" With that, all four of our visitors moved swiftly towards the living room door.

After my startled shock at what happened before me, I said no words beyond starting to wail. I felt so scared. Dada picked me up with his big hard hands in one gentle, smooth motion, pulling me close to his chest. My wailing instantly stopped in such a safe place. Dada just stood where he was in the living room, glaring sternly at the departing, almost fleeing, family of four. Mama was following them silently, almost shooing them out the door like they were an unwanted neighbour's cat that had suddenly turned up in the house. The lads were out the door first, shoved and thumped by their Dada as they went. The lads' Mama's head was turning round and round, back and forth, still babbling ignored apologies, as Mama determinedly marched behind them all. As the still-grovelling woman was on the front step, Mama slammed the door and stormed back into the living room.

Mama began a long rant as Dada placed me speechlessly back down on the faded green carpet, placing my tractors in my hands. I only held them and did not play, too intent in watching my parents after these strange events. Dada sat down on his armchair, as Mama sat edgily on the edge of the sofa, continuing to vent her rage. Dada just sat absorbing what she said, nodding in agreement, but he was obviously noiselessly thinking his own thoughts as Mama verbally conveyed hers. I was confused, thinking I had done something wrong and hoping I was not going to be smacked like the two lads had been. I rose and waddled over beside Mama's knee. She stopped speaking, lifted one of her clasped hands from her lap and placed it tenderly on my hair, rubbing my scalp gently.

"Don't you worry, Joe. Those were being bad boys. You, Joe, are a good boy. Yer Da and me want to keep you that way!" She went silent. Then, for whatever reason, added sadly, "As long as we possibly can, anyway." Just as Dada was about to speak, seizing the speech opening opportunity, Joanne walked over to him, still holding her new dolly by the hair. She jumped up into Dada's lap and he slung his arm around her, snuggling her in.

"When will I be old enough to be allowed to say 'shit'?" Joanne asked innocently. Dada gave Mama a stare. As I tennis-looked, alternating between my parents' faces to try to figure out what was going on, I thought it was a very good question. Neither Mama nor Dada seemed to have the answer at that moment. Maybe I would ask them, I decided, when I mastered what I wanted to say. I started saying, "Ssss…"

Mama and Dada glared at me open-mouthed, Dada receiving a silent hot death stare from Mama, words failing her, as Dada failed to hold in a laughter snort that I sensed spoke volumes.

Lampposts

Neither were in the middle, but both were the centre of attention in their own way. Each was a focal point for all the activity that went on, amidst the concrete block wall surrounded tarmac out front of the massive old building. The squealy gate, with its multiple layers of peeling paint, marked the half-way point along the front wall between the two of them. These steel grey lampposts stood rooted in their concrete blocks against the bland, grey walls at either end of the small playground. Both were used as the starting or meeting point for all the games, fights and just hanging about that happened before school started, and at break-time and lunch. Neither seemed offended, at the end of the school day, by being totally ignored when the bell sounded. At that time, home was a bigger beacon for the escapee youngsters than any attractive light either lamppost could provide. Both tall playground guardians silently accepted that fact. They accepted everything that happened around and to them in the same motionless, silent way. They never judged, never complained, never scolded... These characteristics and more were probably what made them such metal magnets for the school kids.

It was a small country school. Local famers' offspring went there, generation after generation, bringing the baggage of enduring family feuds with them in their hearts and heads, alongside the books and pencils in their satchels. These boys and girls mixed with those of the two nearby clusters of houses that possibly might have grown up to be villages someday. Numbers varied from a low of twenty-seven to a maximum of thirty-eight one year. The cloud of closure had hung over it for years. Gloomy, remote bureaucrats in the Education Department caused the occasional overcast parents' and teachers' moods, threatening the thunderstorm of closure. The Headmaster and Mrs Shortt were well-prepared weather forecasters. They equipped themselves and fought hard and passionately against these recurring storms. Both were able to deflect the rain of statistics and accounting, with their own umbrellas of community that meant so much more than just numbers on spreadsheets. Although the sun was not shining brightly when young Joe Average started his learning life there, enough heat and light remained to keep life in the big old building for a while yet. Or so it was hoped. All of that was not the primary concern of the pupils as they were pumped with facts and figures inside, and spilt blood from grazed knees on the tarmacked outside of this historic heart that was loved in the local area.

The rules in the classroom were strict, giving the school an impressive school role model reputation amongst parents and, equally as impressive, dread amongst those actually on the roll there. Those children who were not on the school's line or had moved off it were quickly brought back to towing it by the authoritative power of the two teachers: the Headmaster from P4 to P7 and Mrs Shortt P1 to P3. Although old in the pupils' eyes, neither teacher could be described as in any way ropey. They certainly would never be strung along by any of those in their classrooms telling winding tales for misdemeanours or forging a parent's signature with stringy counterfeit copperplate calligraphy. However, once out of the school's heavy front doors into the playground, technically those school rules still applied, but there was much more room for ignoring or bending.

Although a vegetation-free zone, apart from some intrepid and strong dandelions and grass tussocks sprouting randomly across it, the carnivorous laws of the jungle were adhered to outside at break and after lunch. Eat or be eaten certainly applied in the playground as much as in the room that served up the usually unexciting school dinners. Or perhaps it would be more apt to describe the small play area like an open, although more tarmac black than the brown-grassed African savannah. The big elephant P7s were the undisputed rulers, some straight and well measured, some not.

One of these eleven-year-old bulls used his sheer size to tusk away at the other inhabitants, several being regular victims but all being reminded occasionally who they should treat as their lord. That was until the lionised Mrs Shortt or the Headmaster roared at him, letting him know who the real King and Queen of Beasts in this land were. The zebras and wildebeest P6s and P5s seemed to always be together, mixing easily and coming up with gnu games, no one had played before. The P4s and P3s were like the gazelles and impalas. They were constantly so full of energy it drove their parents up the walls. Sometimes, it could be thought these ever-bouncing young ones would be able to jump higher than the school. They could if they had tried, as the sound foundations of the old building meant it could not jump at all! There were the over-excited warthog P2s too, scampering and squealing constantly here and there, playing games that only they seemed to know the rules of, if any existed. Finally, the shy little dik dik-like P1s, nervously tried to find elusive cover, or seek protection from their rebuffing older siblings. This was all the mayhem that made up a typical playtime.

Joe loved playtime, most of the time. He found it strange, though, that the boys and girls tended to split up a lot of the time. The lampposts were equally split, the western one being the girl's headquarters, the eastern one the boys. No one knew why that was the way it was. It had simply been passed on from primary school class to primary school class, probably since the lampposts were erected, and no one questioned this tradition. Despite such a small number of schoolkids in total, they still split into girls' games and boys' games a lot of the time. However, at least once a school day, all of the boys and girls, from all of the classes, would have a huge game together. 'Stick-in-the-mud' was very popular – tagged kids having to remain motionless until they were touched to be released by someone who was not a chaser. Other times it was a free-for-all game of 'Tag'. This often descended into something more resembling dodgem cars at the funfair with collisions, intentional and accidental, happening often. At such times, the small playground seemed even smaller, unable to cope with so many bodies moving so fast within the walled confines. After the strike rate and crying body count reached a certain point, either the kids themselves or usually the teacher supervising having ran out of tissues to hand out, a halt would be called to the frenzied running around.

One time, and only once, they all played what they called 'Bulldogs' for whatever reason. Joe found it quite weird how kids' games had strange, seemingly totally unrelated names sometimes. Every school seemed to have its unique names for similar games. Anyway, 'Bulldogs' basically involved all the kids lining up along the wall at one lamppost. That was except for the two nominated or volunteering catchers. They stood in the middle of the playground using the paint peeling gate as a guide. The purpose of the game was to run to touch the other lamppost and wall on the other side without being caught by a tagging catcher. These were simple rules that all the age range could understand so, in theory, should have worked out to be lots of fun. Even Mrs Shortt seemed to approve. That changed very quickly ten minutes later.

It all started so well. Joe was in P4 now and, although not a very fast runner like some of his classmates, was usually good at juking and turning quickly to avoid being caught. Joe, like the others, was quite excited about trying out this game that they had not played before. Unsurprisingly, one of the P5 gnus had come up with it. Joe, like the rest, stood with one foot and one hand touching the wall, a few others having to have this starting position reinforced. There was one P6 girl and one P7 boy in the middle as catchers. It was Bull Boy from P7 who had volunteered as a catcher. As would be found out, more concern about this should have been raised at the time. However, all the kids had been too busy organising themselves and hyping up their excitement to think this through. Even Mrs Shortt had not questioned this.

Bull Boy catcher shouted, "Go!"

With rapid running and shouts, this tide of mixed-size bodies flowed towards the two larger bodies in the middle. As it approached the two catchers, this moving sea split in two, half going towards the outer wall at the roadside, the other half towards the side of the school building. One catcher moved left, the other right, eyeing up targets amongst the funnelling, speeding youngsters. The more the catchers approached the tighter these two targeted escape points, at the outside wall and at the school building, became. Then the faster, perhaps smarter kids, cut inside and ran up the now open middle, joyfully running through to touch the other lamppost on the other side. Joe copied these tactics and made it through the middle, jumping happily with the others that had made it untouched.

However, most carried on into the bottleneck at each side. As could have been predicted, elbows were scuffed against roughcast walls, and legs and arms became entangled. The catchers tagged one each side, then succeeded in tagging three more who had fallen together in a knot of limbs. The other kids who had made it through looked back but remained beside the safety of the lamppost and wall den, not offering help in case they were caught too. Besides, they did not need to do anything as Mrs Shortt had quickly arrived and untangled them all. She assessed all three of the tumblers, straightening them up, wiping away tears, checking that there were no cuts, then kindly ordered them to carry on playing. No one disobeyed Mrs Shortt, even parents, so all three wiped away any still-existing snot from their noses, rubbed their bruised knees and, rather downcast, took up position in the centre with the other two original self-congratulating catchers.

Joe looked at the much more formidable row of catchers now. They spread out across the width of the playground. To Joe this looked as intimidating as the pictures of those men in balaclavas, he saw painted on murals, on TV and sometimes in real life. Still, he readied himself, physically assuming the start position and mentally planning in his head a route through this open wall of bodies ahead of him. With a bugle-like 'go' from the P6 girl catcher this time, a charge the Light Brigade would have been proud of ensued. That was an apt description, as the results in that playground were about to have an even higher casualty rate, although, amazingly, no fatalities!

There was no split in the tide this time, all the runners gathering into several small clusters as they tentatively approached the catchers. They were not so fast this time, running then stopping, jigging left and right, trying to distract the catchers, looking for and trying to create openings. One P6 boy ducked under P6 Andy's flailing hands. The Andy catcher shouted loudly that he had tagged the P6 runner. The P6 runner vehemently disagreed and turned sharply, and Andy the catcher, without a doubt, caught a left hook to the face. Andy fell to the ground, ending that debate so suddenly that Mrs Shortt had not seen it. Meantime, a catcher and three others had ended up in a crumpled pile at the wall. The catcher had simply bulldozed the other three but had overshot. She collided with the solid wall herself, making no demolition impact on it, only on herself. This turned it into a wailing wall that was no Jerusalem for any of those involved. Another P5 lad went belly surfing for a surprising distance along the tarmac, having been tripped whilst running full pelt. He stood up, his jumper in more shreds than it originally had been. He raced over and began punching away at the boy attached to the leg that had caused his fall. Mrs Shortt broke this up quickly then scurried hither and thither, sorting out other confrontations in turn.

Nor were the girls very ladylike either. Most, even the shyer ones, seemed to have become possessed by the Celtic warrior spirits of their ancestors. Their screams would have deafened dogs as they tore at each other. In two cases, this applied quite literally as dresses were grabbed and ripped, causing tears that resulted in huge amounts of tears. Two girls began hitting at each other too. This was, as in international politics, after negotiations over having been caught or not had failed, and violence was resorted to between the two involved parties. Three P1s saw what was going on and decided they wanted no more of it. They ran back to the starting point lamppost and huddled around nervously, hoping for its ever-silent protection.

Then there was Joe. He had his spirits and blood up to such an extent he could take on anything. Or so he thought. As he began to run forward, straight ahead of him was the P7 Bull Boy. That did not daunt him too much. Joe had a plan to juke and jive, beginning to dance repeatedly as he neared the large, almost stationary lad determined to beat him. Joe feigned a left, then quickly went right. There he was stopped right in his tracks by a thrust-out right forearm. Bull Boy shot out his arm like a clotheslining professional wrestler. It caught Joe just under the chin. Joe's head remained where it was, as the rest of his body carried on with its forward momentum. In a split second, his toes were almost at the same level as his eyes, before gravity took effect and his whole body splatted onto the tarmac. Joe felt the back of his head bounce painfully off the ground. He felt his shoulder blades and hips hit hard as well. His open hands landed too, with Joe feeling little shards of black stone cutting into them with the force of his fall.

As he lay there flat on his growing-in-pain back, Joe looked up through his swirling, star-filled eyes. He saw the bent head of the lamppost with its bulb alight even though it was daylight. It seemed to be flashing, sending a message somehow. Joe blinked hard, again and again, ignoring Bull Boy loudly and sarcastically saying, "You're caught!" There seemed to be an aura around that lamp in the sky. As the pain spread through his body, Joe felt calmed by this radiating light. It was mesmerizing and thankfully distracted him from the pain, for a little while. He could feel a hot bulge begin at the back of his skull that was almost soothing. Then everything went black.

Joe awoke, probably seconds later, to Mrs Scott leaning over him and fussing anxiously. He felt the cold cloth she was gently holding at the back of his slightly-raised head in her slightly-trembling hands. He could not figure out if this was the cause or if it was the hard, cool tarmac that had shivering chills rushing through him. There were other distorted, peering faces on the edge of his vision. He focused blurrily on the bright light surrounding the lamp head above him. He felt himself being lifted. At first, he thought it was the light pulling him upwards, worrying and comforting him equally strangely. As he realised it was hands and arms raising him, he groggily stabilised his jelly-like feet and legs. From the corner of his eye, he could see Mrs Shortt, waving her other hand that was not under his armpit, gesturing to push a wall of curious kids back.

"Joe!" the Headmaster said calmly, appearing from nowhere. "Joe! You are going to be fine. You've just had a nasty bump on your head." He mumbled something else about telling his mother, but Joe drifted off looking upwards at the boys' end lamppost again. The golden aura was still there, he thought he saw the lamp still lit up, despite it being sunny daylight. In a blink of an eye, he could have sworn it flashed a wink at him. This gave him a surge of strange feelings, all of which culminated in him receiving a reassuring message. Whatever this other worldly source was, or whether it was his own imagination, Joe was certain he heard, "You'll be all right. Don't worry." He smiled despite the weird but warm feeling that he was being watched. These words in his head comforted him, not scaring him at all as they probably should have. He clasped the back of his head tenderly and winked back up at the light as a 'thank you'. His eyes went to the ground as he tenderly touched the large, egg bump on his head. Wincing, he looked up again and the lamppost's bulb was no longer shining.

Leftovers

What she did shocked Joe in a way. The casual way she did it made him a little bit angry too. The fact that she acted like it was 'no big deal' and carried on doing the same thing as she cleared up for the others increasingly frustrated him. But he could do nothing but sit and watch it happen. He was at his mate Brendy's house and had stayed for tea. Politeness ruled that it was their house, so their rules applied. No matter how much he did not like it, Joe Average had to remember his manners, sit quietly and suck it up; even if there were loads left that should have been sucked up or saved for another time, but was not.

In his home, 'there are starving kids in Africa!' was the encouraging statement to finish off anything left on the plate before them. Joe always wondered why the starving kids in his own wee village and in neighbouring towns and villages were never mentioned. He had heard it was even worse in parts of the city. And what about the adults? *If they were starving did that not matter so much?* he wondered. It was always the suffering of children that was harped on about, using these long fingernails of guilt to pluck at the heart strings. Regardless of what happened outside the walls of the Average house, this phrase always had the same result. Plates would be cleared of food, no matter how disgusting it tasted. Sprouts and cabbage regularly needed such encouragement. Or it was used if the food was badly cooked, which was rarely needed.

If Ma had burnt something, or forgot to include something, she would usually be in such a bad mood, angry and embarrassed, that plates were polished clean to ensure there was no reason for her to flare up. Even the charcoaled crumbs would be forked or spooned into mouths to ease Ma's mood and thank her. However, in those circumstances, the main reason for doing this was that everyone sensed that Ma was simmering away, and no one wanted to do anything to boil her over the edge. Da cooked sometimes too, usually on a Sunday, and his servings were always easily gobbled up for two reasons. Firstly, he was actually a really good cook within his limited culinary range of stews and fry-ups. Secondly, he never took criticism well, so everyone always enjoyed it, in reality or falsely, even if things in the kitchen had not gone according to plan for him.

In Brendy's house, they obviously did not follow the two main mealtime rules in the Average household. There, the first commandment to be adhered to was 'thou shalt not leave any.' Plates had to be cleared of food, full stop, and usually were. There were a few exceptional circumstances, such as when there was legitimate illness. No messing about at all! It had to be genuine sickness! That was one of only two reasons for any reprieve. If all the tastier bits were eaten and then 'I don't feel well' was falsely used to escape from the rest…! Well… that never ended well! Joe, his brother and sister had all tried to test their acting abilities with that one when they had been very young. They had all failed in such auditions, never seeming to get the part they wanted or liked. Chips did make an appearance as special takeaway treats, but these happened randomly with long spaces of time between encores. Usually, they had to stick to the exact same script every mealtime – eat it all up regardless of what part it was.

There was one other means of possibly being allowed to leave food but had, in the history of this wee Average family, only ever been used once. The repercussions from that well-remembered time meant there was more chance of mushy peas having a conversation with you than there being a repeat performance. The mentally painful memories of this ensured it was never used again, and never would be. Drinking someone else's vomit was a sickeningly preferable option to what a very young Will had done. A four-year-old Will had said at the dinner table what Joe and his sister Joanne had been too fearful to even think about uttering. The resultant outburst from his Ma and Da made it feel like an earthquake of ingratitude had erupted, not appreciating the hard work of both parents to provide the food on the table, etc, etc, etc. And etc! This scarily justified Joe and Joanne's decision to never have said it. So 'I don't like that!' never crossed any of their lips before or after that one time. No matter how much they did not appreciate the taste or texture, even if they gagged as forkfuls and spoonfuls of it passed their lips to be chewed and swallowed, they kept going until the bitter end of a clear plate or bowl. That was the preferred, hassle-free option, and, besides, the food was usually simple but great.

This was never as dictatorial as it seemed, as there was always the 'I'm full' option. However, Ma usually had used another of her mysterious parental powers to portion out the food on plates. Whatever advanced

34

mathematics she used to calculate the quantity of food ratio to stomach capacity, she almost always received a tick for a correct answer. As her kids grew, so the portion proportions grew too. These were always fairly divided. Even when the housekeeping budget was smaller than it should be, this was squeezed tight to ensure food was always put before her family. Sometimes there was not that much to go around, but she would still circle the table with her pans, everyone would receive a fair share. So 'I'm full' was rarely said. When it did happen, this would have to be parentally certified to ensure that an appropriate amount of food had been eaten to qualify for this reprieve. The number of leftovers would then be approved after perhaps one of two more forkfuls or spoonfuls had been consumed. This would usually be followed by the circling sibling vultures or Da, swooping in as soon as the remains of the dinner carcass were left and the porcelain plate picked clean.

Within these very clear parameters, whenever food was left, there were three leftover options which were considered right. First there was the saving. It was either left in the pan to be heated up the following night, or put into little bowls to be eaten cold for lunches the next day. Alternatively, it would be packed into plastic bowls and covered with thin, sticky plastic sheets. These would then be added to the assortment of mysterious brown and red-filled tubs filling a corner of the small freezer above the fridge, or plates would have their food contents covered in plastic food wrap and precariously balanced in the small fridge. These were usually emptied by supper time.

Secondly, there was the dog. Finn, his predecessors and successors lay in a well-worn spot under the kitchen table, where they were sneakily fed little bits by all of the family seated around during mealtimes. This was not meant to happen but always did. It was at the end of the meal, when there was food left on plates as a result of the 'I'm full' belly-busting avoidance that the dog suddenly became a lot more alert. Everything, not saved or cleared by the family vultures, would be scraped into its bowl and, being true to its genetic heritage, it would wolf it down. The dog, after all, was as much a member of the Average family as the humans, so the same rules applied to it. Everything would be scoffed; no matter if it was cabbage or Brussels sprouts. This did not improve these green vegetables' image in the kids' eyes at all. Maybe this was why a dog's breath was like dog's breath, Joe always thought.

Finally, and the least used option, was the bin. Wrappers and rubbish were put in it, but food hardly ever. Binning food was seen as verging on sacrilegious, and 'disrespecting the human efforts and natural processes that had ensured this wholesome nutrition had ended up on a plate', so Da had read one time in the newspaper and adopted as his own saying. The exception was really off food, including strange-smelling ham with blackening corners, green, moulded yoghurts and cut off bits of blue, moulded bread. However, it was very rarely food in the fridge or cupboard was there long enough to go off in the first place, thus avoiding such a fate. One-time cooked fish was scraped into the bin, but that was only after it had been regurgitated. The tiny bones had caused a major panic when the dog had choked and choked on them. This only ended when a huge splurge of dog vomit had him wagging his tail again. With a contorted-with-disgust face, Joe had held him by the collar to stop him trying to eat it up again. Ma had wiped it up into the kitchen bin, before taking the ominous-looking and smelling bag to the steel one outside. Joe could remember this very well, especially the smell, but blocked it from his mind, especially at mealtimes.

That was Joe and his family's simple attitude and routine with regard to food. Brendy's family was almost the complete opposite. Joe was still overcoming the fact that Brendy and his three siblings were each given choices of what to eat! The only menu option in the Average home was limited to one. 'Today's special is…' and everyone had it. When asked by Brendy's sweet but seriously overworked Mum what he would like, Joe had just sat flabbergasted and simply said he would just have the same as Brendy. When the meal was ended and the other three younger kids ran off, leaving half their meals on the plates, Joe stayed behind to help clear up. It guilt-tripped a begrudging Brendy into doing the same, but he later appreciated the good Brownie Points this earned with his ma. Joe found that very strange too. At his house you either helped prepare the meal or you helped clear up afterwards. Those were the only two choices. Da was the only one who managed to, the odd time, get out of both, as he was usually too tired or too late back from work, but he mucked in when he was not.

"Where do I put the leftovers?" Joe had asked as he brought the plates over to the sink. She had given him a strange look in response, wondering why he did not know. To prevent further confusion, Brendy's mum took them off him and casually scraped everything into the bin. Joe was stunned but had the courage to ask, "Does the dog not even get some of the leftovers? Not even the sausages?"

"No! No! He has too delicate a stomach. We buy him special dogfood and if he eats anything else it… well, let's say it upset his little tummy … both ends!" Brendy's mum spoke caringly as she reached down and made 'poochy-poo' noises to their black, barrel-shaped Labrador. Joe laughed a little as he realised Brendy's dog certainly did not need any extra food.

Joe became a little bolder and said, "My Ma and Da always tell us to eat up all our food, as there are lots of starving children in the world." Brendy elbowed Joe in the ribs thinking he was being cheeky, but the kindly woman scolded her own son with her eyes.

"I know!" she said. "It's terrible when you see them on TV with their faces like skulls and ribs sticking out. Makes your heart bleed for them, so it does!" she said this, paused a contemplative moment, then scraped a sausage with one bite out of it, and some chips and beans into the bin. Joe waited for her to say something else but that was it.

Later, they were out playing in Brendy's huge garden with its metal swing and a red, plastic slide. They had even brought out a paddling pool on this hot, sunny, autumn day, which Brendy's wee brothers and sister were splashing around in, fully dressed. Leaving them to their fun, Joe and Brendy climbed up into the biggest of the three apple trees in the corner. It was a place they often went to escape the others. Joe reached out and grabbed an apple, rosy-red one side and glossy-green the other. He twisted it, the stalk broke and he took a big bite out of it. He offered it to Brendy as he had done before, and he took a scrunchy bite out of it as well. Suddenly, there was a female shout up from a few feet below, asking loudly what they were doing.

"Eating an apple!" Joe and Brendy said together.

"No! Stop that! Don't be eating them straight off the tree like that! You need to bring them in to wash them first! All sorts of bugs and things will have been crawling all over them. Birds will have probably pooped on them as well. Come down, both of youse!" She let out a shivering sort of sound as she stood waiting for them to clamber down.

Once their feet were on the rotting, apple-strewn ground, she took the twice-bitten apple from Brendy's hand and threw it into the thick, pine hedge beside them. Joe did a sort of double take looking up at her, then over the hedge and back again. *What a waste!* he thought silently It was a very tasty apple. He consoled himself by hoping the birds and mice would enjoy pecking and nibbling it. "Now go inside and wash your hands, Brendan. You never know what germs you will pick up from those. Joe, you wash your hands too, please." Joe nodded and followed behind Brendy. It was their house, so their rules, he chanted to himself as they walked over to the house.

The next early morning, Joe and his family were all sitting around, slurping porridge. Joe told them, as he had told them before after every visit, he had to Brendy's house, all about how they ate as a family. As before, this always provoked strange responses. Ma and Da were fairly disgusted with the waste, but justified that Brendy's family could afford it. Joe could never figure out that reasoning. If you were rich, it was okay to waste a lot of stuff, but when you were poor, you could not afford to waste it? That melted his young head quite a bit.

Joanne, Will and Joe were slightly jealous at being able to have a choice of what to eat. When Joe told them about the five different varieties of cereals in the cupboards to choose for breakfast, Will and Joanne's enthusiasm for porridge dwindled severely. The fact that the dog did not even get a taste of any leftovers surprised all of them. Even Finn let out a little whimper in response. Joe wondered if Finn was either showing sympathy for his canine colleague, having understood what Joe said, or maybe he was just hungry and not a porridge fan either? Joe went for the latter and passed a burnt toast crust under the table for him to chew on.

Joe finished his porridge and toast as they all did. As they always all did. They headed like a stampeding herd for the front door, off to see what school and work delights awaited them. They were running late, which was becoming a normal part of the morning routine. Ma's face and mutterings showed frustration at her children and schoolbag-loaded car being stuck behind the bin lorry. It was stop-starting on its collections down the street, which was not helping them to get there any quicker. Joe peered through the front windscreen, it being his turn for the front seat. He had eventually won this argument after a decisive gulder from Ma. He saw the burly men slinging the contents of the metal bins into the back of the slow and smelly truck. As the big compactor door reached out to crush everything smaller, Joe was amazed at how much discarded food was in there. He caught sight of a whole uncooked chicken and a full unopened loaf before they were mushed into the rubbish carnage.

The next bin chucked in had prepacked food, unopened, to be churned up with the plastics and cans. The smell was gruesome, and Joe wondered if there was less food in there perhaps the lorry might smell a bit better. He battled with the decision of whether to screw down the window to let air in to dispel the stinking air, but would that only bring in more smelly air? Or maybe he should leave the windows up to try to trap what stinking air there was inside the car and not make it worse? All these solutions still stank, so his hand remained on the window handle and he did nothing. Then he smirked with an idea.

"Will, could you do us all a favour please?" Joe shouted to the back seat where Will and Joanne were doing their usual annoying, repetitive thumping at each other. He agreed immediately and Joe asked, "Could you let our one of your most stinking farts to help the air smell better in here?"

Ma gave Joe a disgusted look. She was even more disgusted when Will concentrated hard and a squeaky little trumpet noise signalled that the task had been completed. How he did that, being able to perform on demand, amazed his family! Although they all knew it was not a talent that would make him rich or appear on TV. Ma and Joanne laughed out loud at Joe's cheeky request but the laughter soon stopped as nostrils flared and mouths gagged. Windows were rapidly wound down to experience the pleasant aroma of a bin lorry in comparison. Joanne squawked at the smugly smiling Will, "Have you been eating from the back of that bin lorry to produce something like that? Ma! Ma! Stop the car! I think I am going to be sick!"

Ma turned up a side street shortcut and the freshness of the petrol and coal smoke air was welcome. When he thought about the stink of the bin lorry, that certainly gave Joe food for thought. He looked at his Ma and thought she was thinking the same. Will and Joanne were very quiet and still, sitting in the back seat. Maybe even they had called a truce to their bickering to think about things. Joe gazed back at them and could see they were both deep in thought. Then he saw a wicked smile cross Will's face, heard the trumpet noise and grabbed the window handle to wind it down as a matter of urgency.

Ma spluttered a little and asked, "What on earth have you been eating, Will?"

Will just smiled.

Lignite

As Joe later found out, the fires of resentment had burned for a very long time before the Black War began. This time, however, both sides were ready for that 'big push' for final victory. As Joe also found out, as in the Great War to end all wars, which it most certainly did not, this was a costly tactic. Very costly. Regardless of the price needing to be paid, the scarred battlefield was ready again to pay the price of battle. Everything had ignited over the lignite, both sites having become so furious over the bituminous that their hearts had turned as hard as anthracite. The hateful feelings ran as deep as the historic, man-made tunnels that pierced the earth. The mole-like workers thought they were being shafted just as much, the government feeling likewise. The miners believed they were kept as much in the dark as the underground world where they toiled. They blamed the government for this, mostly correctly, it turned out.

The stopping of work was the only way they saw to strike a light at the end of these dark and sinister tunnels, thinking they knew where these were leading and threading along these to follow a very different seam. The government, they believed, saw only economics and capitalism, not jobs and communities, which they had to protect. The government said its role was to protect the entire nation, both internally and externally. The miners had hung the government up by their entrails too many times before, and now the government had the guts to sort out this problem from the bowels of the earth once and for all. These government and the miners' polar opposite views on keeping the home fires burning sparked and sparked until the fire started, which set mainland Britain blazing. It set young Joe's mind alight as well.

Television showed the conflicts of this war to a young Joe Average. His eyes and ears devoured the images and reports, hungry to find out the how and why. He saw daily when it happened, courtesy of the small, family TV in the corner of their living room. At that time, he did not know all of the troubled history of what had gone before. Nor did he fully understand all the politics behind it, but he was old enough to understand enough. One thing was for sure: he, glued like everyone else to the television, understood that what he saw unfolding across the nightly news reports was as dark and dirty as what they were fighting about.

Each side's rhetoric and actions always fanned the flames, rather than making any attempts to quench them. What burned brightly as a result was pure hate. Those television images showed it so vividly young Joe sometimes found himself reaching towards the screen to touch it. However, he would pull his hand away quickly before any chance of contact. It was just too dark, hot and scary for his fingers, or his other senses, to grasp. Joe always believed, from he was really young, that no one could or ever would handle hate. When they had tried to, it only ever ended up making it grow more monstrous, until a battle or war was needed to try to be rid of it. As 1985 and the legacy left showed, even that does not always work. Joe knew many argued convincingly that it never does, at best only removing the original hate and replacing it with a different version.

Joe saw it at the time, and even moreso later, akin to a medieval royal ego conflict that emotionally, politically and financial fired the whole of the realm. Unbeknown at the time, the embers of it would still glow decades afterwards, in mining communities and beyond. Margaret styled herself, a queen, sitting on her throne in 10 Downing Street, miles apart from mines, and not just geographically. Her blood and her opinion polls were both still riding high after her vanquishing of an enemy far, far away to the south, on two little pin pricks on a global map. She needed a new foe to direct her energy at and keep this momentum going. That foe had already been identified years before and was, unknown to them, next on her list. She could not and would not be restrained from this new mission. Her court of royal advisers cowered to her will.

Rather than counselling her, they entered the fray on her side, arming themselves with bureaucratic policy paper shields and swords. She, in turn unleashed her weapons of choice, her sharp schoolmistress voice with words that cut deep. The pen used for her signatures delivered deadly blows as lethally as any axe. She saw immense honour in having been labelled made of metal by other world leaders. Maybe it had been forgotten by her that metal needs heat to be made? Coal traditionally provided that necessary forging, real heat and she certainly stoked that fire into a furnace. Hard were her methods, hard was her desired legacy, and it was hard, nigh impossible, to turn her from her course. A collision course was set, not only by her, and she meant to hit as hard as she could.

Opposing her was King Arthur, who did not have a round table of knights or maidens. He instead had a union that he sat firmly at the head of the table of. This he felt provided him with the almost divine right, as an elected leader, to lead in his own way, bringing glory to the miners and undoubtedly himself. Even a young Joe could have told Arthur that glory is not always glorious and usually gory. The difference between the wondrous words on sectarian murals and reality of life in Northern Ireland/North of Ireland showed this all too often in Joe's bloodied corner of the world.

Arthur tried to be a shining light, a beacon of hope, but his multitudes of followers were not renowned for being angels. They were tough workers burrowing down towards the fires below rather than the heavens above. Yet they had voted for their leader who used this fact, in exactly the same way Margaret used her mandate, to each justify their chosen actions. His Excalibur was all these votes of his hundreds of thousands of paid-up union members that had put him where he was. He had drawn this sword before, thrusting into the government's weak and energy addicted body, cutting a better pay deal for his army of followers and leaving a festering wound. They hero worshipped him for it. Queen Margaret hated him even more because of it, underlining and highlighting King Arthur and his followers' names even more on her 'things to do' list.

When the miners erupted from the earth and poured their heat into protests and pickets, Joe saw it purely as a spectator through TV. To his young eyes, what was happening across the water, between the miners and police, was so, so different from local violent protests his side of the Irish Sea. A lot of the sporadic, sectarian protest and riots in his homeland sometimes only had the briefest of mentions and images on the local news. Rarely did they make the national news. These were sometimes described as spontaneous, which Joe always found strange, wondering where all the petrol bombs, stones and all sorts of other chuckable things suddenly materialised from. These riots fell into two categories.

Firstly, there were the bored teenagers wanting something to do, so they would decide to start throwing stones at their supposedly culturally different 'enemy'. Surprisingly enough, the almost identical bored teenagers wanting something to do on the other 'culture' side would decide to retaliate or do the same, to exercise their throwing arms as well. This happened so often in the cities, and sometimes the towns, it was mentioned more in the local traffic reports on delays and detours than on the main local news. Strangely, Joe always thought, he, his siblings, his neighbours' kids, his schoolmates – none of them were every bored enough in their local area to start rioting. Where his family lived, the closest Joe's little hamlet of houses and scattered nearby farms ever came to a riot was when the ice-cream van arrived one time. Having drawn everyone's attention with his loud jangly music, a very red-faced Vince Manning, or Van the Man in the Ice-Cream Van as he was known, had to announce from his cold cave of delights that the pump had stopped working. He drove off at speed to angry, abusive shouts, with a couple of disgruntled potential customers throwing empty tin cans aimlessly. Vince nor his van, very sadly for the local kids, ever came back after that, leaving no one a winner.

Secondly, and much more seriously, were the full-blown mini-uprisings or outflowing of rage following some bombing or shooting or change, or not, of legislation. Or there were also occasions when it was the price of a pint going up, or other less serious economic factors, being the reason. These happened often, far too often, but were certainly mentioned on the local, and often on the national news. These would usually last a day or possibly two. They would then stop, with the threat of them starting again simmering for another day or possibly two. Then the reasons behind them would-be put-on hold for a little while, before they were used again at the next opportunity for another run about the streets destroying stuff and people. Then this too would stop after a day or two, and the reason for this one added to the ever-growing lists of rioting reasons. And so, it went on until nobody actually paid a blind bit of notice to the reason for it, just seeing an opportunity to fight; or it was a Tuesday, and there was not much on telly!

After many, many years, what the real reasons were became immaterial and all that remained was this need to show hate. Images of these left a tainted stain on Joe's homeland, dragged out by media archives regularly, regardless of the modern, current situation. This stain could never be removed by a local council clear-up crew brushing the stones and broken glass aftermath up and taking it away. It was even harder to sort out the stony hearts and broken lives, caused by and resulting from the street violence.

Even these, to a young Joe at the time, seemingly huge televised local riots and fights in his homeland were so minor in context compared to the miners' protests. Instead of groups of sectarian gangs wanting trouble, Joe avidly watched the huge armies of hundreds gather in the towns and fields of north England, mostly. The dark, uniformed and regimented ranks of police formed up in orderly squares behind their Perspex shield walls. Armed with their batons; protected by their helmets; radios communicating to them from a command centre covering the whole of England, Scotland and Wales; cavalry and vehicle support; and able to draw on reserves from across the land – they were a formidable force, more army-like than police. They were disciplined and fully trained. Ironically, Joe found out later, it was the training and experience gained in dealing with the riots in Northern Ireland/North of Ireland that made the police such an effective force opposing the miners! He always snorted sarcastically when he thought of that.

Then there were the miners, looking on in their jeans and t-shirt uniforms with a copy of the local paper their only shield. They would nearly all have had dangerous things in their possessions. Lit fags and packets of cigarettes are, after all, deadly nails in coffins! They always seemed to mill about, chatting amongst themselves, waiting for instructions that never seemed to come. From the TV screen it would sometimes look like it happened almost out of boredom that groups would approach the police lines. Mostly the shouting and shoving would start with the arrival of the battered buses. Their war wounds from previous perilous journeys would be clearly visible, having been inflicted because 'Scabs' were their non-striking worker passengers.

Then, the missiles would be thrown, and the police would hold the line for a while. Sometimes there were no horses so there would be policemen hoofing it into the midst of the gathered throngs. When there were cavalry, these would come charging through like modern knights of olde in very different armour, easily dispersing the disorganised, only fist and feet armed infantry ranks before them like they were a minor nuisance. If anyone had ever stood in front of a charging horse and rider, even without a lance and suit of armour, personally Joe knew it removed the need for any laxatives for a month at least! So, Joe totally appreciated how effective the cavalry charges were. Once the horses had hounded the miners, the baton-wielding police on foot would plod in, picking off pickets and protesters seemingly at random. As Joe watched the TV he began to wonder if it was the day before footage they were showing? It all started to become the same, day after day, akin to the local riots. The outcomes were always the same, with bloodied heads, arrests and more bitterness to put into the next day.

On the television screens the confrontations looked like the miners were the native peoples, chucking their local dialect spears at a smartly-uniformed colonial army. As with native peoples, they threw all they had, keeping going even when their obsolete weaponry fell far short of the intended targets. The miners' strike sucked in everything and unleashed it. It became much more than uneconomic coal mines having to close. It became socialism, even communism, versus conservatism, even fascism.

Unlike Northern Ireland having a distinct, if controversial, geographic line on a map with southern Ireland, the North/South divide of England was just as potent and potentially toxic a divide without the need for distinct cartography. Northern versus Southern rivalries were brought to a bitter head, and not just the one on top of a pint. Working class against middle and upper, rich opposing and oppressing the poor, all became embroiled in it. Joe watched the rather incredulous TV reporters inform of the part international politics played a part. As the National Union of Mineworkers funds bled dry, life blood aid packages were sent to the miners from many countries, including those that were a much deeper red than even the government opposition Labour party. This was a small part of the international Cold War being enacted to heat the Coal War in Britain up. Such events made the infuriated government even more blue than its party colour, before it became red with rage instead of sad. The US and Europe breathed heavily down the government's neck because of this Second World support in a major first world country. It led to the British government not seeming to be concerned about the country being bled white in its quest for victory.

Joe could see the miners were fighting for their cause too. Literally they were fighting, with bare fists against the perceived fascism, fabrications and ferocity of the state. Fighting for a cause was a phrase Joe had heard since he was a boy. He continued to hear all the talk of the need for blood and sacrifice and sweat and toil and will and bravery from leaders and wannabe leaders, who only a few ever seemed to lose or give as much of any of this list as was needed. Yet this was expected and demanded from their followers? As he grew older, Joe realised such things never really changed. Back then, as Joe watched the screen night after night, the thousands and thousands of gathered miners on those streets and fields gave

45

that entire shopping list, some even the ultimate sacrifice of death.

They gave much and more, some everything, but they did not receive what they needed. They believed in a union mighty in numbers, with the tried and tested tactics of the 1970s. But these were being used to meet the radically different 1980s, and a new standing tall political leader. She would not be bending the deferential, fearful knee her predecessors had. The need for investing in change was ignored or derided by the union leadership, despite the fact that its financial reserves had been gained from members' contributions. The government reaped the dividends of this, and it was the miners who paid the cost across the board, not just the Coal Board. Even a young, square-eyed and mesmerised Joe could see the way things were going and found it hard to control the sadness this evoked.

As the strike went on, heels were dug in instead of picks, attitudes became like rocks that no blasted words could crumble, and neither side would give an inch of ground. When the government was not talking to them, or not saying the things they wanted to hear, the miners went on shouting abuse at the police forces that opposed them instead. When the government did not listen to them, or want to listen, they gathered in their thousands to try to close access to the veins of black blood that kept the power network flowing. When the miners had got what they wanted so many times before, why, they no doubt asked themselves, should this time be so different? Oh! But even a young, historically naïve Joe realised early on that this was! The miners passionately believed they were striking a blow for fairness and for their communities. However, with the forces arrayed in front of them, over that year they should have realised earlier the need to strike a new deal, instead of just another strike. The news programmes would, after all, have found something else to report on.

The war in his homeland was certainly not about mines. A curious Joe had asked his family about these. His Da and Granda, mainly, told him about the still-thriving salt mines, which, they half laughed, did not have the ominous implications Stalinist Russia had given to being sent to these. There had been mining for metals too which were all gone, some not lasting long, others long enough to create entire communities. Some only lasted a few decades, some not even one. There were the coal mines at Ballycastle and an amazing number of Ulster people who had not realised why Coalisland was named such. These underground enterprises were on a small scale compared to across the sea, employing hundreds rather than hundreds of thousands. Although there had been strikes, these were sorted very quickly at a local level. Mining was a minor industry in his homeland but major for many blackened mainland John's who pitted themselves against the might of Maggie.

Joe's da came out with many words and phrases of advice. It took him until later in life, when he was experiencing these for himself, for a lot of these to come back to him to guide and protect him. Lots he got straight away. His da's telling him about mines, being like human nature, fell into that latter hole, pigeon not mine. He said it several times, as he did with all his wisdoms which differed in their pearl value. "Humans treat this world like it is not only 'mine' but like a mine too. They take and take and take based on their belief that if they don't someone else will. They take until the mine runs out or the cost becomes too high. They will take the last fish from the sea, the last tree from the forests, for these same reasons – greed and stupidity. What do we do when the last mine closes, when we kill the last fish, kill the last tree?" Joe did not know when he first heard his da's wise question how the stark truth of its terrifying answer would haunt him for the rest of his life.

On mainland Great Britain, it had gone far, far beyond local to having a national impact. This was shown by the National Union of Miners leaving a nation numb, when they eventually had their spirits and finances shattered. The NUM defeat was necessarily and realistically accepted, forgive and forget not included in the final paperwork. The Black War ended with the government gaining a bitter victory by force and finance. Successful battles in the fields and towns forced the dwindling numbers of protestors and pickets back again and again. Injuries and arrests, even briefly of King Arthur, continued to weaken what had been an army force of miners.

Despite the love the TV cameras had for such live action, it was the mining communities being financially strangled and the starving families that brought the Black War to its conclusion. Unable to claim dole money, and union funds gone, debts and feeding their families at soup kitchens sucked the strike resolve from many. More and more returned to work as the calls of 'Scabs' dwindled. Although not picked on any more, little healing happened. When a court case judged that the strike had been in fact illegal, as it had not been properly voted for, that was a killer blow to King Arthur's ambitions and his armour dissolved after that. He did not sign a peace treaty but ended the strike by simply and factually announcing that colliers were to close, thousands of jobs were to be lost and those coal communities were to be destroyed. Anti-climax was the end result.

Joe had waited all his life for the violence destroying the communities in his homeland to end. In the mid-1980s that seemed far off. It seemed even further away when, probably carried away with her Malvinas and Miners victories, the very next year Queen Maggie thought she would sort 'The Irish Problem' out as well. Instead, her signature on the Anglo-Irish Agreement in 1985 brought thousands onto the streets of Ulster to protest and vent their fury at this believed betrayal. However, these hot demonstrations, words and actions, like all previous ones, cooled eventually. It, like most protests, changed nothing, apart from more resentment always left behind. This agreement failed, as many before had, but it provided an ember for future peace seekers to blow on and rekindle.

Coal is like all protests, Joe realised back then. Nothing had so far happened in his life since that time to change this viewpoint. The black and dirty issues will lie there for a long time, nobody doing anything about it. Then someone or something will come along and put a match to it. It will burst into fiery flames. There will be intense heat and injury resulting from any brief physical or verbal touch of it. At the time it will feel like this ominous fire will spread to consume and blacken everything. However, as with coal, the government forces will contain it within a fireplace, within a grate of its making. The great and powerful will sit tight, keeping the hot coals under control and well watched, and they will wait. Then they will wait some more. Joe had watched it happen with all sorts of riots and protests, including the Miners' Strike, which had taken a year of government waiting. But they had waited and won.

In Northern Ireland/North of Ireland, this need to wait usually just took a day or two for flaring riots to end. Then a day or two for the next one to start! They seemed to be waiting decades for the ignored or not wanting to be understood reasons for these to somehow end. However, the bright, burning coals of protest would always become mere embers, with their glow fading rapidly. Eventually, the fire would go out completely. No matter how much the cinders would be raked, no burning ember of reignition would be found. Nothing would change until these cinders were piled on top of the next coal fire, to burn again and go through the same process. It was a cycle of heated outrage that, unbeknown to Joe back then, he would see happen again and again and again.

As with the miners, the Anglo-Irish Agreement and every other protest that Joe could think of, there was always the call to make a 'strike for freedom.' Freedom, to a young and especially older Joe, always seemed to be very elusive. Like the head of a struck matchstick, it would flare up spectacularly just for a moment. Then it would just as quickly burn out, leaving only a black residue that could be easily crumbled away. No one could or would define what exactly freedom meant, it having a thousand different meanings to a thousand different people. Like cold cinders, freedom continually seemed to be struck out very quickly. As he thought when it happened back then and reflecting on it in the years that followed, Joe saw the defeat of that Miner's Strike as a real turning point, to the right rather than left. Regardless of direction, Joe wondered back then, and still, if that was a good or right road to take. The miners were forced to admit defeat, but who were the real winners afterwards and, in the decades, since? Joe had no answer to that. That did not scare him at all. What terrifies him the most to this day is when he wonders who, if anyone, was?

Last-Time

"For Fuck's Sake, Ma!" Joe half-shouted at her, throwing his schoolbag angrily onto the kitchen chair, causing it to rock slightly. His messily-uniformed brother Will was close at his heels, standing rigid and just staring at her with a shocked sadness.

"Don't you use that swearword in my house!" she spat back, in a viciously angry but subdued voice. She had remained sitting motionless as she spoke, only her head nodding upwards towards him. Her red, bloodshot eyes had briefly hardened. She returned to the table staring she had been engrossed in before they had walked into the unusually cluttered kitchen. She had tried to use the 'look' tactic to assert her control, but that was fading. Her older kids were teenagers now, and young Will soon would be. It was clear to see that she was also too caught up in her own painful thoughts to force the issue.

She was sitting at the kitchen table, a sodden, snotty tissue clasped tightly between her slightly shaking hands which lay limp on the empty table before her. Her left cheek was crimson red and, as soon as he saw it, Joe knew what had happened. This had prompted his outburst. As he peered closer, he was sure he could actually see the red outline of thick fingers on her pale, white skin. Silently he looked down at her and, although the only jewellery his Ma ever wore was her wedding ring and earrings, she had a newly-added thick, purple bracelet on her wrist. Worryingly, there were a few spots of blood on the wet tissue that was exposed from her prayer posed hands.

"He said the last time that that was the last time! It would never happen again he said! He promised! He swore! What good is that's bastard's word now when he goes and does this!" Joe ranted as he slumped down to sit on the edge of the chair where he had just thrown his schoolbag. He bent his tensed body across the table towards his precious, long-suffering mother.

"Don't you ever call your father that! EVER! You hear me?" she shouted back, the steel of anger in her eyes shining brightly through the pain and hurt that was not stainless. Joe sighed and leaned back against his bag, unconcerned about the discomfort of books and buckles digging into his back. It confused him so much when she defended him like this. He had hurt her physically. Again! He had hurt them all emotionally. Again! True it had been a long time since it had last happened. There had still, since that lashing outburst last time, been fierce arguments, about money, as usual. These always threatened to go to the next violent step. For whatever reason, they had thankfully not. The Average kids had actually begun to think things might be getting a lot better. They had even begun to wonder what a normal family life might look like. They wondered if anyone had one of those? Now all those dreams and plans were gone! What had happened now crashed Will and Joe back into the darkness of a sadness and powerlessness they had started to dare to hope and think they had left behind.

The front door slammed and Joanne quickly sauntered into the kitchen behind her bothers. "Aw, for fuck's sake!" she guldered, staring hard at her ma who seemed to have shrunk somehow. "The bastard's done it again, hasn't he?" she questioned, but what she saw before her answered it instantly.

"Don't you use those swearwords in my house! NEVER! Never refer to your father like that!" Ma spat back at her in the same angry but subdued voice in response to Joe's swearing. "He has his faults but he works so, so hard to provide for this family! To put food on our table! To put a roof over our heads…" She broke off and tears started flowing erratically down her cheeks. A long, pent-up sob exploded from her, like the sound of a whale breathing, before she started emitting haunting little cries as her defensive wall crumbled under the sheer weight of what had happened. The still silent Will was beside her first, his arms wound tight around her neck, kissing her twice on the forehead. He remained there, saying nothing, but through his touch reassuring her that he would stay there as long as she needed him to.

"We are definitely getting the police this time!" Joanne raged. "Definitely! How many more chances are you going to give him, Ma? Seriously! You cannot take any more of this! None of this family can take any more of this shite!" Ma just silently sobbed now, dabbing her eyes and not even reprimanding Joanne for using the 's' word in her presence. "I am going to phone them now!" Joe nodded in firm agreement. Joanne turned on her heels and was about to head up the hallway to the phone by the front door. Her ma's voice stopped her in her tracks.

"NO! NO! No! No! Don't do that! We don't want the Peelers involved!

51

We would be the talk of the neighbourhood! Do not ring them! I am telling you! I am begging you!" Ma stammered out in panicked loudness. Her voice was as cracked as this new damage that had been caused to the fragility of the Average family life. It was as clear as crystal what had happened, but the ding of intact family purity now thudded dully. Joanne wanted something done about it. Joe too wanted something done to stop this evil ever happening again, for good. Will just hugged tightly, saying nothing, not even a nod or smile. His white, stark face just stared numbly and lovingly at his ma.

"What then?" Joe asked, failing to keep a lid on his temper and frustration. "Do you want us to contact Women's Aid? Or the Samaritans? A solicitor? Nan? Who do you want to speak to, to try to sort this for good? What do you want us to do about this? Because one way or another, this is definitely the last time! This never, ever happens again! You hear me! Even if it means moving out and staying at Nan's, that is what we can do. Is that what you want, Ma? Tell me, what can we do to stop this and sort it?" Joe felt hot tears welling up but swallowed them back down again into that inner watery pit of despair that he had hoped he would not have been topping up any more.

"NO! No! None of that." Ma replied weakly, her chin buried in her heaving chest. "We will sort it out! We always sort it out within the family. He is away now, but will have calmed down when he comes back. We will talk about it then. No police! No solicitors! And definitely no Nan! Do not mention a word of this to her!" She paused a moment, then looked sternly at all the faces around her. "Okay?" she added brusquely. None of them spoke. "*Okay*?" she repeated, giving each a taste of the 'look' that turned them all back into obedient seven-year-olds. Disgruntled nods and 'yes's followed from all three.

Joe knew that Nan knew but never said she knew. Neither he nor his siblings had told her. He also knew that most of the other family members either knew or suspected, just as a lot of the neighbours did. He tutted as he thought everyone in a ten-mile radius of their house could hear the arguments when they were in full throttle, so were bound to know what was going on. A small wave of melancholy came over him as he realised how often he heard muffled, arguing voices coming from the few houses surrounding theirs. When those sounds came to him from across the road, or from those next door and further up and down, he felt a strange sort of guilt for the very weird reassurance this gave him. Despite how personally his ma and da barging away at each other affected him, hearing it happening elsewhere meant that his family rows and arguments were not unique. Other families had loud fights, verbal and sometimes physical, too. It gave the whole fractious thing a sort of normality. He knew, from a very young age, that arguments happen; that is part of life. But should they ever be considered normal just because they happen? Violent ones, even if they were frequent, should most definitely never have a shoulder shrugging, 'ah well' acceptance of them.

Joanne and Joe both sighed heavily. The still-hugging Will smiled, nodded and kissed Ma gently on her forehead again. She moved her arm up around him and pulled him close until their cheeks touched. Then Ma winced in pain at the skin contact and Will edged away, concern on his face. He placed an ever-so-gentle kiss on her still bright, red cheek, hoping it would have the same healing powers as his Ma's always seemed to have had on his battle wounds.

Joanne thrust a chair out from the table and plonked down hard on the wooden seat. She leant forward, arms across the table, her hands balled into fists against each other. "Leave him, Ma! Just leave him! All three of us are big enough now to understand and make our own way in life. Hell, at least a quarter of my college class have divorced or separated parents. It seems to be the normal thing nowadays." She snorted sarcastically and paused, her eyes flicking with each blink from anger to sadness and back again. She sighed heavily. "It's nothing to be ashamed of. You have suffered for far too long with all this shite. We all have! No court in the land would not grant you a divorce!" Joanne added with a determined resolve. Ma's face was shocked at the use of the word 'divorce'! "Or chuck him out! That would be a lot easier for all of us! When he does stuff like this, he doesn't deserve to be part of this family! Does he?"

Joanne ended staring with an angry expectance of an answer from her Ma. Ma's initial response was physical, suddenly reaching over and grabbing both Joanne's fists. Keeping one touching Joanne's hand, she swiftly moved the other over to hold Joe's that lay flat on the table, trembling slightly with inner rage. Joe felt the clamminess and heat of the touch. "No one will be moving out! There will be no more talk of divorce, or solicitors, or any of that! We will work through this. We always have before and we will again! You hear me?" she spoke quietly but with conviction. Her three children slowly moved their heads up and down, although very reluctantly. "The thing is I love him. And he loves me. We both love all three of youse. That's the truth. Plain and simple. He has his faults. I have mine. Love is what has seen us through all this. It always has and always will. All the money worries, all that family shit with your uncles – all of that." She smiled warmly, and a little glimmer of light returned to shine from her eyes.

All three of her kids did a quick double check of their hearing, to check if Ma had used the 's' word. "Sure, this is a bad time. And, before you say it, yes there have been bad times before. More than there should have been, I know. But! And it is a big but! We have had lots and lots of good times too. Sure, we have never had much money, even though both yer da and me work hard. But we have always got by and made the most of it. Always! There have been fun times, too. We are a strong family and I need all three of you to be strong now. For me! For yer da! For yerselves!" She smiled that special smile that showed a love words could never express.

The three of them muttered 'yeah's and 'yes's. "We will sort this out between the five of us. Okay? We do not need to involve anyone else. This is our business and no one outside of these walls knows about it and never will." She paused after speaking, and then added a final authoritative, "Do you all understand what I am saying?" Joe tried not to show his quizzical stare at her, wondering if she was just pretending that no one knew and wanted to keep up that pretence. Or did she genuinely believe that no one in the family or neighbourhood had ever heard the arguments and fights? They would have heard about the hospital visits for sure, as the two nursing sisters who were sisters, living further up the road, were as leaky as sieves with juicy gossip, real and fake. Joe was a little baffled by this. However, as with everything, family loyalty came first.

He accepted his ma's wish to maintain this imagined Average perfect family image, regardless of how deluded and distorted this thing was. Despite his rage, he did have to admit the fact that, even when his wee family unit had this painful, ugly side fully exposed, it still showed the love that glued it all together. However, as he sat now, his anger was too hot and had melted that bonding. The bulk of his rage was directed at his da for doing this. But some was at his ma too, for not doing anything to stop it, perhaps even pushing Da too far to cause it? No matter how far she had shoved him verbally, it still did not justify what he had done. There was a chunk of hot anger at himself as well for not stopping it. He had thought he would not have returned to this reason for rage again, but furious at the very fact he had had to. Boiling anger took away his words as his brain heated, his heart pounded, his hands sweated. His Ma clenched his hand tighter. Her touch, as he always remembered, was like a cooling balm and it worked its magic. But only a little this time.

Joanne was about to speak but only got as far as a 'but...' before Ma's intent stare silenced her. Joe quietly fumed inside, unable to look at his ma, despite her squeezing his hand.

"Look at me, Joe!" Ma demanded. He refused. "Look... at... me!" she repeated more slowly, deliberately and unaccepting of disobedience. Joe did not move his slumped head but peered at her from below frowned eyebrows. "You understand, don't you?" She smiled at him.

Joe slumped back in his seat, looked her fully in the face and yanked his hand away from her grasp. "So, what happens when it happens again? Can you sit there and tell me that you will never suffer any more pain from his hands or feet? Can you guarantee that, because I certainly can't! Can you, Joanne? Can you, Will?" Joe yelled, jumping to his feet when he finished and started pacing the kitchen floor. Joanne nodded her head in agreement with Joe. She changed to frantically shake it side to side, with a little confused look, to clarify that she, like the rest of them, could not confirm it could never happen again. Will just stared blankly, not really knowing how to respond.

Joe found a new fury for his da, partly for his ma but also a lot for himself. Family was meant to protect each other, and he had failed to defend his ma. He had overcome his own fears and tried before, but was physically not strong enough to win. He was also not psychologically strong enough either, loving his father too deeply, but changing to loathing him just as much when the likes of this happened. This left respect in some sort of limbo Joe could not quite figure out, unsure if he ever would.

"Sit down, son!" Ma stated softly. Joe hated being called son, but accepted that this was family and his ma was one of only two people who had the right to call him that. He was unsure, judging by how he felt now, if he still wanted to be known as his da's son, beyond anything more than biological. He gave a few final stomps to the fridge and back before another more urgent plea of 'sit down, please' was obeyed.

She just smiled at him. The bruise on her wrist seemed less vibrant.

While Joe had stomped, Joanne had risen to run a cloth under the cold tap and place in delicately against her ma's red and slightly swollen cheek. The redness had eased quickly from the cold contact. As all four of them hushed to listen, the redness returned with a flush. All four swallowed hard in unison. They sat or stood where they were, Will clinging more tightly to his ma and Joanne clutching her ma's hand like she was trying to wring it out like the wet cloth. Joe stood still. He breathed deeply several times. He focused his mind and gathered all of his body's strength, then stood by the fridge and waited. They had all heard the distinct sound of their da's van pull up onto their driveway and the driver's door squeakily slam shut.

Learner

"Right, let's get these Hell Plates stuck up, then!" Da smirked wickedly, knowing it would press the right button of teasing annoyance on Joanne.

"Would you stop calling them that, Da? I am NOT that bad! I'm NOT! AM I? Seriously is it so terrible sat beside me? NO! I am doing, okay. I am getting better. Aren't I?" Joanne rambled as she paced up and down at the roadside in front of their home. Her anger and confidence thumped it out in a verbal fist fight, her nervousness and insecurity joining in the melee, with doubt doing referee. It was only her second lesson, so Joe thought she should not be so hard on herself. He regretted having teased and wound her up before about it, his silent encouragement now an attempt to ask for forgiveness.

Da stepped over and hugged her tight. He kissed her on the forehead as he had done since the day she was born. Seventeen years had passed since then and now she was practicing to take another step towards her womanly independence. It was clear in Da's blue eyes that he was proud of her for doing this. However, there was a growing sadness leaking more and more through the cracks in his hard exterior. Once Joanne had achieved this, she would be able to be much further apart from him and her family. She could go to explore the world when she wished. That was, of course, if the family car was available or she was able to afford one of her own. Joanne had an over-exuberant excitement at her potential freedom and the prospect of car shopping. This was matched, and more, by her parent's reflective recognition of the mixed emotions of this major milestone to adulthood and independence.

"And why does he have to come?" Joanne snapped with a vicious look that stemmed more from her own nervousness rather than anger at Joe. That was what Joe hoped, anyway.

"I already explained. Twice! We are droppin' him off at Terry's while we are in town. Okay? He will be no trouble at all. Will you, Joe?" Da winked over at Joe as he said it, holding Joanne tightly by the shoulders with his big hands. He kissed her again on the forehead and went around to the passenger's seat. "Besides, it won't be long before Joe will be doing the same thing, so he needs to learn, too!" Joanne just grunted and Joe smiled excitedly. His da was right; in two years, three months and twelve days, he could apply for his own provisional licence. Not that he was counting at all!

Joanne reached in to the back seat and stuck up the floppy, sticky square bit of white plastic with only a red L on it. She slapped it onto the corner of the back windscreen. It wouldn't stick, as usual, so she delicately spat on it and did it again. This time it stayed, adding a little more to the smear on the glass in the corner that would be cleaned at some stage. Da stuck one on his side of the front windscreen. Joanne looked obviously relived that he did not need to gob on his to make it stick. Before Da spat, you would have thought he was trying to hack up stuff from his toes, judging by how long it took and the amount of noise. Nevertheless, his side also had a square smear stain on it too from previous mis-sticks requiring some saliva adhesive.

She sat in the driver's seat, put on her belt as Joe jumped in the back. He shuffled over into the middle seat to give himself a good view of gear changes and all the rest. He leaned forward, an elbow on each corner of the front seats. "Sit back and put your seat belt on!" Joanne snapped. Joe just smiled silently and did as he was asked, or was it ordered? Anyway, he sat back, pulled the black, thin, fibrous length across him and clicked the silver, strange-shaped hook into the little holder. Then, he sat forward as far as he could and watched. "Sit back!" Joanne definitely ordered this time, her flaring eyes showing her seriousness. He said nothing and slouched back, still watching her every move closely.

"Right! You know what to do. Just take your time. We are in no panic. Are we, Joe?" Da said very calmly and deliberately, staring at Joanne and then back at Joe.

Joe, after glancing at his black strapped watch with the chipped glass, uttered a, "Well…" but his words were stopped by a semi-loud repeat of 'are we, Joe?'

Joe muttered an, "Of course not, Da!" back. Da gave a nod of approval and looked with nervous care over at Joanne again.

The knuckles of her long-fingered hands stood out like the Mourne Mountains in response to her attempted strangulation of the steering wheel. If she had succeeded in this circular murder, the time of death would have been a quarter to three. She had been told the time of steering wheel holding, but no one had yet told her the strength to be used. Being unsure, she had gone for the option of competing with boa constrictors. Da said to ease her grip and she did so. For at least thirty seconds.

Her knees moved up and down as she worked the pedals, Joe able to hear her mumbled 'clutch, brake accelerator! clutch, brake, accelerator!' mantra chant that seemed to bring Joanne no additional inner calm. Joe could have sworn he heard her knuckles crack as she released a hand from the steering wheel. She flicked the lever to put the windscreen wipers on, even though it was not raining. She let out a little frustrated groan, before flicking the indicator lever up and down, even though she was not turning. She reached down and pushed in the cigarette lighter, even though she did not smoke. The knob for the lights was turned on, then off, even though it was not dark. Da had sat quietly watching as she went through all these motions. Trying and failing to hide a hint of sarcasm, he said, "Now, will we start the car?"

Joanne took both hands off the steering wheel suddenly and shook them in front of it in nervous little waves. "Sorry! Sorry!" she repeated in another anxious mantra, glancing over at her Da back and forth. Joe could not resist a little smirk until Joanne's death stare backwards wiped it away. She reached down and turned the key. It started first time and Joe was about to applaud her. He then changed his mind and did not, knowing she would think he was piss-taking. Joanne moved her foot on the accelerator and a roar erupted from the engine like the start of a stock car race. "Sorry! Sorry!" she repeated and then did it again, apologising again for another surge of engine power.

"Okay! You certainly know where the accelerator is!" Da quipped, surviving not having his blood spilt from Joanne's cutting look. "Let's try a gear!" Joe could see Da's face wincing in anticipation and wondered why. He found out almost straight away. The agonising cries of the gearbox made Joe's eardrums jangle and his teeth tingle. Joanne clutched again and proceeded with round two of the mechanical and passenger torture session.

"Da, don't you need to find the bite of the clutch?" Joe piped up, genuinely trying to learn and be helpful.

Joanne's head snapped around and snarled, "I'll bite you! What do you know about driving?" Joe was about to snap back about his driving the wee red tractor on Granda's farm. He realised Joanne had done that too, so remained quiet. Looking around, he realised tractors and cars were very different. Everything was all to one side in a car for a start. Maybe he would struggle the same as Joanne when it was his turn in two years, three months and twelve days.

Da asked her to calm down and take her time. Third time lucky did indeed prove to be so. Joe thought his bite advice must have worked, even if she did nearly bite his head off for saying it. Joanne slid the knobbed stick into first gear with a flowing smoothness everyone, especially the gearbox, appreciated. She smoothly pushed the button and lowered the handbrake. Joe could see the concentration on her face, with even little beads of sweat forming on her brow. She leant forward, her chest almost touching the steering wheel. Joe wondered what she was doing and why it was taking so long, before he noticed her left knee ever so slowly moving up. It was as if time stood still as Joe and Da watched Joanne closely, waiting and waiting for that moment of movement. That moment came a lot more suddenly than expected, and for a much shorter distance too.

The whole car gave one big lurch forward and the engine cut out. Joanne swore very loudly. Da gave her a slight telling-off look, after he had finished a muttered one word swear under his own breath. Joe had been sitting forward, straining a bit on his seat belt. He was flung back into his seat, a little seat belt edge burn mark on the side of his neck as a memento.

"Right, let's go again," Da said. Joe was amazed at the patience his Da was showing. It was not normally a talent he was renowned for, but he was showing absolute oodles of it now. Joe began to wonder how long it would last, but, to his surprise, reckoned Joanne had a good few more goes yet before she reached that point.

"Sorry! Sorry!" Joanne repeated.

"Stop bloody well apologising! You are only learning! Remember that!" Da replied, slightly annoyed, before touching her shoulder briefly for her reassurance and perhaps a part apology for snapping. Joe was seeing a few cracks staring to appear in the patience wall. "Try again! As Joe helpfully said, feel for the bite of the clutch."

She quickly turned the ignition on, and the engine purred quietly. Joanne assumed her knuckle mountain grip on the wheel. She intently focused her stare at the dashboard, sitting far forward and her left knee rising again. Joe could feel the car respond as the bite point was reached as it moved ever so slightly forward. Joanne must have thought that was it too, but she responded by letting the clutch all the way out in one swift motion.

The car lurched again, the engine sounding like a scalded cat just before it stalled. Joanne swore as she yanked the handbrake on, then apologised again and Da muttered a clearly audible curse this time. Joe added a second seatbelt graze to his collection as he was bounced back again by another round of this corporal punishment.

"Right!" Da said a little too loudly before he breathed and went back into cool, calm and collected mode. "Take your time. Feel for the bite. Then ease the clutch out. Okay? Nice and gently!" Joanne nodded nervously, was about to apologise but did not, the sweat freely flowing from her brow, now.

She turned the ignition on and released the handbrake again. She assumed the same clutch release posture as before. This did not inspire Joe with confidence, so he sat back this time to avoid a third painful little stripe on his neck. However, he was happily surprised that third time lucky did prove worth its salt yet again, as Joanne did indeed move the car slowly, if stutteringly, forward. She revved the accelerator a little too much before she found a steady flow. A smile actually succeeded in appearing on her red and flustered face. Da smiled too. He congratulated her kindly, but a little too soon.

There was a slight hill on the road up from their house. Joanne did not do as Granda would have instructed when tractor driving to 'give her some welly!' So, only twenty yards up from their front path, Joanne stalled and stopped again. She swore again. She thumped the steering wheel several times, only stopping when she hit the horn. The loud blare on a Sunday lunchtime echoed even more so around the surrounding scattered houses and laneways. A neighbour walking his dog close by jumped a little. He smiled and waved as he dandered over, possibly to have a chat. Maybe it was Joanne's fire-red face, or Da giving a big thumbs up and shouting out the half open window, "All right, Tom, catch up with you later. A bit busy now!" Whatever it was, Tom decided to take himself and Fred on his way. Joe looked hard as he always did at what all the local kids had christened 'Furball Fred'. As he always did, he tried to figure out which end bit and which end pooped amongst that fluffed up, blurry ball of red fur that constantly twirled around on its red lead. Joanne briefly waved but did not look as Tom passed on by. Joe just gave a brief nod.

"Don't worry. Take a breath and everything will be fine. You're doing grand," Da said quietly, taking his own advice as well as he loudly sucked a large gulp of air into his lungs. Joanne nodded and took a deep breath herself, followed by another even deeper one and released them both very slowly. Yet another one was taken and Joe could not resist having a quick look at his black, strapped watch with the chipped glass. He thought about saying he would catch the bus to Terry's, but it was a Sunday so there was only one bus into town, which he had now missed. He would have to stick it out, hoping to reach his mates house sometime before the school bell rang on Monday morning. He sat back and waited, impatiently trying to control his impatience.

Joanne took one short but deep breath as she turned the ignition on again. Joe admitted she had at least got that bit of the driving process off to a good start. Joe resigned himself to another jolt, gripping the plastic seat covers in preparation. Happily, fourth time lucky worked as well, and Joanne moved slowly off again after another successfully smooth handbrake release and move of the gearstick into first. With a little bit more rev, she moved a hundred yards up the slight slope. "Okay. Great. Let's go for second!" Da requested, unable to hide another little wince on his face. This relaxed as Joanne moved very smoothly into second, but Da's face turned almost prune like as she let the clutch out too quick again. The car jolted, and stopped. Joanne swore. Da swore. Joe swore and succeeded in becoming a seat belt sergeant as he obtained his third stripe on his neck. Joanne thumped the steering wheel again but avoided sounding the horn this time around. A passing blue car, containing a couple of hat-wearing elderly ladies returning from church, slowed and peered in at Joanne as they passed. Joanne did not even look at them. Joe stared out at the inquisitive ladies, giving a little wave, wondering why they still wore their hats when they were inside the car.

"Right! Okay! We are doing grand." Joanne glared at Da as he spoke but said nothing. "On the bright side we have not hit anything!" Da joked and Joanne frowned, although she still remained silent. "Seriously. You are doing fine. It is a lot to take in!" Joanne turned her frown upside down, smiling at her Da's encouragement. "Now let's try that again."

The ignition key grated a little as she turned it. Joe took this as not a promising sign, taking away the one positive achievement of Joanne's driving day out so far. Then, he was shocked and stunned that within a few seconds they were moving forward again. "Well done, Joanne," Joe shouted out a bit too loudly from the back. She turned to the source of the unexpected noise, took her eyes of the road, mounted the roadside kerb, bounced back down again as she rashly turned the wheel before Da could grab it, and stalled the car pointing at a strange angle on the road. Joe pushed his backside hard into the plastic of the rear seat, trying hard to make it swallow him up. Despite his efforts it did not! He received the full blasted tirade from Joanne. In amongst her yelling there were all sorts of names that were in the dictionary, and many that were not, verbally slapping him. He may have resented his recently inflicted seatbelt cuts but was very relieved Joanne was still constrained by hers. Da just gave Joe a single hard stare that told Joe to 'be quiet', 'don't do that again, ever', 'have a bit of patience', 'help your sister', and finally, 'you will get to Terry's when we get there.' All in that one look.

"Okay! Joe's going to be quiet from now on. Aren't you, Joe?" A quick glance back at Joe from Da made sure that there was not even the remotest possibility of Joe opening his gob before this never-ending journey was over. "Take a breath and let's try again." There was a little growing sharpness in Da's voice. This made Joe think more cracks were appearing in Da's previously solid patience wall. He began to wonder if the next mini driving lesson rumble would cause the final earthquake to crumble it down.

Joe slouched back in the seat grumpily. He was becoming fed up with this. Da had remained remarkably calm, well, calm-ish, for all of these past ten decades of minutes, but Joe could tell there were ripples forming. All he wanted was to get to his mate's house. He would have been quicker taking his bike, he thought. He wondered a moment about walking back home for it. They were, after all, not that far away from where they started. The burst inner tube from a too-speedy connection with the sharp edge of a deep pothole would have made that pointless. As he shook his head in frustration, he also realised such an abandonment would have had the potential to fire both Joanne and Da up, in an already incendiary situation. However, as Joanne fired up the engine, again, things began to look very promising.

The car moved slowly but smoothly forward and Joanne pressed on the accelerator gently. There was the stunned silence from Da and Joe as they tentatively waited for what turned out to be a another very successful gear change into second. Joe leaned forward slightly and began to smile as he saw the speedometer reach an astounding nineteen miles per hour. Joanne held this speed, prompting Joe to try to calculate how long the five-mile journey to Terry's would take at this speed. He gave up when he came up with the answer of nine hours and twelve minutes. That was bound to be the wrong answer, he chastised himself. However, as they continued to toddle along, he started to fear that his answer may have been right. Yet, he said nothing and mentally willed Joanne to go for third.

Joanne must have heard his telepathic message and she scrunched a little as she clicked into the next gearbox slot. Joe was impressed at how she had done that relatively easily. Third was definitely a tricky one going up, then across, then up some more. He would remember that for the future. Glancing at the speedo he saw that they were now travelling at twenty-seven miles per hour. Trying again for an ETA at Terry's, he came up with seventeen minutes. That did not sound right at all, despite how much he convinced himself it should be. Joe hated that part of maths and, as his recent erratic answer had shown, was not very good at it at all. A moment of panic hit him as he wondered if that was needed to learn to drive. Although he thought not, he decided he had better get better just in case.

Joanne leant back in her seat. Her brow was sweat free. Even her clenched jaw had relaxed just enough for her lips to part and there was the vague possibility of a small smile forming. When she moved smoothly into fourth gear a little smile did form for a second or two. Da too looked a little more comfortable, although his right hand still hovered right beside the handbrake and his face remained hard. Joanne's eyes kept moving from wing to rear, rear to wing, with the odd glance at Da to try to assess his reaction. He sat motionless with his eyes scanning left and right too, with Joe glancing into the rear-view mirror occasionally to see Joanne's face.

They had travelled to the end of their road and arrived at the needing-its-white-blocks-repainted junction. Joanne moved down the gears a lot easier than up, with only a little bit of jolting as her foot bounced on the footbrake. The car absolutely crawled towards what remained of the white line running at right angles to the slightly askew 'give way' sign. However, she stopped without stalling and pulled up the handbrake. Joe could not help but smile. There was even a bit of pride in his sister starting to shine through, as her earlier stinging snaps at him faded. Tension was flashing in big neon signs above her now though as two cars came along the main adjoining road. Da was on high alert too, his hand actually on the handbrake in readiness. The two cars passed and Da assertively stated, "All clear! Are you ready to go?"

Joanne nodded nervously but did nothing but grip the steering wheel even tighter. Da looked at her with a 'let's go!' message which she did not receive or reply to. "If nothing's coming. Come on, let's go!" Da said out loud and snapped Joanne out of whatever her thoughts had trapped her in. She revved a little too loudly, clutched a little nosily into first and Da let the handbrake off. She accelerated more than she needed but moved forward slowly, out onto the quadruple checked traffic free main road. Turning the steering wheel left her pointing in the right direction, and she accelerated some more. Joe could see she was absolutely crapping herself but he could smell nothing and hoped he would not. Finding an inner strength, Joanne moved up into second gear and sped up a little. Another brief smile crossed her face as her stony, focused stare returned to the road ahead.

It happened in a noisy blur. From nowhere, a blaring horn and a large flash of blue bulleted past them. It was so fast it created its own sound wave, the impact of which rocked their car from side to side. All three of the Average family members swore out loud. Da continued to swear as he watched the split seconds it took for the wannabe rally driver driven car to disappear around the next bend. Joanne ever so slowly pulled the car over to the side and stopped. Eventually being able to release his grip on the back-seat cover after that turbo experience, Joe leant forward. Her shoulders shuddered and Joe could see tears flowing down Joanne's cheeks. He genuinely felt terrible for her. It has scared the life out of him and he was only a passenger. He reached forward to place his hand on her shoulder and, although she did not say anything or react, he sensed she appreciated it. Her hand reaching up to briefly touch it reassured him.

Da went off on one. "Who the Hell does that arsehole think he is? What is he playing at? He could have killed us all! What have I always told you, Joanne? It's not you, you have to watch on the road, it is complete arseholes like that! What was it? Some big flash German car probably? Big Massive Wanker! Did you see, Joe?" Da did not look round to even see a response from Joe. Joe was still a bit too shocked to have replied anyway, even if he had known an answer. Da continued to mutter 'arsehole!' several times under his breath, and Joe was not sure if his Da's slightly shaking hands were from shock or anger or both.

Da's rant ended immediately when he looked over at Joanne. Sobs were coming out of her regularly. Joe removed his hand as Da reached over and put his arm around her, causing her to lean over into him, as much as her seatbelt would allow. "Look! That was not your fault at all!" Da said calmly. "Not at all!" he repeated loudly and firmly. He paused a moment then asked,

"Are you okay? Do you need a minute or two?" Joanne nodded between sobs. "Okay! Let me drive for a bit, then?" Da half-asked, half-instructed as he undid his seatbelt and moved to go out the passenger's door. Joanne did the same very quickly, arriving in the passenger seat before Da had even crossed the front of the bonnet. Joe reached over and silently touched her shoulder again. She reached up and held her sweaty hand on his.

"That's a hell of a thing to happen on only your second lesson!" Da commiserated to a silent Joanne. Da effortlessly went through the motions and pulled the car out onto the road, although he did scrunch the gears a little, forgetting he was in the old family car and not his even older work van. A few seconds later Joanne took a huge breath and wiped her eyes. Staring back at Joe, he saw a scared kindness there as she patted his hand some more. She gazed over at Da who looked back at her with a big smile.

"Right, Da! Pull over when you can! I need to learn to do this! I have to! No Big Massive Wanker arsehole in a big flash car is going to stop me!" Determined anger flared in her words. Da beamed with pride, relieved that his daughter had found her spirit again. Joe smiled too as he felt the warmth of his family in that moment. Da pulled over into a gateway and swapped seats with Joanne, pausing briefly in front of the bonnet for a hug. Joanne swiftly belted up, slotted the car into first gear and, with only a slight engine splutter, flashed the indicator and pulled out onto the road after her twenty-third check of her mirrors. Joe and Da smirked as they heard her muttering, "To hell with it all. I am going to learn this. I AM! I AM!"

Joe smiled admiringly, wondering if they might arrive at Terry's a bit quicker now. He was sure by now that Terry had learned that Joe was never exactly on time. Joe could not wait to tell him about this hell of a day so far and all he had learned, good and bad. Learning to drive was going to be a hell of an experience.

Land

"Are ye digging a grave for yersel'?" Frank hollered with a laugh, as he arrived on the spade cut edge after trudging through the mud.

"Hope not? But it might be the death of me yet," Joe replied, looking up with a frown on his mud-streaked, reddened face as Frank responded with a little laugh. Joe thumped the spade back in again, loosening yet another cuboid of earth. He muttered, as he had been doing several times for the past hour or more, "Sod this!" Before he raised the spade and shoved it into the soil again with his squishy feeling, sweat soaked inside, boot.

Frank hunkered down until his backside almost touched the heels of his clay clad boots and spoke quietly, "I had a serious barney wi' the architect, and the Clerk of Works as well, about this. It was their fault but they gave me the same old spiel about dominos!" Joe looked up confused, and Frank continued, "You know! When you change one thing, that has the knock-on effect on having to change somethin' else, and so on. They could not get it into their thick heads that it would be so much easier to make the connection over there instead. There we could use the JCB. But no! It has to be here where we can only get a man wi' a spade in. And that man is you! But no better man for the job!" he said as he looked towards a gap in the density of scaffolding-clad half-houses where the hole could have been, far across from the thorn hedge beside them. When he returned his gaze to look back at Joe, Joe could see a kindness and a little regret in Frank's eyes. The kindness he had seen before occasionally, but, apart from that one time with the cowboy hat, regret, never!

This thick hedge held back the nosy cows behind, dividing them from the tightly-packed, semi-constructed houses, inserted into the stone and mud that covered all the way down to the road. This large construction site had probably had cows and crops in it not so very long ago, Joe thought. Planning had eventually allowed new houses to be the only things growing daily now out of this former field. This crop of cement, wood and brick would only ever be harvested by estate agents in the near future. It was a lasting change as permanent as the concrete and tarmac covering where grass had once been. Joe thought, a little sadly, that it would never be farmed again. Lawnmowers would be replacing tractors, petunias instead of potatoes, with yapping dogs and skulking cats the only domesticated livestock. Joe and the rest of Frank's lads were sweating and grafting to make this dramatic change happen as soon as possible. It was happening everywhere across the country, with land being chewed and swallowed up for new houses. Joe smirked at new sites like these. These fast-erected houses were often smaller, less solidly built and with less room around them than the former homes on terraced rows and in council estates that the buyers of these new homes were sacrificing.

"I heard about wee diggers..." Scrunch. "Ones that are less than half the size of a JCB..." Scrunch. "They would be able to get up in between the houses..." Scrunch. "They would have this dug out in no time..." Scrunch. "Think it's the Germans that make them..." Scrunch. Joe spoke quietly in between digging, continuing to work, thus denying Frank the opportunity to make any of his unsubtle comments about chatting too much and not working, that he was prone to do. It was his right as the business owner, but it was still irksome.

"Nah! Why would I need to get one of them? I saw one of them wee things that looked like a big Tonka toy. You could shift more with a spade, just like you are doing. Sure, you are getting on grand!" he replied with a strange smile.

Joe just glared up through his sweat stinging eyes and wiped the back of his muddy hand across his mouth. Even though no soil had gone into his mouth, he loudly gobbed a spitball onto the bankside. He had felt the need to spit, possibly as a token protest, as he replied trying to not sound sarcastic, "Using a machine is a lot easier on the back!"

Frank just laughed. "Aw, you're young and have a strong back. Sure, it keeps you fit and gives you the muscles all the girls like!" Joe just snorted with his head down, rolling his eyes and feeling the growing painful twinge in his back. "Give Jimmy a shout when you find it and he will sort it out. Need to go. See you later on," he said as he stood up and started to stride back towards the scaffolding. He shouted something Joe could not quite hear up at a couple of the brickies, who were acting up as they treaded the boards. They waved back down and ignored him, but returned to carrying on slopping cement onto the blockwork of the third storey instead of messing about.

Joe saw Frank reach into the leather tool belt he wore. He had brought it back from the States when he had been on holiday last year. He always wore it on site now despite there being no tools in it, just a brick-like mobile phone in one side holster and a huge measuring tape in the other. He had brought a still-talked-about Stetson back as well. When he had arrived back, he had worn it, but only for a couple of hours on his first day back on site. The laughter and piss-taking from his workforce meant it was flung in the back of his car with frustrated embarrassment, never for his employees to see it again. In that short time, the slagging he had received was endless, not just asking where his horse was but other sarcastic, but funny, comments about cowboy builders. He still wore the belt, though, whipping out his large mobile phone like it was a six shooter, even when he did not need to take or fire off a call. He had pulled the phone out now and started yakking away on it as he splashed through the puddles, walking further away from a muddy Joe.

Frank Napier was a character for sure. He was funny, tough and slightly dodgy, but in a just-this-side-of-legal way. He took no shit whatsoever, but he was fair and good to his workers. He had recently insisted that all his work vans and his construction machinery were newly logoed up. It was another source of mickey-taking but he actually seemed to enjoy the attention. After carrying out two jobs in County Monaghan last year, Frank had changed his business name to include 'international'. He saw absolutely no reason to question this at all. "It is technically another country over the border, so I am now an international business!" he repeatedly argued and forcefully stated, despite the questioning looks and smirks. The gentle mocking continued when Napier International Civil Engineering became a NICE company. As Joe looked at himself clarried in mud, he was certainly anything but nice, and his armpit aroma was definitely not. Still, he reassured himself, it earned him a good few pounds during holidays for his studies at university and, as the sun shone, at least the weather was nice. Joe smirked as he thought of the new company name and logo that appeared on his payslip, thinking it could be a lot worse. He thought of his mate Jonnie No H working for Thompson's International Transport Services.

Despite his dismissal of Joe's wee digger suggestion, Frank had taken the trouble to check on him, knowing that it was not that handy a task. Now Frank was away, Joe paused a moment, swigging brown lemonade, finding it difficult to hold the slippery, brown, soil-covered bottle in his slippery, brown, soil-covered hand. He looked around at his achievement so far. He snorted again as it was like a grave, about nine feet long and four feet wide. The pipe had meant to be four feet down, but, although Joe was only dead tired and certainly not dead, he was six feet under the surface. This was what was frustrating him as he was starting to think he had been told to dig in the wrong place.

He raised the spade for the hundredth and more time and struck the spade in again. It hit an unseen boulder. The jangle went up the shaft, through his right hand, up his arm, across his shoulder and shot down his right side. The tingle only seemed to end when it reached his right kneecap. He grunted, recoiled, and began gently scraping the loose soil away until he could find the cause. Digging around he levered it out, lifted it on the third slippery attempt with a grunt and threw the large lump of rock on the growing piles at the edge of his hole creation. With relief he saw the T-junction of the pipe he had been searching for. This big boulder that had caused the reverberations in his ribs had been used to mark it. "Pity they hadn't put it on top of the ground instead! Would have saved a lot of hassle!" Joe muttered, a bit pissed off, under his breath.

He sighed and leant back against the crumbling soil bank, stretching his back muscles as much as he could in the confines of the muddy hole. Before he went to find Jimmy the plumber, he lifted his drink bottle again and took another large swig, wiping the sweat from his face and felt more squidgy mud smear across his chin from his clabbered hand. He looked at the bank as he swallowed, seeing how the soil colour and texture changed on the side that obviously had never been dug up before to put in this elusive pipe. The opposite side was a mixture of small drainage stones, soil, building site debris and a drink can sticking out. He reached over and ran his hard, calloused palm down the length of what would have been the natural, untouched side until he had come along with his spade. Joe looked in awe a little at how it appeared either precisely engineered or artistically drawn; he could not decide. The thin black line at the top, with the plant roots in it, had a band of orangey soil immediately below it, filled with more roots. Then there was another line dividing this from a darker brown band, which, in turn, changed subtly until it was black at the bottom of the hole. Joe looked between both sides, comparing how nature had neatly constructed the soil layers on one and what it was like after mankind had finished with his building work on the other.

Joe reached over to the layers and picked out a little leather jacket grub from it, peered at it closely and then set it carefully into the dug-out spoil pile. He looked even closer in the orangey layer and saw worms, lots of them, randomly spaced across the soil bank. They peeked their heads out to see what was happening and then wriggled back through the soil grains. A round little robin bounced down beside Joe, only inches away from him, grabbed a worm and flew off to perch on an overhanging thorn branch nearby. With a gulp, it swallowed its squirmy lunch whole, then came back for seconds, then thirds. Another robin appeared and a noisy and flappy fight briefly began. It ended just as quickly with the new arrival bullied away.

He glanced over at the other rubble and litter-strewn bank, and it certainly did not seem as alive, so he returned to gawping back at the natural one. Joe watched a huge, sleek and shiny, black beetle scuttle across the face of the bank, lose its footing and fall to the floor of the hole. Totally unperturbed, it just carried on scuttling. Joe was amazed when he thought that was the equivalent of him falling five stories and just walking away. He had read somewhere about insects being called invertebrates, their skeleton being on the outside, rather than having bones on the inside and being surrounded by all the organs and other squishy bits. From a biological engineering point of view, that, to Joe, made so much more sense. It meant he admired these little creatures even more. "You are one tough little critter," he said admiringly out loud to the fast disappearing beetle.

"Yeah. I know I am but less of the little!" came a voice from above. Joe knew it certainly was not God speaking, and recognised Jimmy's dulcet tones. No matter what religion, if any, they followed, this was a big man that Joe knew most of his workmates feared and respected more than God. He always thought even God might take a moment to compose himself before taking Jimmy on. Joe looked up a little embarrassed. "Sorry, I was just watching the biggest beetle I have ever seen…"

Jimmy interrupted, "So have you found this bloody pipe yet?" The half-smoked, unlit cigarette hung loosely from his lower lip as he spoke. It was an almost permanent feature on Jimmy's hard life, deeply-lined face. Joe always thought he must stick it there with something as he never saw it fall off. He never remembered seeing him actually smoke it either.

"Yeah, there it is!" Joe pointed, then grabbed the spade and exposed a bit more of it.

"Good lad!" Jimmy said. "Will you gimme a hand when I get the gear?" He turned sharply and wandered off, back towards where his van was parked on the roughly stoned area beyond the houses. Joe did not have to answer, so did not, as it was really a sort of rhetorical question, with 'yes' the only answer. No one said no to Jimmy unless he wanted them to. He was a man of few words that he more than made up for with his very large, slightly intimidating presence that spoke volumes. He was tall and nearly as broad as his height, heavy but not overweight and was a solid giant of a man. Not surprisingly, Jimmy was well respected on the building sites. Respect sounded a lot more courageous than shit-scared. Joe did respect him though, as well as fear him. Joe had seen Jimmy's kind heart in action, he worked seriously hard and was abrupt but never rude to Joe. The occasional, unexpected bottle of fizzy drink or chocolate bar he threw Joe's way was appreciated too.

Joe returned to his bug hunt in the soil as he waited, knowing if Jimmy had needed a hand he would have said. He saw more black beetles of all shapes and sizes. Then he spotted a centipede and wondered if they did in reality have one hundred legs. He picked it up but gave up counting very quickly and dropped it gently back where it had crawled out. He had to confess that, although he had done lots of this sort of spade work before, he had never taken the time to appreciate how alive the soil was. This underground world was a mysterious place with strange, alien-looking creatures. He always laughed when he imagined if centipede's and beetles were the size of dogs! People would have a lot more respect for them then, he thought. His brow furrowed as he realised that if that was the case, humans would do what they always did to anything that remotely threatened them. Instead of using the sole of their boots to crush these incredibly resilient creatures, they would just use more violent means to wipe them out. Joe considered how many hundreds, probably thousands, millions even, of wee beasties that had been and were being squished across this site every day. He felt a little guilt at his large hole, ruining their home and probably having contributed to the fatality list as well.

As often happened, his thoughts wandered. This soil, this land was the reason for so much bloodshed and turmoil to try to control or own it. Political and physical battles were fought over what flag should be stuck into it. His Granda had taught him so much about how precious the soil itself was for the farm. 'If you lose the soil or lose its fertility you lose the farm,' was Granda's simple way of stating its importance. Granda always tutted when he saw neighbouring bright green grassed fields turned black with plastered and pooled gallons and gallons of slurry. Joe remembered him saying angrily one time, as they drove along the road, past one of these acrid smelling fields on the tractor, "The soil's a living thing! That slarrying o' shit only drowns it and gives ye an inch of fertility at the top. Ye need more than that to be a good farmer. Then ones put far too much o' it on and most o' it just washes off into the rivers and kills the fish." As those words came into his head, Joe recognised he was seeing more and more of the fields around him like this; either bright, almost unnatural looking, grass green or slurried a stinking black brown. Maybe building houses on this one was actually saving it, in a way, from that artificial-looking and smelly fate, he thought.

He looked again at the worms and other creepy crawlies. He contemplated that they just carry on about their business without a care in the world about maps, or governments, or who owns what. All they worried about was eating, not being eaten and finding a mate. His admiration for such a simplistic life grew and he smiled, watching one beetle only half playing leap frog with another. It clung on tightly to the back of its chosen concubine who was trying to scurry away, having failed at playing hard to get and maybe regretting her choice. Although they were probably totally unaware of his watching this beetle porn, he looked away and gave them some privacy for their copulation.

He rested his back against the bank again, stretching his weary muscles to try to bring some ease. There would no doubt be more digging to make the trench for the new pipe that would connect into this one. Sure enough, he saw Jimmy with a full length of plastic pipe over his shoulder, like some Highland caber tosser on his way to show off his strength. He sniggered, thinking he would never call Jimmy a tosser to his face. Jimmy's other hand, not gripping the pipe, had his tool bag. There were orange plastic pipe joints sticking out of it as he bounced along towards Joe, the bit of cigarette still hanging from his mouth.

Joe watched him coming closer, like a mountain slowly moving, as he peeked out over the rim of the hole. He watched in powerless amazement as Jimmy tripped on something, then stumbled forward. With both hands full, this avalanche of bone and muscle landed heavily on his front. Maybe it was because he saw it happen, but Joe was sure he felt the earth vibrate as it absorbed this large man's belly flop face first into it.

In a flash, Joe scrambled out of the hole, definitely reburying a lot of his new insect pals and probably the recently revealed pipe connection as well. That did not matter as he ran across the mud and stones to Jimmy. The brickies on the scaffolding had seen it happen too, but they started laughing and cat calling instead of racing to help as Joe was. With each step he took, more mud gathered in the remaining grid-lined grip of the soles of his old boots. This meant that by the time he reached Jimmy, it was if Joe was wearing six-inch mud platform heels like some seventies glam-rock star.

It took a mere second for Joe to lift the pipe length still on Jimmy's shoulder and throw it to one side. He, in almost the same movement, took Jimmy's bag from his hand and set it a foot away to the other side. Then he knelt down with a squelch beside Jimmy who lay with half his face buried in mud and slight groans coming out of the clean corner of his mouth, his exposed eye closed tight. Joe spoke quickly and maybe louder than was needed, as Jimmy's ear was only inches away from Joe's mouth. "Jimmy! Jimmy! Are you all right?" Joe placed his hand on Jimmy's back, not sure whether to try to attempt to turn him over or lift him, doubting if he had the strength to do either anyway.

Jimmy must have had the air knocked out of his lungs for a minute or two, but started sucking large gulps of it in through the one nostril and half his mouth not buried in mud. Then, a stream of loud swearwords came out of him. Then, a loud single one, followed by a brief pause, before even louder shouts of pain and profanity came as Jimmy's arms moved and he dug his spades of hands into the mud. He eased himself up very slowly, Joe still kneeling by his side. Then, he spoke quietly and tightly, reaching slowly for his guts. "Aw, that was bloody sore. What the hell have I landed on?" As he straightened, he swore even more. Joe could see two half bricks sticking out of the ground within the large body shaped dent on the ground surface. Joe felt like he was on one of those crime TV shows, with the body outline of where the murder victim had been found. He briefly wondered if he should draw a white line around it? Thankfully, this large body was still breathing, even if it was painfully wheezy. Joe tutted as he had a little think back to the large beetle that had fell so far and still just carried on as normal. Humans definitely were not built like that, as even rock-solid Jimmy had just proved.

Jimmy pushed himself up further and slumped back into a sitting position, not caring about the wetness or dirt. He pulled up his completely soil-covered shirt to expose his massive, gorilla, hairy stomach and chest. A huge purple bruise was already starting to form across his ribs on the right side and he reached over tenderly to touch there. Joe just watched, not sure what to do. Jimmy seemed to be coming around. Nothing seemed to have been broken bone-wise, or else Jimmy was really good at tholing pain. Joe waited to see what Jimmy needed him to do.

"Aw, what is it they say? It's not the falling that hurts or kills you, it's the sudden stop at the other end when you land!" Jimmy joked a little breathlessly, his laugh cut short by the pain in his side. Joe laughed and rested his hand on Jimmy's shoulder, glad this hard man with a roughneck reputation was okay. Joe slid his arm in below Jimmy's mud-soaked armpit and across his broad back. Jimmy gripped Joe's shoulder as he rose to his feet. Jimmy winced in pain but stood up straight. Joe winced too, worried he was being pushed more into the mud than he was lifting Jimmy out of it. As they rose and both reached almost vertical, Joe released his hold and Jimmy stooped over, putting his hairy hands on his knees and sucking in huge breaths of air. Jimmy straightened up, his chest heaving and turned the top half of his body slowly towards the scaffolding behind. He gave a one-fingered salute and shook his fist at the still-laughing brickies. They went immediately silent knowing that they may be safe up in their scaffold tower now, but none of them were Rapunzel. They would have to drop down sometime for a hairy encounter with this winded but huge, fiery dragon that was not in a Prince Charming mood. Joe laughed a little, knowing they should have known a lot better than to laugh at Big Jimmy. His simple single-finger salute had sent that message loud and clear for sure.

Jimmy went to reach for the pipe and his bag again. "Wait! Catch your breath. We can sort that out later on. Tomorrow, even?" Joe gently reprimanded him. "That was some landing! I was just like your wife and felt the earth move!" Joe joked. He froze for a nervous moment as Jimmy gave him a hard, adulterous accusing stare before getting the joke and laughing as much as his aching ribs would allow. "You only half buried yourself, when I have a perfectly Jimmy-sized hole just over there to bury you in completely." Joe thought he had maybe pushed his luck too far as Jimmy stared back suddenly. Thankfully from Joe's perspective, he got it and laughed again. Laughter was always a good medicine, Joe believed, taking everybody's mind off pain and injury.

"Sure, that's all we get in life, isn't it?" Jimmy said a bit wheezily. "A time and a place! A time to die and a place to get buried!"

"Well, I'm glad this wisnae yer time or place, even if I did have a grave all sittin' ready close by. We would have had to do the pipe connection first before we put you in, though!"

Jimmy laughed. "That can bloody well wait, like ye say, until tomorrow. I'm goin' home to have a lie down."

"You have covered yourself in a field's worth of muck. Maybe a bath as well?" Joe chipped in with a smile. Joe looked in total amazement that, although totally soggy and brown, the half cigarette still hung from Jimmy's lower lip on the mud-covered side of his face.

"Aye, to think of all the fighting they do over this land. I could give them a pile of it for free!" Jimmy replied as he scooped his large hand across his shirt and presented a huge handful or dripping mud to Joe.

"I think I have enough on me to share as well," Joe replied, scooping a smaller handful off his knees as they walked slowly but smiling back to Jimmy's van. "What on earth do you want me to tell Frank?" Joe asked with a sudden realisation, as he set Jimmy's mud-encrusted tool bag in the back of the van. He slid the side door closed as Jimmy very slowly lowered himself into the previously clean driver's seat.

"Tell him the truth that I was brought down to earth with a bump and gone home. If he doesn't like it… Tell him he can shove it up his own pipe up and smoke it!" Jimmy replied with a painful wince. "I'll be back the morrow to finish the work, if the earth does not stop spinning in the meantime. My head feels like it is going around just as fast but its easing."

"Okay! At least you didn't fall on stony ground. Well, apart from a couple of brick bits," Joe replied with a laugh as he pushed Jimmy door closed. He flicked a small blob of wet soil from his hand, making sure it landed short of Jimmy's van. "Here's mud in your eye and keep your feet on the ground next time! Take care big man!" Joe said as he waved him off thinking Big Jimmy certainly did not treat him like dirt and was the salt of the earth. Jimmy smiled back at him as he revved the engine. As Joe walked off to find Frank, he thought they both had been brought down to earth with a bang today, Jimmy literally. Then he heard and saw Frank yakking away loudly on his large black mobile as he walked along.

"What do ye mean the land's no longer for sale? I've the money sitting ready to transfer o'er. Now ye are telling me the bastards have pulled it! Ye can tell them from me…" Frank ranted increasingly loudly as rising blood pressure made his face an ever-increasing red. Joe knew timing was very important, and now was not the time. He thought he would come back later to tell Frank about the pipe and Jimmy. Landing that on him now would have probably landed Joe in trouble. Joe wandered back to his hole to fetch his spade to dig his next hole.

Live

The double thumps were not as loud as the yells of pain, or the furnace of hot curses that followed from their entombed hell. Brendy's bad driving was condemned to be with them in that hell by a battered and embittered Joe and Brian in the back. They had lost count of the times a pothole was hit at speed and they were both jettisoned upwards for Brendy to see if his old Transit van's roof could be used as a nutcracker for Joe and Brian's increasingly lumpy noggins. To ensure neither of them defied the laws of physics, after the thin steel roof painfully stopped them both going up, they came back down again just as fast. It was also just as painful, although at the bottom rather than the top, adding more misery to the entrapped duo. The rough wooden crate they both sat on was not secured to the van floor, so it moved up and down freely. Joe winced, rubbing his head yet again with one hand and pulling a long splinter out of his bruised left buttock with the other, for a third time, making him wince even more. Brian was moving his hand from his scalp to before his face repeatedly, silently checking with serious concern if anything was bleeding or any brains had seeped out. Joe muttered angrily, "And we are not even at Newry yet!"

Joe reached over and banged on the mesh grill beside them which separated the comfortable front seats from the lack of proper ones in the back. "Here! Youse two! We are definitely... definitely swapping at Dundalk! No pissing about! At Dundalk!" Brian shouted even louder in support. "Dundalk! Youse both swore it!"

"Yeah! Yeah! Course!" The three in the front only half-heartedly replied, causing Joe to shout loudly over the noisy engine. "Brain and me are not staying back here in this cocktail shaker all the way to Slane! Youse two will take your turn – AS AGREED – when we reach Dundalk!" Joe certainly felt woozy and not from alcohol. Both he and Brian had become Van Wallbangers rather than Harvey Wallbangers. There was a pause with no answer so Joe put on his Da voice to say "AGREED?" No H and Builder turned their heads around to half look back, unable to resist smirks. No H replied, "Keep your hair on! We will sort that all out down the road!"

"AT DUNDALK?" Joe said again in his Da's voice.

"Yeah! Yeah! Down the road," No H replied but without any conviction, criminal or otherwise. His failure to mention Dundalk caused alarm to the battered two. As No H spoke, Joe could see Builder and No H's shoulders wobbling to contain laughter.

Joe and Brian, or Brain, as the lads still knew him, although this nickname might need to be reconsidered if there was any more van roof battering, had literally drawn the short straws. Grass had been hastily pulled from the roadside verge by Brendy before they set off. Brian's protesting that it was ridiculous using this as a way to decide front or back was ignored. Brian was even less keen on the selection method when he was one of the ones that lost. Joe, the other one, was equally unimpressed at his lack of luck in the straw draw. As they bounced around in the back, they both had had major doubts about the Dundalk compromise. He could hear the 'just a little bit further', 'sure, we are almost there' and such like comments once Dundalk was reached. So, Joe doubted very much if the agreed swap would take place.

He leant back against the side of the van, springing forward slightly with a painful scrunching showing on his face as one of the fresh and tender, swollen lumps on his skull touched metal. Rubbing it slowly, Joe plotted that, as the arrangements were too fishy, if they both ended up sardined in the back of the van until Slane, he was damned well sure Builder, or Robert as his Ma called him, and Jonnie No H would be travelling all the way back up the road home! Anger rose in him but then a contented little smile crossed Joe's face, as he thought of those two being ricocheted around when they returned with a raging hang-over and no sleep! Maybe he would stick this all the way to Slane after all? Another bump in the road and another added to the back of his head made him reconsider for a moment.

Brendy had managed to acquire five tickets from somewhere. None of the lads never really asked where Brendy acquired a lot of his 'merchandise'. Brendy never really said either, sometimes not even sure himself! That was the way it was usually left. Both reassuringly, and not so reassuring, Brendy had told all of them, as he dealt out the embossed cards, "I can assure you that these ones are the real deal!" His emphasising 'these ones' made the rest of the lads wonder what poor sods would end up going all that way to be turned away, their worthless tickets not even letting them enter a raffle, let alone a music festival.

However, what confused the lads was that Brendy had never, ever been in trouble with the Peelers, Tax Man or Tax Woman, the council or anyone from officialdom. Brendy was small in stature and a bit fly by nature. Sometimes this flyness was midge-like, just a teeny tiny bit the wrong side of what would have been called legal. At times, this morphed to bluebottle proportions, causing Brendy to buzz more than usual. Even then, his mates admired how cool he kept the bottle he never lost and always, amazingly, came through as vinegar and newspaper squeaky-cleaned glass. True, he associated with some characters who were so dodgy they could have ran across a minefield without any chance whatsoever of going boom. There were a few of such characters that did miss a step and paid the explosive price, but Brendy never seemed to put a foot wrong. However, his mates did not judge Brendy. After all, everybody knew those types of people they admitted.

So, the joint agreement amongst the four of them was that Brendy was probably a dodger, but he was certainly jammy enough not to get caught. Brendy was even possibly, although not probably, totally above board. At worst he was well over halfway up towards being there, by taking gambles left right and centre without placing any bets. They decided that Brendy only acted the wide boy the width of an ocean, as well as sometimes only a sea, sometimes a mere stream. However, the reality that he was really straight as a rush they not-quite-totally believed. The wind did blow occasionally, very strongly at times to bend things Bendy Brendy's way. When his cheeky chappie charade fooled even his closest mates, it most certainly fooled everyone else, including those with the peaked caps and clipboards. All of them could not help but admire Brendy for this.

Joe held tightly to an empty beer can in one hand and the millimetres of edge on the moveable wooden chest with the other. It was in the vain hope of providing some sort of anchorage in this turbulent storm of bumps. Both he and Brian sat rigid and silent, preparing themselves for the next big upcoming bounce they knew for certain would happen but not when. Neither of them even thought about delving into the crates of beer piled along the other side of the van amongst the sleeping bags, very small-looking tents and tired-looking holdalls. They would just have created mini beer fountains as they travelled along and that would have been a sad waste of good alcohol. The couple they had before they left sloshed about in their guts, only once or twice threatening to move all the way up instead of sideways. To take his mind off more beer, and settle both his stomach and his head, Joe did, as he knew he did too much of and despite his pounding headache – he thought. He thought Brain was doing the exact same, although Brian was distracted, still having to check if his scalp was bleeding again.

Reputation is an important thing, Joe thought. Brendy had a reputation for wheeling and dealing to obtain whatever someone wanted. How he did that was not questioned. The item or items were simply gratefully received and the money handed over. Robert had a reputation as a very handy builder. Brian's was brains. No H's was his amazing abilities with romancing the ladies but never able to hold onto one for any length of time, let alone permanently, so far. Joe had no idea what his was – probably being average, he thought, to match his surname. He did know the reputation of his homeland, having lived through it all his twenty years of life so far. All that did not matter. It was the reputations of those they adored that made them jump at the chance Brendy's ticket offer gave. Brendy's business dealings may have been a bit wonky but he never dealt much in chocolate. Nor did he have some fantastic factory, but it was still a golden ticket he had given them all, even if it was only printed manilla paper. Their idols, their heroes, their gods were why they were headed south. Slane was their destination, with their hearts singing at the prospect of live music. They were going to see and hear bands live, beyond the rectangular confines of TV or a stereo. As Cockney's would say, they would be having a butchers of their heroes giving fresh, meaty performances in the flesh.

There were some awesome local bands, thumping out cover versions of hit songs, sometimes even better than the originals, in pubs and clubs. There were even local groups with the courage to perform their own material. For some showing off their unique musical talents worked awesomely well, becoming headline acts that made local and international news. For other wannabe original pop and rock stars, they hit the wrong note with the crowds of teens and twenties in the pubs and clubs. 'At least they tried', or 'give them a chance' was not often heard at such gigs. Joe's own dearth of any melodic talent made him simply admire and enjoy whoever and whatever was playing, harmoniously or not.

Joe had head bobbed and banged and boogied along to all of them, even dancing on stage with the lead singer one time. That was until the bouncers chucked him off without any chance of an encore. It was all part of a night's craic, and music was always a big part of a night out. Although the only thing he could play was the fool, and his dance skills were at best passable, Joe loved music. The castrating cat sounds of screeching operas were about the only type of music that he truly hated. Country and Western he could love and hate, depending on the song's depression levels of how many dogs had died or lovers had run off with someone else. Everything else, even sometimes overcoming the snobbery associated with classical, he could listen to and enjoy. His record collection was not large nor remarkable, consisting of his own carefully selected rock, punk and a bit of pop. All these he cherished, even a few impulse buys that needled him when played. There were those he revered as gifted geniuses and musical masters that reached idolic levels of his personal worship. The bumps and grumps of this journey were going to be worth it to see some of his musical gods become mortal.

It was not just its smallness, but mainly it was Northern Ireland/North of Ireland's reputation that, not surprisingly, deterred a lot of the titans of the music world from even visiting, let alone touring. Bombs, bullets and bigoted bullshit will do that to celebrities' opinions of a place. A few bands and solo artists did very gratefully come. Joe had scrounged up the cash for a few tickets to have his brain reverberating for days after jumping and singing along to rock and pop bands in a packed-out Ulster or King's Hall. Slane was known to be so different from those. It was all the talk of his generation. Those who had been to this Irish musical Mecca were envied and interrogated beyond belief. It showed how the power of music cut across all faiths, providing minutes of escapism harmony in what was Joe's very inharmonious homeland.

Slane promised and would deliver global live music by the big boys and girls of the rock and pop worlds. There were even the mega groups that alien spacemen would have heard of and bopped along to. The power of their band name put to a song was sometimes all that was needed to send it into the top ten regardless of its quality. Slane was the Irish equivalent of Glastonbury, and none of the five of them crammed into Brendy's van had ever been before. This was a lads' adventure that promised to hit the high note above anything that had gone before, setting a standard for anything else that followed.

As suspected, Dundalk was passed without stopping, Joe and Brian only realising when they managed to catch sight of a road sign out the steamy front window. They very loudly protested, banging on the front/back separating metal grill like chimpanzees at the zoo and sounding similar. Joe's suspected 'sure we are almost there!' and similar other comments came from the three-up front, as they monkeyed around smugly behind the protective grill that kept Joe's and Brian's bodies and rages caged. There was a moment of nervousness when the front lads thought Joe and Brian were going to Tarzan-like rip the grill off. They did not manage it and eventually accepted their fate, returning to their moveable wooden crate seat. Joe whispered in Brian's ear about what he had thought earlier about the return journey. Brian's loud sniggers caused the Builder and No H to look back suspiciously.

The three members of the Front of the Van Boys were first to set foot on the muddy Slane field stage. Their support act, the Back of the Van Boys jumped out very soon after for their debut, spilling out the back doors a little battered, bruised and bitter at being deceived. After venting with shoving and gobbing off at their jailers, as soon as the back-van doors were creaked wide opened, Joe and Brian had quickly begun to take it all in. It had stunned them into stopping their protesting. In awe they scanned, seeing so many people scattered amongst the landscaped parkland. When they saw the stage where it was all going to happen, they froze in a moment of reverential respect. All five, forgiveness expressed with beer cans in hands, stood and watched scurrying roadies lift and lay all sorts of lights, mikes and speakers in endless repetitive action.

Crowds were already gathered in front of the stage, some already dancing drunkenly from an excess of alcohol or stronger stuff. Like a scene from a Western, the five of them strode in a line down the hillside, six packs holstered at their sides and cigarettes, not cheroots, hanging Clint style from their lips. They did not speak as they walked, savouring this iconic moment, each with a different tune in their head. These were blasted away as the roadies began the guitar and drum sound testing. Joe nodded to let them know that 1. they worked; 2. they were more than loud enough; and 3. that was exactly what they were here for. An extended drum roll rattled off across the fields and beyond, dramatically welcoming the five of them, and the thousands of others.

"Aw! Come on. You said Dundalk..." No H and Builder yapped groggily from the back unheard. Their heads were violently throbbing from a cocktail of alcohol, van roof thumps and the sound residue from a hundred speakers and amps. Joe and Brian slept soundly in the front seats. A bleary-eyed Brendy looked over at them from the driver's seat, seeing Joe and Brian's tired eyes tight shut but faces beaming contented happiness. Brendy smirked as he saw both slumbering lad's lips curl up every so often in strange little smiles proving they were still alive. Brendy smiled himself, thinking that, although tired, what they all had just experienced gave him and the others even more reason to live to tell the tales when they were back home.

If I was a musician, I would have wrote a song about this... Brendy thought ambitiously. To the tune of something vaguely unrecognisable, he began loudly and croakily with, "Slane! Slane! Slane! When will I see you again? Will I..." Before Builder did succeed in ripping off the metal grill in one pull. Builder's tender brain obviously was unable to cope with any more music. Right in his ear, he loudly and sinisterly told a shocked and stunned Brendy to stop singing, which he already had done from the shock of having part of his van interior partly renovated. Builder slumped back down on the wooden crate and winced as he pulled a long skelf out of his thigh. Whether deliberately or not, Brendy hit a massive pothole catapulting No H and Builder upwards.

Lifted

Joe was drunk. He had been before, more times than he could remember, or not remember as the case may be. He was at that stage where it took every cell of his jelly-like body to focus on one single purpose; moving forward and getting home. This simple task was proving more complicated to complete than it should have as his mushed brain wibbled and wobbled as much as his body. Many times before he had awoken the following morning when pure panic had, for an instant, overridden the booming headache, queasy stomach and foul-tasting furry mouth aftermath of the night before. The same question would flash frighteningly in his mind – *How the hell did I get home?* Somehow, he always managed to end up in his own bed. A few times, nowhere near as often as he would have liked, not being that lucky or talented, he ended up in a female someone else's bed. Other times he awoke with his entire body aching. either from curling his six feet two inches onto a two-seater sofa at a mate's house, or, when another alcohol-sozzled body beat him in the sofa race, from the grounded chill of a thinly-carpeted concrete floor ingrained into every bone of his body. Nevertheless, he had always made it to a home, even if it was not his. As he moved slowly along this street, insecurity soared as he struggled to find his homing instinct.

Joe's mind was set. He had always made it before at least to somewhere safe. Safe was much more important than warmth and not just because beer money to students trumped heating. These thoughts were bouncing on top of the swirling, nauseous, alcohol-induced waves surging through his mind and guts. He was convincing himself he had always made it before, despite usually having absolutely no idea how long it had taken or what not so scenic or direct route he had taken. Doubts incessantly crept into this head and he just wanted to lie down, but he pushed himself onwards, always onwards, up the street. Maybe onwards was too ambitious, with there being as much lateral movement as there was forward. A little retreat happened sometimes too as he staggered along. Regardless of the total lack of consistency in his direction, he just kept moving on. Where he lived was his only destination as he swayed and drunkenly apologised to the fences or walls he bounced off. He simply had to get there and forced himself to believe that he would at some stage of the night.

Joe was alone. The reasons for that were complicated and would fill a chapter and more of a book. He was not in a good place, in lots of ways, including romantically, but geographically was his most important concern. Vaguely recognising the street, he ever-so-slightly managed to sober up as it was the wrong one in so many, many ways. The only positive thing he could think of was that he was positive he should not be there, and he tried to speed up, attempting to flee. Trying to hurry only made his circular walk more pronounced, his legs flailing like some puppet having a dizzy fit. Taking smaller steps meant he was a lot slower but looked a lot less conspicuous. It meant his sea legs were a lot easier to control, as they bobbed along on the small ocean of beer consumed from several hours previous. He was just forming a rhythmic stride when a chill going down his spine caused him to stop completely. Three burly, blurry men on the other opposite pavement drunkenly shouted over at him. With his hand on a lamp post, he stayed leaning there, pavement staring until they passed. He did not respond to their incoherent taunts and he most certainly did not try to make eye contact. He may have been seriously drunk but he was not that stupid.

Joe was moving. It was as constantly forward as he could manage, as he saw the corner pub ahead. It was a place he had never been in and, based on the true stories and possibly feasible rumours, a visit was not in either his short or long-term plans. A lamplit smoky cloud hovered above those waiting outside it. They loudly laughed and talked as they waited for others, or just delayed going home for their own reasons. Joe, a good few yards away, straightened himself. He rubbed his hands across his face, the smell of stale beer, cigarettes and other unknown acrid aromas from them irritating his nostrils. Standing stock still and tall, he put one foot forward, wobbled like he was a toddler learning to walk again, but managed to hold himself more or less upright as he moved his other foot.

It was slow and needed all his concentration, but he congratulated himself that he was walking as normal as the far too many pints swishing in his gut would allow. Once he was past that pub, he had orientated himself; he was just three streets away from his dingy student digs. *Hold it together until then!* he inwardly yelled at himself. *Once I am past that pub! Once I am past that pub!* he repeated and repeated as he purposefully kept going close and closer to it. The rowdy noise increased as he approached, as did the smell of cigarette smoke, mixed with the stink from nose-scrumpling piles of vomit he noticed against the wall. There was the slightly salty smell of fresh piss from the littered alleyway, along with an assortment of dog crap and degradation also coming from there. All this contributed to the fact his current situation stank.

Joe was listening. As he drew nearer, the voices of those milling about aimlessly became clearer. There were voices loud and clear above the rest, others so slurred that, despite Joe speaking the same intoxicated language, he could not understand. His legs were shaking from the muscles straining to do the totally normal task of walking in a semi-straight line. As a river never flows straight, meandering due to gravity and obstructions, so Joe flowed along the street more like a piece of string than a ruler. His eyes were dry and sore, yet he kept them wide open, watching as his pupils darted from one to another to another of the men ahead of him. It was all men he began to notice, and he held his hands free of his jeans' pockets, nervously hanging them loosely by his sides. This meant, if needed, he was action ready, very aware the consumed alcohol would slow his response time to lame donkey rather than pony express speed. With a drunken urgency, he tried to sharpen his dulled senses but had to content himself with a wooden spoon cutting edge. Slowly he kept progressing until he was right beside a group of three leather-jacketed, barrel-shaped men of hard-to-guess age. They had not noticed him at all. Joe wanted to keep it that way but then it all kicked off, quite literally, just around the corner.

Joe stopped. It froze him in his tracks like he had ran into a glacier. The wall of noise that suddenly hit him was intense. It was a hard wall, spiked with vicious anger and huge sections of it almost melting from the hot sectarian yells he could not ignore hearing. The three men beside him, despite looking more like Labradors on a high protein diet, moved like whippets around the corner. Everyone Joe could see in front of him moved speedily around the same corner at the same speed. Their cigarettes were chucked up into the partial street lit darkness, scattering the air like nicotine fireflies. Smuggled out of the bar pint glasses and bottles, empty or not, crashed and shattered on the concrete, dropped to free hands for the vicious sounding fighting around the corner. Unlike Joe, they were all drawn, rather than blocked, by the ever-increasing volume of shouts, grunts and dull thudding noises.

Joe was curious. His head was starting to throb badly. Thinking about whether he wished to try to resolve his ever-growing curiosity as to what was happening did little to help. That was the way home, so he was going to have to go past it, finding out what was happening on the way. He could turn back, of course, but that would mean even more attempts at walking and being even later home. After some serious squinting, his black, strapped watch with the chipped glass had eventually revealed one thirty a.m. a good while ago. Now he had no idea of the time, but knew it was time not to be here with this going on. The noises were louder and becoming even less inviting, but he edged forward and peeked around the corner.

Joe was amazed. It was totally full on, like wolf packs that truly hated each other had been unleashed in the confines of a narrow street. There were snarls, ripping of shirts and jackets and blood curdling and letting of screams. The intense fury was as if all of them had been told the world would end in a few minutes and it was the other lot's fault, with their joint final decision to try to kill each other before that happened. Bar fights in movies looked like toddlers' brawls with soft teddies in a nursery compared to this. Joe just stood in absolute shock and awe, his eyes and ears becoming sponges to soak in every morsel of this feast of violence. This looked to be only for starters, so what would be served up for main course scared him considerably. Seeing and hearing, he could also certainly smell the sweat and thought he could even taste the anger spewing out into the air before him, but he was terrified to reach out to touch it. Then it touched him.

Joe was drawn in. Before him, the constantly heaving mass of leather and denim sprouted flailing fists and boots randomly in all directions. Sometimes a beer bottle or glass was thrown wildly. These numerous, free-for-all, in-no-way-refereed rugby scrums surged and swayed almost as much as Joe had been a few minutes earlier, Joe unable to try to keep up with it. As they moved erratically, these groups of bodies became like flocks of hens but instead of eggs randomly deposited, bloodied, groaning bodies were left lying behind as they moved. Clucking was replaced with ducking, diving and digging as they all strived to prove, regardless of the consequences, that none of them were chicken. Two bodies were eerily still and silent. Joe felt strangely and attentively sober now, alert to the enormity of the danger before him. Despite this he was frozen to the spot. A ball of grunting lads wrestled as they rolled towards him, but he could not move.

It quickly bounced closer and closer but still he could not make his feet sidestep, quickstep or take any step in any direction. Then, their dangerous dance ended as Joe became an unwanted partner with all of these scuffling, punching lads. He was knocked over by their not-choreographed impact, landing a backwards move to dance flat on the tarmac. Three, four or five blattering bulks, with sharp elbows and acidic bad breath, landed on him. Every cubic millimetre of air was pumped out of him in one motion. He felt like a lilo being jumped on hurriedly as rain drove beach holiday makers away. The seething mass on him rolled away, scrambling to their feet to dance to the swing beat of more punches and kicks. That was apart from the one who was left still lying horizontally across Joe's flattened guts and agonisingly sore ribs. The prostrate fella's head was bleeding, although not as much as the bloody blob of mince where his nose used to be. Joe was in too much pain, struggling so much himself to breathe, to even worry about the mistimed breathing coming from the large heavy lump across him.

Joe tried to move. He pushed at his slumped, unwanted pavement buddy, but could not get the angle right to move it. Joe tried to roll over to shift it but his ribs were too painful and he had nowhere near got his breath back. Breathing deeply and heavily, each in and out causing his ribcage to squeal, he eventually retuned his air intake to semi-normal. It was then he heard the intense blare of several sirens. Looking sideways, he managed to see the flashing blue lights coming fast and probably furiously down the street. They were swaying left and right past badly parked cars and through the few badly driven cars. Joe pushed again at the solid mass over him. He shoved both his arms underneath on each side and tried to shift it. Any direction would have done. After muttered grunts and groans he only managed to move it a couple of inches above him, but the pain in his ribs insisted so very persuasively that he decided to stop doing that.

Joe was stuck. He gave up and lay there as he had no other choice. The slight movement of this ton weight of a duvet made it an ever-so-slightly more comfortable wet, tarmac bed. So, he just lay there, repeatedly thinking of his limited options as he sucked up the pain. Sirens came closer and closer until they stopped just a few feet away from the entrapped Joe. His sideways glances saw boots moving fast as his ears heard the thumping of running feet and shouts of 'the peelers are here!' He knew he had to follow them but could not. He could only lie where he was, awaiting his fate as the cold of the hard road chilled his body, perhaps providing an omen of things to come.

Joe was lifted. The body weight was suddenly gone. Within a couple of seconds, both his arms were grabbed and he was pulled roughly to his feet. He was left alone for a moment which allowed him to lean forward and groan. Realising the pains in his ribs were not so bad now vertical, he gratefully gulped lungfuls of air. No sooner had he caught his breath, that he thought had escaped for far too long, then he felt a hand on each of his forearms and shoulders as two uniformed men shunted him towards the open back of a grey land rover. "No! No! No!" was all he could stammer as he pathetically attempted to dig his heels in, to prevent the forced movement towards the intimidating vehicle. This was not because, although he had been swimming in beer earlier, and in many ways still was, he was not an amphibian. Being frog-marched in this way and the sobering prospect of what could await him did make him feel ill and a bit green around the gills.

His dry throat made him croak as he argued and physically tried to stop himself from reaching that looming land rover. It all made absolutely no difference. He was shoved up the metal back step and plonked down hard in the far corner of the cavernous gut of the metal beast that had just swallowed him. A dazed and bloody-eared, short-haired lad faced him. A manic grin was permanently stuck on his face as he vacantly stared at Joe. Joe looked only once at him and then stared at the blood dripped floor. He looked out the open back doors to where he had lain, seeing a large motionless lad lifted onto an ambulance trolley and wheeled away. He could not see if they covered his face with a sheet or not. Although a complete stranger, who he had not enjoyed the company of, Joe silently prayed that they would not need to.

Joe was asked. A stern policeman jumped up in, slammed the door behind. He sat down confidently, a foot away but beside Joe. Another large officer opened the ominously squeaking land rover door again and swiftly moved beside Bloody-Ear Boy. This newly-arrived uniformed and bullet-proof-vested man sat, directly opposite Joe's identically-dressed bench-mate. In total silence, he ignored both Joe and the squirming slightly injured lad in the corner. It hurt his neck to look around at him but Joe's gut instinct told him that eye contact was essential with this man beside him. He fought the deep desire to look away from those intimidating hard eyes alongside. Simple instructions were barked at first. "Name? Address?" Joe, feeling remarkably soberish now compared to what he was, answered directly and strangely calmly, despite his heart racing.

Joe squirmed. "What were you doing here?" was the next question which unnerved Joe slightly as he knew it required a little more thought before answering. There was still too much blood in his alcohol system, so he ignored the need for thinking and just blurted it all out. He told them where he had been and briefly mentioned the hot argument and presumed dumping of him by his girlfriend. This did not even register one iota of compassion on the hard face in front of him. Bloody-Ear Boy opposite did start to say something sympathetic, but a stern look and a barked 'wait your turn!' silenced his yapped attempt at sympathy. The angry stare from the officer beside Joe's fellow land rover detainee also helped silence his wish to tell his own broken-heart story. He fell nervously quiet, touched an already red, saturated cotton swab to his still-bleeding ear yet again, and Joe filled the silence with more words of very debatable relevance and coherence.

Joe talked. Then he talked some more. Nervousness and adrenaline took over and he became a flowing fountain of facts; trying, he hoped, to avoid any fictions but some might have crept in there. Maybe not fictions, so to speak, but certainly a few embellishments of the truth poured easily out of him. There were definitely no lies though, or at least he was fairly sure there were not. He told the officer, wondering why he was not taking any notes or writing anything down, about his university course, his digs, his homeplace, his family… He just rambled on and on. It felt like forever, but he was cramming as much as he possibly could into the few minutes his questioner seemed to have allotted to him to answer. He gave the officer what he thought was his summarised life story, to which the face remained as impassive as it always had. It did not look bored, maybe a little angry, but mostly it did not seem to really care as it filtered Joe's information for truth.

The concentrating face opposite him just seemed focused on extracting the bits of information it needed from the huge jumble of stuff exiting Joe's mouth. Joe switched tactic a little, knowing when he had started talking about his Nan, he had gone too far away from what the peeler needed. He started talking about how he had never been in the pub behind them, never wanted to be, never been a member of any balaclava-ed acronym and so on. He was trying to evidence his good guy, or good-ish, credentials and appeal to the 'wrong time, wrong place' instinct he hoped the cop was sensing.

Joe was let go. Whatever he had said in the last few minutes of confinement seemed to have done something. The questions stopped, a notebook was taken out and scribbled in with a pencil. His name, student address and home address were hurriedly written down, probably for future checking, Joe very impressed that these had been remembered so accurately, even the postcodes. Phone numbers did need repeated though. Joe had nodded to confirm. With a brief 'we will be in touch if we need to speak further', one of the back doors was opened by the officer's muscled forearm. Joe hesitated a moment before an unsubtle head nod towards the door granted Joe permission to leave. He stepped out onto the tarmac as his interrogator slid up into the corner and, staring impassively at Bloody-Ear Boy, barked 'name?' at him. The door was closed loudly by the other still silent officer.

Joe was out but not free. There was still noise going on around him, with the wailing sirens of ambulances shuttling new customers to Accident and Emergency. Policemen and women were holding back a surprisingly large number of rubberneckers, gawping as they stretched to see what was going on. Two policemen were on the back of a prostrate bloke, who was loudly voicing tantrum-like. What he said in much less polite statements was that he most certainly did not want to be handcuffed or taken to wherever they were wanting to take him. His yells of police brutality and even 'SSRUC!' were greeted with a few unlocatable repeats and cheers from the watching crowd. Staring around, his head absolutely booming with pain and his ribs still aching, Joe knew he had to get away. The tension in the air was so thick he could slice it like a loaf of bread, increased by the faces of the policemen scattered around being deadpan. More people were gathering as more and more lights went on in the street's houses. This was not over yet and, as more RUC land rovers arrived and spewed out riot police, this made Joe's decision to leave not only necessary but urgent. He hurriedly orientated himself and pointed his body in the direction of the street he needed.

Joe ran. He ran like he had ran few times before, but his sprinting had waited until he had left the ongoing chaotic scenes outside the pub. Walking very quickly he had barged his way through a small gathered group of onlookers. Two of them patted him on the back and congratulated him as he excused himself past, something which he had no time to question their reasoning for. As soon as he turned the corner his legs moved. Although rather wallop-y and ungainly, his drunkenness fading, he definitely ran. It was as close to Olympic style sprinting Joe would ever achieve, looking like he was in a three-legged race, even though he only had two. He kept going despite his lungs on fire and his ribs burning, completing the first hundred metres of his homeward journey in five minutes and eight seconds he over ambitiously estimated. Such a time would certainly not win a medal, or even qualify him to compete, but Joe was racing for something much more precious – safety.

He ran again, gaining speed and endurance the more he did it. He went the wrong way once, then twice but he just kept running. He reached his front door, had no normal fumbling about for his key and then he was in his bedroom. He breathed, steam-train heavily as he sat on edge on the edge of his bed. His lungs were ballooning but he craved more and more air. His leg muscles felt like fireworks were going off within them, his brain a Catherine Wheel. He snorted angrily as the image of Catherine came into his brain, what she had said, what he had said… He forcibly rubbed all of that so-long-ago-feeling row out of his mind bit by bit.

Joe stared. His head and eyes were pointed towards the floor in the darkened room, not really sure why he had not switched the light on but not really caring either. He breathed heavily, slowing his air intake until he was taking breaths big enough to fill his entire lungs. By releasing these slowly, every time he did this, he felt a little calmer. He kept going until he almost felt slightly high on too much oxygen, even though this still did nothing to ease the rhythmic thumping inside his skull. His brain was rabidly going through everything that had happened to condense it into bite size chunks, wondering if he had been bitten or not by any of these. Some of it was too drunkenly blurry, but he was still able to pick out loads of the story that had happened a short while ago. He wanted to save the memories, to add it to the 'Joe's Journey' file in his head. It was not a classic tale to be told, but not a fairy tale, even though he was delighted it did seem to have a happyish, if not a charming, ending for him. At least for now.

Joe laughed. Why he did this he had not a clue, but he started laughing. It was a few sniggers to begin with, progressing to proper laughs, until he could not contain it any longer. He laughed so hard and for so long that he reeled backwards on his bed, even the pain in his ribs not able to stop him. Even the loud whacking and muffled shouting coming from the floor above, causing dust to drift from the ceiling hanging room light, could not prevent his noisy outburst. He did not know if it was just relief at escaping, or excitement at the end of an adventure, or simply facing the facts that this could have ended up so much worse than it had done. It was a kind of madness that took over him. Whatever it was that caused it, did not matter. What did matter was that now he felt lifted up into a happy place. Even his raging headache and queasy stomach could not take him away from this. His continued upstairs neighbour-annoying laughing was his attempt at trying to keep himself there as long as possible. Then a spasm of pain in his ribs stopped it immediately. He slumped onto his side, both the bed and him groaning for very different reasons. The face of the man with mince for his nose came into his head. The scary, staring police officer's face flashed before him. Then her angry face appeared. His laughter totally stopped and the sight of her paused his breathing momentarily.

Joe felt dropped. He had gone up the high road for a short while but was now back on the low one, not sure where this was going, let alone if he would be there before anyone else. His eyelids dropped and he drifted away, going up and down as thoughts and sleep intertwined until dreams and reality merged. Her face disappeared and he felt a smile creep across his face as other thoughts came to him. He was gradually climbing back up towards the sunshine, when sleep or drunken passing out overwhelmed him, and pitch-black darkness smothered his mind.

Joe woke up. He blinked his eyes, muttered his annoyance at the beaming bright sunlight streaming through the non-curtain covered window. His head hurt. His stomach and ribs hurt. He felt churn-y sick. His tongue had turned into a hamster. He overcame all this to ask himself *How the hell did I get home?* This was quickly followed by the even more disturbing and sobering question statement, *Did I get lifted by the cops?*

Left

Why was it so different? Difficult, as well. Alien, almost. It looked and functioned exactly the same as the other one, but when it came to certain, even very simple, tasks it was like he had someone else's attached to his body! He practiced as much as he could and was successfully, if slowly, feeding himself and drinking from a cup now. There had been several very messy first attempts but he had got there in the end. But it was writing that was the major stumbling block. They may as well have given him a crayon and told him to pretend he was a five-year-old from the childish results of his scribblings. Hindsight, he was learning more and more, was a wonderful thing. How he should have not bothered reacting if he had known the amount of hassle that moment of reaction was going to cause him in the immediate aftermath and weeks to come. This played constantly on his mind to irk him even more than an immobilised hand.

It was not that the jaw had been a lot harder. It was more to do with him angling his wrist wrongly when he did deliver the punch. He was only defending himself from a pushy pain in the arse that seemed determined to hit someone and had decided on Joe. The gobshite had swung at Joe, three times with his right. Joe had ducked to avoid these easily but painfully caught the unnoticed left flying fist on his shoulder in the process. Joe had then forced and fended off more punches with both his hands. Joe's right was so, so much stronger than his left, and so he favoured hitting with it. That was until he felt the shooting pain in his wrist as his right fist forcibly connected with the jawbone of the flailing firecracker fornenst him. Thankfully, the receiver wobbled away holding his face, blood seeping through his fingers from a busted split lip. This left Joe to feeling the pretence of manliness in the boisterous, goading crowd at the chippy van outside the pub. The very short fight had added to their night's entertainment, as happened most Friday and Saturday nights to fill the time gap between last orders in the pub and burger orders at the van.

Immediately afterwards, all Joe had wanted to do was yell in pain, potentially even cry, as the sharp throbbing intensified. Determinedly, he had silently stepped back into the three deep and six wide queue in front of the van to collect his burger. He remembered how hot it was as he grabbed it with his left hand, his right too sore. Loosely holding it, he remembered how the grease had dripped out from its paper to splatter, sizzling onto the pavement. Joe had sarcastically laughed then, wondering if it had been sizzling from heat or radio-activeness? He had looked sadly and uncertainly at his loosely described as food purchase. However, his hunger had been increased by the adrenaline rush so much that he did not question it any more. He could only hold it one handed, making it awkward and having to accept the loss of some of the burger's contents to the not hungry tarmac. On reflection, that was probably a blessing, but at the time he had wolfed it down, partially to sate his churning stomach and partly to stop him barking out in the pain from his wrist.

Concentrated positive thinking had, not surprisingly, not stopped the pain. He had refused several times, with an increasingly delusional 'give it a day or two, it will be fine' response. However, his mates had eventually encouraged him to 'get that seen to!' After a long-waited-for taxi ride, followed by an even longer nervous wait in the crowded, pain surrounded waiting area, it was only sprained the flesh treating, not eating, zombied doctor at A&E had told him. "Aye. Only!" had been Joe's response, thinking how sore a break must be. There was the possibility of a cracked bone but they could not tell until the swelling went down. Thick bandages had been tightly wrapped around and around by a stressed-out young nurse until she was content with the resultant white boxing glove. The tiny tablet contents of the small plastic pot she gave him rattled constantly in his pocket as he had walked home. They were given to torment him, he thought, as there was too much alcohol coursing through his veins, which prevented him from sinking a couple of the tiny, pain-relieving pills. He had been instructed to take these in the morning and, despite waves of pain, he had waited.

It was a troubled sleep, awoken often in agony when he had rolled onto his injured hand, but he had eventually dozed off. He had swallowed several tablets the following morning, two more than prescribed, for good measure, he hoped. They did, after an hour or so ease the enduring pain. Making cereal for breakfast had been much slower and more complicated than he had thought it could possibly have been. Toilet visits proved to be equally so, treating the previously underappreciated potential dangers of a zip with an alert carefulness. Everything was then, and still remained, so frustratingly awkward. He needed extra time for everything and repeated swearing did nothing to benefit speed. There was still a lot of pain when he, out of pure instinct, tried to lift things will his still heavily bandaged right. This slowed him down even further. He reluctantly had to face up to the fact that for the next while all that was left for him to do was accept that left was the right thing to do.

It had been three weeks since that had happened. His anger had grown in that time, which was only outdone by his ever-increasing grumpiness. His friends asking if he was 'all right' was said with genuine care but seemed mocking in his life being up the left circumstances. He had stayed up in his student digs and planned to do so for the next few weeks, to avoid his family's interrogation of 'how did that happen?' He had told them by phone, as well as calling in sick for his weekend labouring work, saying that he had sprained his wrist but without the precise details beyond 'I hit something with my hand.' They had probed a bit but gave up quickly and wished him well.

Meantime, he was muddling through. His left writing in lectures and tutorials had improved slightly, he thought. A few of his classmates had even joked it was easier to read his left notes than his normal right writing! He was grateful to his lecturers for giving him extra time for assignments and essays, most giving him until the end of term to submit work. The happiness at the novelty of such reprieves was soon quashed when he realised how much coursework was building up. He was managing to work around things fairly okay now after weeks of practice. He was able to cook, which was a relief, and not just to ease his hunger. Visits to the toilet were still a bit slow, but had been safe, straightforward and left no mark on his credentials. Long would they continue to be so, he hoped sincerely. It was writing wrongly that was the biggest problem he found.

Was it a tenth of the world's population were left-handed? he tried to remember having read somewhere. It definitely was not a rare thing if that was the case. As he had watched them at school and work, to him they always looked a little peculiar when they wrote and drew. Maybe that was not the right word? It was not abnormal certainly, just not normal to him and possibly other right-handed people. Sure, he pondered, were lefties not meant to be much more creative than righties? He had read many times, top artists and designers all skilful left handers. Left handers and footers on the sports' fields gave them a little extra advantage over those favouring their right side. Then there was the crème de la crème, such as the couple of people he knew who were ambidextrous. Now, there was a skill that he truly admired. He dearly wished he was like that now, to save all this weird unfamiliarity an unusable right hand had caused him. Watching these people swap from left to right with effortless ease was truly amazing, he thought. It was strange, though, that they usually favoured one hand when they wrote, usually the right.

He often wondered why that was. His most plausible theory was that historically this was one of the strangest of the many sufferings beliefs and religions had imposed on people's natural instincts. The left hand was associated with the devil, supposedly. Having personally never having shook hands with the devil, or watched Lucifer write a letter, he was never wishing to or planning to either, Joe could neither confirm nor deny that Lucifer was a leftie or not. The left-handed and footed people he knew were not evil as far as he could be certain. He had heard sad stories of left-handed kids at school in olden times being constantly caned and beaten for using their left hand and forced to write with their right. He sympathised with them so much more given his last few weeks of his own traumas of unnatural hand usage.

It was not just about evil but there was lots of folklore about lefties being unlucky too. To Joe it seemed to be that demonising left handers would not do much for their luck at all and that was probably the main reason for their perceived bad luck in the first place! They were persecuted into being unlucky and not simply by being a lefty in the first place. It was not fate, but what was inflicted on them wrongly by righties. All of this lefty demonising stuff sounded to Joe like it was just another example of the majority picking on the minority, yet again. He imagined judgement being passed as to 'why should we kill, or banish, or treat this person badly? Oh, they are left-handed – that's a good enough reason!' It is just another factor to use against someone, same as religion, skin colour, lack of wealth or whatever has been, and still was, used to reportedly rid society of what 'they' had decided was evil. Joe snorted yet another laugh at the madness of the world and the pettiness of many of the people on it.

Joe steadily lifted his mug of tea left-handed with ease, slurped a little from it and placed it back on the table without a single spill. He congratulated himself and realised his right hand was easing. The big bandages had been removed yesterday, and now he had this orange sock thing that itched a lot. He could flex his right hand a lot more and bend his fingers easily. It was quite strange that, because he had been using only his left for the past while, he was starting to favour it. He had found a new respect for lefties that he realised he had not had before. Maybe he would keep using his left as he was even starting to write much more legibly left-handed. Well, only legibly to him he had been told, a few times, so maybe not, then. He would continue nevertheless, training to be, if not achieving the goal of ambi-, at least able to be a little more dextrous.

Even that phrase about being up the left was applicable to Joe all the time and not just over the past couple of weeks, when he had been left without use of his right. Being up the left was in fact not that bad, he pondered. The more he thought about it, the more he realised that those ones that thought they were always right were usually complete patronising pains, who deserved to be left well alone. Perhaps it should be left solely to the individual to decide what they wanted to do. That would be right, would it not? 'Each one of us can then be left to do what we feel is right.' There was nothing wrong with that, Joe thought, as he reached out with both hands and brought his mug up to his mouth. It had left a ring on the table.

"Ah well," was all he said and left it at that. There were plenty of other rings already on the old table, so one more would make no difference. Some things are better just left as they are, he decided. Then his brow furrowed as he asked himself, *But what if they are not right?* He reached for a leftover takeaway napkin, stuffed in a cup on the table, and began wiping...

Line-up

There was a strange, nervous, unknown tension in the air, even for those who had been before. Some of the others gathered in this spartan, white walled large room talked quietly; most were silent. A few, sometimes rather manically, laughed and joked with those beside them. Joe could hear the jokes easily, as could the rest of the room above the general low hubbub of other voices. The purpose of the loud laughter for two fidgeting lads especially, on the far side of the room, was certainly more to dispel nerves than for what the jokes deserved. Joe scanned the assortment of faces around the room. All of them had the look of apprehensive expectation.

Joe's study course mate Stevie beside him did likewise out of a mixture of inquisitiveness, trepidation and boredom. There were fresh, clean-shaven ones contrasting with rather haggard, stubbled ones. Joe stoked his rough chin and slowly rubbed his tired eyes, knowing he fitted into the latter category. They had both been doing this quietly for half an hour or more, neither in much of a mood to talk, the weight of the atmosphere in the room supressing their usual excited conversations. Both of them were careful to ensure no direct eye contact was made. If eyes did meet, heads were quickly nodded and lips turned into brief smiles, before moving their vision onwards quickly, before any potential 'what you looking at?' accusations were fired out in response. To Joe, awkward and tense, with a fair dollop of fear of the unknown thrown in, was certainly how this whole room and situation felt.

There were twenty-nine late teen and twenty-ish-year-old lads all gathered together. The number was exact, as Joe had counted them all three times in his quest to find something to do to kill time. Some were sitting on the few hard seats available, with two centrally placed soft armchairs left vacant for some unknown reason. Most stood about quietly, paced idly or chatted randomly to those next to them. Joe guessed most were like him, having never been in this situation before. Stevie had been, once before, and leaned semi-relaxed against the wall. Joe was itching to ask Stevie more about what he had let himself in for but remained silent, leaving the questions scratching about in his head. As the time passed, Joe had increasingly doubted, several times, why he had come. This niggling regret grew as the minutes tortoised past. He sensed he could not leave, and that none of them could. Actually, that may have not been the case, and they possibly could have left when they wished. However, despite the anxiety clear on some of the others' faces, no one seemed anxious to test out the potential for freedom. There were two large policemen at the closed door, the sides of their faces visible through the rectangular door glass with its squares of wire mess within. They were possibly the main deterrent. Until the police were finished with them, whatever that involved, they could not go anywhere. All of the room occupants seemed resigned to this unknown time of release.

Joe and Stevie had been dawdling up the street, slightly late for a lecture but not feeling the need to rush. They had been stopped by two very pretty, uniformed, female police officers, who had smiled warmly. In hindsight, Joe actually remembered what this situation was called on TV and in the movies. Honeytrap had sprung into his mind hours later but had not done so when Stevie and him just met them. Maybe that would have changed his mind, then? It would have still been very hard to resist as they had so sweetly and politely asked if Joe and Stevie had some time to spare to help. The two lads were somewhat enthralled by the sparkling eyes of the young officers, although they both did glance over briefly to register the two large, bulletproof-vested male officers standing alert a few feet away in the shop doorway, machine guns straddling their chests. The female officers chatted away as they placed a clipboard in front of both of them, asking Joe and Stevie to fill in a few details. It was just name, address and age, nothing too time consuming, so both of them scribbled down the information.

Immediately the form was filled in; although both were very thankful, the friendly brightness in the officers' eyes dulled noticeably. The dark-haired one spoke to Joe, the other blonde one to Stevie, directing them to go to the police station around the corner. Joe had a sudden feeling of questioning what he had done, but obeyed and followed behind the striding Stevie, as the two officers approached another group of three young lads. The trio waved and shook heads, apologising profusely as they semi-jogged on up the street. Joe remembered seeing them do this and, in hindsight, thought that those three had been better prepared for a honeytrap that he and Stevie had willingly fell straight into. Joe felt a bit sticky when he thought of this later, but in a good way.

Joe had not been in a Police Station before. He never had a reason to be and never wanted to have one either. Well, there had been that one time when he had come very close. He had had a few too many pints and had been in the wrong place, most definitely at the wrong time. However, that was another story for another time. He continued down the pavement, his rapid heartbeats adding to the percussion to his bass beat footsteps, as the Cop Shop loomed before them, Joe wondering what was for sale there, and at what price? Maybe there were offers? Instead of that being a funny thought, it somehow had a sinister edge to it that did little to help Joe's nerves. He had heard about 'special' treatments inside some stations and did not want to know more.

Police Stations in Belfast in particular, as across the rest of the towns and villages of his homeland, were not designed to be places you voluntarily visited. Foreign tourists would meekly cower as they passed by, the same way locals did. The ongoing, strange, war-zone this land had become was reflected in the formidable fortress like architecture of these buildings. They had been built to withstand all sorts of potential attacks, using the same defensive principles of medieval castles. Twenty-feet walls, some as thick as they were tall, were topped with neck cricking heights of wire fencing. At the very top, just in case some madly athletic assailant ever reached there, were rolls and rolls of, still visible from a pavement viewpoint, vicious-looking razor wire. Joe stared nervously up as he walked past, feeling the structural intimidation this bunker of a building emitted. At the fortified entrance, Stevie spoke briefly to the heavily armed officer sentry, who with a nod and a point spoke quickly to direct them both. Joe made his way through the ice-cold-to-touch, metal turnstile that blocked the entrance instead of a portcullis. He felt his heart race and a feeling of dread come over him. Images of dungeons and torture chambers kept coming into his mind and, no matter how he tried, he could not dispel them, too late doubting why he had volunteered for this.

They had walked slowly over to the interior building ahead of them. Its outer appearance surprised Joe, looking more like an ordinary office block than he had expected. Although, it still did have a resemblance of a strong walled inner keep. Joe paused a second to wonder what inner secrets it kept and a shiver went down his spine. It had thick, concrete walls with horizontal slits for windows that gave the building a sinister, yet almost sleepy appearance, as if it was slumbering but ready for action if needed. Another shirt-sleeved and bulletproof-vested officer stood at the front of the strong, glass entrance doors. With a polite but woolly-sounding grunt for a greeting, he entered and they followed him, sheep-like. He led them down a white-walled corridor, Joe and Stevie gazing all around, even though the white walls were blank. No pictures, or signs, noticeboards or anything to read at all. After a few yards, he swiftly opened another door and waved them silently in. Joe entered first and was greeting by the synchronised stares of those already in the room.

A couple of ones in the far corner nodded to Joe and Stevie; Joe knowing he knew them from somewhere but struggling to identify them. After a brief brain rummage, he gave up and concluded their names were unknown to him. Both Joe and Stevie nodded in return and smiled over. As they moved over to an empty spot by the wall Joe whispered a, "Who are they?"

Stevie said huskily back, "Not a clue!" They thought no more about it as they stood with their backs to the wall. In some situations, this was always seen as a bad and desperate situation to be in, but not to Joe at that moment. Having the solid, cold plaster touching his shoulder blades felt reassuring to him, offering rear protection as he surveyed the room for any potential attacks from front and flank. It felt surreal that he was in a police station, which should have been the safest place possible but did not.

Joe and Stevie had actually started wishing they were sitting in their so, so, much-less-boring lecture on… Neither of them could remember its title. They did know the very elderly professor taking it who was so, so, admirably knowledgeable. He was indeed a leader in his chosen field but listening to him was the aural equivalent of watching grass grow. Joe had asked Stevie in a whisper about his level of boredom. Stevie replied something about it being almost like watching the paint dry on a cricket pavilion and he was so bored of being bored it was becoming boring. Joe had just finished sniggering when the door burst open. Four men urgently charged in causing every single body in the room to jump to attention. Those seated automatically jumped to their feet and Joe would have not been in the least bit surprised if some had saluted. He, inexplicably, had actually resisted that urge himself.

One of the men was very obviously a high-ranking policeman. It was not just the crisp lined uniform he wore with braid around his peaked cap and brass pips on his shoulders. He had that air about him. That aura of power that emanated 'do not even think of not doing what I say.' Beside him was a very expensively-suited and shiny-faced man, with distinguished-looking features and greying hair. Joe sensed he too had a shining aura of power, but this was restricted by the shadow of the top cop beside him. There was another flustered looking young man, probably a few years older than Joe and Stevie, sweating slightly as he tried to hold two briefcases, scribble notes onto a file pad, prevent the contents of paper folders falling out, as well as keep shoving his glasses up his nose bridge every ten seconds or so. The last man was also well suited up, with a shine on his shoes that would have demanded sunglasses. The glinting sparkle from his watch, several rings and seriously large cufflinks dazzled as he fidgeted to adjust his tie. Joe sensed he was powerful in his own way too but was making sure his aura was well hidden, for whatever reason. Joe watched him closely as this man silently scanned the room, like a security camera closely manoeuvring around and recording everything methodically. The others talked in babbles, constantly consulting the paper folders' contents.

"Line up along the back wall, if you please!" was the sudden, loud and impossible-to-ignore demand that came from the uniformed policeman standing in the open doorway. Surprisingly enough, there was absolutely no delay and this was actioned immediately, with the rapid noises of footsteps and chairs moving filling the room. As they walked smartly over, bumping shoulders with others as they all packed into the same area, Stevie quietly asked if Joe wanted a blindfold or a last cigarette. Joe had a genuine second of panic, images flashing before him of white squares placed over hearts on uniforms, before he saw Stevie's grin and shouldered him gently as a rebuke.

They stood in three lines, the entire length of the room. The policeman that had been at the doorway had moved over to ask, nudge and tug them until their lines were straight. It was not alphabetical, or height or any other criteria-related, just straightness seemed to be the aim. This, very surprisingly, was achieved in a minute or two, with very limited cajoling. Joe remembered back to his schooldays when such a simple task would have taken so much longer. He realised that messing about may have been tolerated a bit at school but definitely not here. Everyone was compliant and did exactly as they were instructed. Joe and Stevie were in the middle of the middle row. Joe smirked as he thought that appropriate. After all, his name was Joe Average, so he should be in the most average spot, even though it felt like a mean one. As he stood silently, he wondered, using the same rationale, if Stevie should actually be over at the very far end? West was his surname.

Before Joe's mind could wander off in any more obscure tangents, the group of four then moved over to the end where Joe had thought Stevie should have been. All four looked, with similar frowns and serious expressions, into the paper folder laid flat on the grey-haired suit's briefcase. The lining-up cop followed behind them. All five looked at the folder then up at the first slightly sweaty, angst-ridden face before them. He nervously said, "Hello!" and was met with a sharp 'no talking'. All four shook their heads and the line-up cop gently grabbed the lad's upper arm, moved him aside and directed him with a head nod towards the exit door. There was the same look and shook with the lad now exposed behind and he was gently moved aside. The same with the lad now revealed on the back row. Again, there was the look and then all four heads were shook.

Joe could not see the faces of those not chosen, for whatever reason, to see if it was relief or disappointment. The four just kept moving along the rows like they were Quality Assurance Inspectors of a dodgy batch of action toys, although their ponderous moving along the rows was the only action happening. Rejections seemed to be the main result, as one after the other the door creaked open and closed, as the twenty-nine were whittled down. By the time they speedily approached Joe in the middle, only three lads were left conspicuously standing on their own in the first half. They stood exposed, like they had charged as a battalion and had been machine gunned down to these last few survivors. When they glanced nervously around now and again, Joe saw they had a similar look about them.

"Remove your glasses, please," was asked of Joe by the glitzy, cuff-link suit. Joe had been caught a bit unawares by how fast they had reached him.

"Yeah, sure!" Joe replied as he grabbed them off his face, only to be rebuffed with a 'no talking'!

"Sorry!" Joe replied to be rebuffed again with a sterner 'no talking'. Joe hung his head, a little embarrassed.

"Head up, please!" he was asked, realising they had had more conversation with him than they had with all of his dozen or so predecessors.

"Sorry!" he said instinctively again, then hung his head in embarrassment, then straightened up and looked straight ahead, before he was told off again. There was a moment of pondering as all four of them looked thoughtfully at Joe, then the folder, then Joe again, then the folder. Joe became a little nervously excited at the prospect that he might be a chosen one but then there was a final look. Then the heads all shook and he was ushered to the doorway.

As he exited the door, he quickly looked back and saw Stevie standing along with the other three chosen so far. Joe smiled, giving Stevie an unseen little wave as he went out the door. Joe was not sure if he should be happy for him or not. He closed the door quietly behind him and was about to walk past the little table set up in the corridor, with the dark-haired officer from the Honeypot earlier. He stopped and decided to stick around for a little while.

"Hi, again," she said, appearing genuinely friendly this time. "Don't forget your money." Joe almost had, as she had whizzed so quickly through her words earlier that Joe had not really taken them all in. To be honest, he had to confess, he was looking at her more than listening when he had met her previously. She reached over a five-pound note, as she had been doing to all of the previous rejected lads. Holding a pen towards Joe, she directed him to sign that he had received the fiver, smiled and wished him well. Immediately, she said the same, "Hi, again. Don't forget your money," to the next lad leaving the selection room. Joe wondered if he should call it the rejection room instead, as more were turned out than kept in? Walking up the still, boring, white corridor, Joe overheard the two lads in front say that if you got picked to line up in the proper official one, with the accused bad guy standing beside you, you were given a tenner! Sometimes even twenty if it took a while longer the other one said he had heard. Joe reached into his jeans pocket and checked his boredom-earned fiver was still there and was quite content with not having been picked.

Joe squeaked his way out the still-freezing, cold-to-the-touch turnstile. He ambled slowly up towards the street corner, wanting to wait for Stevie but not wishing to look suspicious loitering about outside a police station. He lit a cigarette, pulled on it long and hard, letting a billowing cloud escape from his mouth and nose. He felt like he deserved it, feeling the relief of having that over with. As he tugged again on the orange butt, he wondered what he had made of that experience. He had a fiver he did not have before, which was a good bonus, even if it was very unlikely to survive intact after a couple of hours in the Student Union bar later. He had missed a boring lecture which he would need to catch up on, but that was a bonus too. He had seen the inside of a police station without being handcuffed or reporting a crime, which was good too. So why did he feel so strange? It was very hard to describe, almost like he was needing a shower, feeling dirty, somehow. It felt like that time they had been working on the building extension at the local abattoir. Despite daily showers and scrubs, even days later he thought he could still smell what he could only describe as suffering on him. That was how he felt now, like the inside of that police station was stuck to him like a bad smell.

The dirty, smelly feeling felt so wrong, but it was the only way he could describe it. He may not have agreed with the actions of the police in some cases but he still had a lot of respect for them. They were brave, committed and always polite, in his experience. As he puffed as he waited the unknown length of time Stevie was going to be, he thought about this dirty feeling. He came to the conclusion that it was right to feel like this. A police station was not somewhere you wanted to be, whether perpetrator or victim. So, by feeling freaked out by being in it, wanting desperately to be rid of the smell and feel of the place, Joe decided was perfectly normal.

He had touched the law and it creeped him out a bit, which, he decided, was totally natural. The law always did win in the end after all, but not like on TV or in the movies. Despite the fantasy portrayal of super sleuthing, in the real world the bad guy or gal was only caught maybe a quarter of the time at best. The many, many unsolved cases cooled and cooled over months and years until no one but the victims and their families continued to search for the warmth of justice. He knew all too well that it was not always the judicial law that punished the bad guys and gals. There were other laws, on the streets with their jungles of murals and flags and painted kerbstones, that sorted out certain problem people before or after the police, judges and juries had got to them. Or sometimes they removed the need for the legal forces to be involved at all, as 'disappearances', 'accidents', and simple brutal murders served the wishes of those administering the ironically-named community justice. Joe was adamant he never, ever wanted to be lining up at the request of either justice. There was a smell of death associated with those conducting those types of vigilante trials that Joe was sure they would never wash away. Joe shivered a little as he remembered an article from last night's paper with sledgehammers involved.

His thoughts were creeping him out. He decided to give up waiting on Stevie and stubbed out his cigarette on the pavement. He headed home for a very hot and soapy shower. He hoped there would not be a queue for the house's one and only bathroom for six people. He had lined up enough today to do him a long time.

Lady

"She certainly gives a whole new meaning to the word cocksure, doesn't she?" Jonnie No H slyly stated with a quick flick up of his eyebrows. The other lads at the table burst into projecting spittle and beer droplets at each other across the table in synchronised laughter. That was except, as usual, for Robert, or Builder, as the lads knew him.

Every time she was mentioned, he would redden slightly in the face, go even quieter than normal and then chip in at random points in the conversation to try to change it. None of the lads truly knew the reason for this. They had all tried to worm it out of Builder over the years. He would just gruffly dismiss it, not wanting to talk about it. He would add 'ever!' as the decisive finish to Joe's attempt at fishing out what troubled his mate when she was mentioned. Without any evidence Builder's mates had all decided on a plausible unsubstantiated scenario. They were fairly sure that she had possibly baited him, and it was where his worm had been potentially wriggling that had caused Builder's reluctance to talk. It was left at that until they found out for sure, but they all knew they never would. Builder had built a protective wall around himself about this and none of the lads could or would try to break that. Builder would have to knock it down himself and, despite having all the tools in his van, that was not likely to happen soon.

Catriona White, despite her surname, would have been the talk of the local gossips if she had walked up the aisle in all that was associated with a traditional white wedding dress. Cat, as she was known, had scratched a lot of backs in her twenty-something years. Quite a few local lads had the scars to prove it. This was who Jonnie's 'cocksure' comment had been about. As the laughter died down, pints lifted and cigarettes lit, Joe sat at the table with the six others and thought. He knew he did too much of this but carried on anyway.

He went around the tightly-packed seats, peering over the even tighter clutter of full and empty glasses on the table. The general murmuring hubbub of conversations and clinking glasses came from the other packed tables nearby. Joe's smile was Cheshire as No H caught his eye. Jonnie gave him a strange look, then carried on talking to Brian beside him. Jonnie had no real right to be so catty about Cat, but it was said as a joke. Jonnie and Cat had a light switch relationship, on and off, then on and off again, and so on. Both thought it was just a bit of fun. Then, at times, they seemed so serious about each other, before they would be back to scratching each other's eyes out. Jonnie even proposed to her in the pub one night. Granted it was after too many vodkas, meaning he wobbled a lot on one knee, but he did have a genuine ring. All the gang were there that night, messing about thinking that was all Jonnie was doing. But he had been serious and, even more amazingly Cat had said yes! However, Jonnie was probably glad he had not bought one with a bigger fake diamond in it. It could have had his eye out when she flung it at him two days later! Even after that they fell back into the same routine. They would not see each other for months, then start going out for a week or so, fight like cat and dog, break up, make up, break up again, then go out with other people, then meet up again months later… Jonnie's mates had given up a long time ago trying to keep up with where the two of them were at.

Brain, or Brian as Joe knew he had to start calling him now they were not at school any more, had been there more than once. There was always a coolness about Brian that was never frosty. He was warm and caring, very smart too, in his brain and in his clothing choices. Nothing seemed to ruffle him. With regard to Cat, he simply acknowledged the fact that he had gone out with her a few times, they had both had a nice time and that was all that was ever said. No details were every provided, despite requests, and it was left at that.

Wee Brendy so wanted to 'have a go at her'. He said this many times, in the most unromantic way possible. He never did, possibly because, even with a pint or two of Dutch Courage, he never really tried, clogging up when she was near him. One time he boasted and smiled like Cat had just had his cream but the lads soon found out he was talking through his hole, rather than getting anywhere near any of Cat's.

Lenny, allegedly but with a lot of credible evidence, was accused and had confessed to having been there first, before anyone else. It had been the first time for both of them, so Lenny said. This meant he never wanted to say more about it than that. That was something all of the lads could relate to. It may be a saying but practice may not make perfect. Despite how much you may practice at it, the first real attempt at this is never what you expect or are prepared for. Cat may or may not have been purring after her time with Lenny. Only they both knew the answer to that, as the lads could not claw out any more details.

Finally, with them as well at the table was one of Brendy's mates from another town, who no one else really knew. He was easy to talk to, a good laugh and bought his rounds. So, despite the cramped seating arrangement around the table, he fitted in with everyone else easily. He was very keen to find out who this mysterious Cat was but all of the others, even Jonnie, were very reluctant to tell him more. There were very good reasons for this. That was all that the others would say. Brendy's mate, clearly frustrated by only being told part of a story, was even more so when he was told decisively to drop this heavy subject. Each experience, after all, was very personal to each of the lads around the table, especially Builder.

Joe wondered if it was for the same reasons as him, that the others went silent and hunkered down when Cat was mentioned. He always found it reassuring that all of the lads always sheathed their claws when it came to Cat. They gossiped and teased a bit about her and who she was going out with amongst themselves, but that was as far as it went. They never bitched, intentionally or otherwise about her within their gang, nor certainly did they spread any malicious truths or rumours beyond. That could not be said for a lot of others in the local area, especially girls around Cat's age and old women with nothing better to do! Joe even remembered his Ma sticking up for Cat, who she did not even know, one time. Some auld busybody had been telling her a truly nasty rumour about Cat in the shop. Ma had told Joe about it when she got back, saying no one should have that said about them, regardless of what they did, or if it was true or not. That busybody had gone away with a piece of his Ma's mind. Joe knew, from his own experience of receiving that, it meant it would be a while before that woman's tongue, or tail, would be wagging again telling tales. Joe had been surprised at his Ma but proud of her too.

Then there was Joe. He had been with Cat just that one semi-drunken night. It had happened two years and four months ago. Not that he counted, of course, as he tried to figure out that it was a Friday night. Although not sure of the exact date, whatever the calendar date may had been, he never looked back on that date night with regret. Although his head and guts had been swirling a bit in beer, he most certainly did not see that one night as a mistake. Far from it! Sure, his mates slagged him off about both of them being slags. But he did not feel dirty in any way. Things might have been different if their one night had not happened weeks before the crabs had starting pinching.

Cat was partly blamed but she had told Joe she was clean. Joe was very grateful he was too. He remembered that chat with Cat clearly, as he had initially badly struggled to hide his shock and take her seriously. But he easily believed her when he was able to look into her eyes. Yet still, the Crabby Cat name stuck for days. That was until it was clawed out of him and Crabby Colin admitted he was the source of the infection that crawled around the local pubs and clubs. He had shelled out a bit of cash to try to keep those that knew silent, but that, of course, did not work. People heard about it and most of them, but not all, did not bring their toys out to play for a week or two. Despite all the gossiping and speculation, in the end only a very few local people needed treatment. This thankfully did not involve any of them being boiled alive, despite what some firebrand preachers wished. This whole episode proved that, as with most things, rumours and misunderstanding are much more dangerous than reality. The local fishmonger, not selling any shellfish for almost a month during that time, was a case in point.

Before, during and after that local scandal, Joe always spoke to her when he saw her, making a point of going over to say 'hello'. He would even kiss her on the cheek sometimes if she was not with another lad, so he rarely did that. That was as far as it ever went and that one night was never repeated. Although at times curious and needy, Joe had never asked her again. It was left as a one off in Joe's mind. Likewise, she never even mentioned the night they had, so the prospects of a re-run seemed to slip quickly from slim to non-existent.

This dented his ego slightly, a little part of him wanting to hammer out her explanation for this. For whatever his own reasons, he did not question her. It simply just did not seem the right thing to do. What would he have wanted anyway? To hand her a scorecard for him to be awarded marks out of ten for such things as creativity, endurance, etc. It was better not to go there and, in truth, Joe did not really care about his ego enough anyway. It was not that important to him, too battered and scarred to be worth worrying about. One thing, however, he did find hard to cope with was the feelings he had for her that lingered.

They all knew and trusted each other well enough for a bunch of twenty-something lads. They would do naturally around a pub table what Americans would pay large amounts of dollars to their shrink psychiatrists for. The lads would take their problems and 'share with the group,' but with a lot less patronising and a lot more alcohol involved! But they would not share absolutely everything. There was the stuff all the lads knew about each other, from nights out and trips away together to sports events and pub tours of another town or city. There were all the funny stories and all sorts of jokes about known wounds from broken hearts and bones. They knew each other but in some ways they did not. Although they sometimes did, emotional things were tough for them all to talk about. Especially with regard to girlfriend relationships! Slagging and teasing was how they talked about it, laughing their way in and out of such sensitive subjects. Jonnie was an exception as he seemed to have missed the emotions section entirely when he was being assembled in the baby factory! He was not heartless or uncaring, just way too blunt and about as sensitive as granite. Yet Cat had clawed her way through even Jonnie's tough exterior. That was why Cat was talked about, but never really talked about by any of them, especially Builder.

For Joe it was in her eyes. Joe was always fascinated by eyes. They said so much about a person that Joe often wondered why they even bothered saying words. Many times, he had heard the words 'I'm doing great', when the eyes before him showed they were on the verge of painful tears. Other times 'it's the truth I am telling you!' as their eyes skitted about, fearful their lies were not in a good enough hiding place. When he started going down that road thinking about Cat's eyes, he easily saw them in his imagination and the road they led. They were large, with dark pupils and slightly oval shaped. They were beautiful in an ornamental way. Physically, Cat had all the right proportions, other girls jealous that she was much more than average in some places. Her hair was long and always, always styled, showing off her magazine-cover face. As Joe sat at the table with the lads, sipping his pint, he pictured her small round ears, her narrow, slightly upturned nose, but most of all he pictured her mouth. Her top and bottom lips were nearly as thick as each other. They did not look weird or false, only strangely seductive and providing a sucker effect when other lips met hers. Joe remembered those almost suffocating but blissful kisses very well. However, it was when Joe was sucked into her eyes that he had his own eyes opened.

In behind those dark pupils, he saw nothing! No matter how many times he had looked that night and in the times he had met her since, still there was nothing in there. It was hard for Joe to explain. It was certainly not a coldness in her eyes. It was more like a deadness, like there had been something there before but it had shrivelled up to nothing or had been taken away. Her eyes also revealed a searching which Joe could not figure out either. This was maybe not for what was missing but for something new, something better. In the same way Cat was certainly no shrinking Violet, Joe was certainly no shrink psychiatrist. Nevertheless, he knew what he felt, what he sensed. When he was in her company, he knew he possibly would need a proper brain doctor to try to explain it.

It frustrated him deeply that he wanted to help her but could not bring himself to offer it. For a long time, he had thought that his one night was as if Cat saw it as turning over another rock, to see if it was below. It obviously had not been and she had moved on. Maybe she was sure Joe did not have it after just one try? Maybe she was unsure about Jonnie, and some other lads, having to go back again and again to double check? He could, of course, ask her what she was looking for, but his sixth sense told him that she did not really have a clue herself. The old saying 'I will know it when I see it' possibly applied to her seemingly endless quest. She was looking and looking but could not see. She appeared to become more and more stumped amongst all the woods and trees. As the time went by, Joe realised that, behind the even thicker mascara, her eyes were becoming even emptier. Boyfriends seemed to be almost on a revolving door basis as they regularly and randomly came and went. It bugged him but not enough for him to do anything about it, which meant it bugged him even more.

That night in the pub had been the last time they had talked about Cat. She had, as cats are prone to do, just disappeared a few months soon after that. No one, even her family, knew where to. Her family received the odd reassuring 'I'm fine' phone call, but still gave no information on her location. Everyone kept expecting her to come back, but as time went on, they stopped waiting and watching. Joe concluded she must have finished her search around her home area and needed to look beyond. People moved on with their lives. The gossips picked on some other girls and fellas, who they self-righteously decided they had the right to make judgement on their moral character. It was strange how these busybodies never seemed to actually try to help people, just gloated instead on the damage their wicked tongues caused. However, their tongues were stunned into silence when Cat, just before Christmas, suddenly returned. Then, they wagged at a hundred miles an hour, as she was not alone!

The two of them strolled down the High Street like they owned it, but not caring that they owned it, as there were far more important things on their minds. Their arms were linked, their kisses frequent, their smiles constant. Joe had watched them come towards him as he approached from the opposite direction. He quickly recognised her. She looked as stunning as ever, even more, probably, from the better quality of clothes she now wore that tightly hugged her body. Eventually he took his eyes off her and looked at the man beside her, scanning up and down. He wore ordinary clothes, jeans and a shirt. His jacket looked worn but comfortable. He was tall, over six feet, his hair was blonde and his glasses designer. As he drew closer Joe was surprised that Cat's fella looked very average. He was a little more perturbed as he actually looked a lot like Joe!

"Hi, Joe! How are you?" she almost shrieked, a genuine sincerity in asking how he was. She let go of the man beside her arm and threw both her arms around Joe's neck. She kissed him several times on the cheek and he, after checking it did not seem to bother Cat's man, kissed her gently back once. She held both Joe's hands for a few seconds, staring at him as Joe muttered about great to see her, summarising very briefly a bit of his life working away and seeing someone serious. Then she broke off suddenly and reached up to grab her man by the shoulder. "And this is Robbie!" she squealed as Robbie reached out his large but soft hand, to warmly shake Joe's outstretched one. Robbie and Joe nodded at each other but were unable to speak as Cat jumped in with, "We were married last June, had our honeymoon in Majorca and we have our house up in the city. We also have Robbie's other house near Lough Neagh and the apartment up on the North Coast."

"Have you married Lord Robbie, then?" Joe joked, looking at Robbie to make sure he knew he was only codding and not fishing.

There was a split second when Joe wondered if he thought he was not, but then he laughed and replied, "I am no lord that is for sure, but she most certainly is my lady!"

Cat tiptoed herself up and kissed him passionately on the lips as his head moved to meet hers. They forgot themselves a moment before pulling apart, looking a little sheepish but unregretfully back at Joe. Joe could clearly look into her dark, sparkling eyes. He was hoping not to, but expected to see the emptiness that seemed to have been growing and haunting her more during that last time he had seen her. He could see there was something there now, which he felt a strange relief about.

"No matter what people say, she had always been a lady and always will be!" Joe replied smiling. His cheeks flushed in embarrassment as he realised the connotations of what he said. Robbie just smiled rather blankly, and Cat burst out with a mock embarrassed laugh as she swatted at Joe with her hand.

"Oh, Joe! You have always been kind to me, and never a stranger when I needed help. I always felt I was looking for something and now I am sure I have found it." She stammered a little nervously as she finished speaking, then stared intently at Joe for a second or two too long. It made Joe feel uncomfortable. Glancing over at Robbie, he could see he felt the same way. But he had looked long enough in her eyes to see that there was something very new and bright in there.

"I am really sorry but we must rush on! We have an appointment at the clinic!" Robbie said eagerly, his face showing he clearly regretted mentioning the clinic and was keen to move on.

"Everything okay?" Joe felt compelled to ask.

"We just need to have a few tests done, that's all!" Robbie replied unconvincingly casually, trying to brush if off as if it was as routine as brushing your teeth. His hard, fidgeting eyes said otherwise. He thought it strange that Cat nervously rubbed her stomach, almost unconsciously, as he watched her and Robbie intermittently, as he listened to Robbie talk about clinics. There was a little 'oh!' moment as Joe looked again more intently at Cat. It scared him a little when he saw that old emptiness flashed into her eyes. It disappeared as she laughed, saying, "Sorry, Joe, we do need to go. It is getting dark as well. I am Robbie's lady now and do not want to be a lady of the night!" She laughed again and hurried on.

Joe was left in a blur of thoughts as he watched them go. "That's some lady," he muttered to himself.

Loaded

Joe was groggy and tired, even more so than usual. The trundling train home had taken ages, stopping at every hole in the hedge station regardless if no one was getting off or on. Then there had been the almost weekly bomb scare on the tracks. It always seemed to be rung in on a Friday, just before rush hour to piss off as many people as possible. That was just in case ordinary people were not pissed off enough already with those members of groups wanting to disrupt, change and possibly even end their lives. This one had turned out to be a hoax which made absolutely no difference at all to the general mood of scunneredness. The passengers had trudged wearily off the train and on towards the waiting bus, just trying to achieve the simple task of reaching home. All of the passengers had been taken off at the station to be driven by bus for about ten minutes up the road, to the one after next train station, avoiding the 'suspicious device'. There, despite the sensible requests for the bus to just take everyone home, they were told to get back on the train and carry on their journey, as the bus had to return to repeat the short shuttle service for the next train's delivery of pissed-off passengers.

Then, when Joe did eventually get off the train at his bomb-hoax-free station, the bus to take him the final leg of his journey was late by ten minutes. Joe was not sure if it was due to the driver putting his feet up for a while, or not putting his foot on the accelerator pedal enough. When the bus hissed on arrival the driver did appear to be quite well rested. When he did get on it, as if things were not bad enough, the worst thing he did was fall asleep on this bus from the station. Luckily, or maybe not so luckily, he had only slept for the next two stops beyond his. So here he was, trudging first down the muddy, grass verge, then onto the narrow pavement towards his parent's home. His battered holdall was slung over his denim jacketed shoulder, full of some dirty washing, lots of books that he needed to study over the weekend and a couple of on-offer bun and biccie treats for his Ma and Da.

He was not far away now from his real home, not the rented room he had in the city which would never be more than a place to sleep and eat.

This made him quicken his stride and he smiled contently. As he wondered what his Ma would have cooked for their tea, if his legs had not been so tired he would have broken into a run to taste long-awaited home cooking. He was nearly forty-five minutes late, so he hoped they had either waited for him to arrive or saved him some of whatever it was.

There were not that many cars about on the road at six forty-five p.m. Most people were at home already tucking into whatever feast or not they had for their tea. The one or two cars about were probably swearing stragglers, cursing being kept late at work. Joe's ears pricked up like a Springer Spaniel's as he heard a very different engine sound coming along the road behind him. Its meaty roar sounded like fillet steak compared to the spitting sausages and chugging chops of the usual cars he heard in his neighbourhood. It became louder and he turned to look in the twilight, the street lights just starting to come on. Within a minute or two, there it was, cruising along beside him as smooth and sleek as a bulky, blue bullet. Joe stared at it between the parked cars that looked like metal cubes and so square in so many boring ways in comparison. Then he watched as it indicated. Even flashing orange was done so coolly by this car he almost drooled. It pulled in and he suddenly realised it had parked directly behind his sister's very lonely-looking but much loved, tiny-in-comparison, car. In fact, as he walked forward a few more steps he realised it was parked directly outside their house. His excitement and his curiosity merged and increased together.

He was only a few yards away from the path leading up to his home when the car's door literally swished as it opened. A large tuxedoed man sprang athletically out of the car, closing the door with no more than a brush of his fingertip. He turned, pressed a button on his key fob which lit all his bright, orange lights and Joe heard the locks click. Joe's tiredness was replaced by gobsmacked attentiveness and thought it was the most awesome thing he had ever seen. Maybe one day all cars would have that, instead of all the messing about with a metal key to lock and unlock every door separately.

The tuxed man turned, smiled and shouted 'hiya' as he waved over.

Joe was seriously surprised, saying to himself, "That's Glen Green of Antrim calling to me outside my home."

"Hello, Brother-in-Law-to-be!" Joe shouted over, quickening his pace to reach him.

"Hello, Joe! What do you know?" Glen stepped forward and greeted Joe with a big, rugby, bear hug. Joe slapped Glen's back as they warmly embraced each other. As they unlocked arms and bodies, Joe could not resist commenting on the car.

"Where did you nick that, then?" Joe asked cheekily.

Glen laughed, well used to Joe's piss taking. "I literally just collected it today from the car dealer's. It is a treat for myself, I suppose. I have been promoted at work and received a very nice bonus for being the best sales rep across the UK and Ireland. I even beat that full-of-himself prick from the Midlands..." He paused, stopping himself from a mini rant. "Here! Have a sit in it!" Glen waved his magic key fob and zapped both doors open.

It was just a two-seater but still so cool Joe was almost scared to touch it in case of frostbite. He took the risk, threw his bag beside the hedge, effortlessly opened the door and hopped into the bucket-shaped seat. Joe placed his hands on the soft, spongy steering wheel, pressed the pedals a couple of times and stared at the multitude of lights on the dashboard that made the car look more spaceship that motor. Glen knelt down beside him in the open car doorway. He talked and pointed Joe through a long list of extras that this car had above and beyond others. There were some that sounded so far-fetched Joe thought Glen was just making them up from a movie or something. There were no ejector seas or rockets fitted, Glen told him, adding with a laughing wink, "Yet!" Glen was not long twigging when questions crept into Joe's head. Before Joe could even ask, Glen would be flicking a few switches and pressing buttons, demonstrating before asked to. Joe just sat in stunned silence soaking up everything Glen was saying.

"How much?" Joe tentatively asked.

"Well, you know your Ma and Da's house..." Glen replied and then stopped.

Joe's eyebrows raised and all he could say was, "Is that all? Bargain, really? I'll pop down and get one myself. Maybe two?"

"But this is not just a Boy Toy!" Glen continued, smirking at Joe's sarcasm. "Whilst it is absolutely awesome to drive, it is also an investment. This car will keep increasing in value every year as there were only a hundred of them made in the whole world. I have managed to put a good bit by for a rainy day, but this car means I can have a bit of fun with my money too."

"No shit!" was all Joe could think of to reply. He was not, nor could he be, jealous of Glen. The fella had studied and worked really hard. He came from the same sort of background to Joe and had made it. Made it big! He did deserve what he had achieved. Though, fair enough, there was also the fact that Glen did have that bachelor Uncle who died and left everything to his favourite nephew. Glen shared some of the profits from selling the one hundred-and thirty-five-acre farm with his parents and brothers, but most of it he invested and reaped huge rewards from. He had only recently found out that his deceased uncle owned a huge vacant ranch in Australia as well, but he was keeping that. Australia was where he was planning to settle down, he had mistakenly told Joe after a few too many pints one night. Glen had spent the rest of that night making Joe promise he would not say anything to Joanne. Joe had kept that promise.

Joe had to confess that he genuinely liked Glen. He was a straight-talking, practical guy who miraculously managed somehow, even when he arrives in a flashy sports car, to still seem down to earth and never showy. Joe still felt the urge to be all big brother and protect his sister, but Glen was far more capable of doing that than Joe was. Probably more than Joe ever would be, either? He had been going out with Joanne since they were at college together. Glen had coolly placed the ice cube sized engagement ring on her finger last year and plans were well under way for their big day.

Joe felt he had sat in the car too long and slid out. "We will go for a drive in it over the weekend if you are about Joe?" Joe nodded back to Glen like a kid on Christmas morning. "Sorry I cannot take you now, but Joanne and I are going to this posh awards thing in the city. Not really our thing, but might get a bit of business from it? They are coming from all over the place – USA, Canada, a dozen or more European countries, even South Africans. It a big thing, hence the monkey suit." Glen fiddled with his dickie bow nervously as he smiled, Joe aping him a little as he too fiddled with his own almost permanently tie free worn collar.

They both turned as they heard the front door open. Joe's Ma and Da stood arms around each other in the doorway. Joe waved to them and saw them wave back before his eyes became totally fixed on who was walking down the little path. The street lights were fully on now, lighting her up like she was on a model catwalk. She looked absolutely stunning in a strapless green dress, her hair flowed silkily behind her, her make-up was subtly perfect and her high heels shimmered as she clipped along. Both Joe and

Glen stood speechless. Joe knew there were very different emotions running through each of their heads. Joe's was much more than just brotherly love, it was a genuine pride in what his sister had achieved and how beautiful she looked. Joe was not really a jealous type anyway, especially amongst family, but he was just so glad to share in her happiness and good fortune at going to marry such a decent bloke as Glen. A bloke who also happened to be very rich! To be honest, Joe did not really want to think what thoughts were going through Glen's head. Joe felt neither a 'that's my sister you're looking at' or 'save it 'til the wedding night' speech would really have been appropriate at that moment.

"All right, Bro-Joe!" Joanne said loudly as she neared him. "All right, hubby to be!" She stepped out the front gate and planted a huge kiss on Glen's lips, leaving smudged lipstick redness across his mouth. Despite her glamour, she reached over and friendly-punched Joe on the shoulder. Joe stepped forward and gently hugged her, trying to make sure he did not crease or mark anything on her.

"You look absolutely stunning!" he confessed in her ear. "Stunning!" he repeated. Stepping back, she smiled proudly and thankfully at Joe, although he detected a little additional blushing redness showing through her blusher.

"Thanks!" was all she said shyly. "I scrub up not too bad, don't I?" she asked, not really expecting an answer. Turning, she pretend-angrily snapped, "You're late, Glen! I've been ready ages." Glen sheepishly looked at the thick, shining watch adorning his wrist. Joe knew without looking it certainly did not have any chipped glass on it like his own.

"Sorry! Yes! We do need to go. Catch you later, Joe." Glen waved and shouted a goodbye to Ma and Da huddled hugging on their front step. He reached round opened the car door flamboyantly for Joanne and overemphasised his gentlemanliness, causing her to smirk at him, as he helped her in. With less ceremony, he jumped-feline like into the driver's seat, made the ignition purr and they were off down the road like a cat with its tail on fire, disappearing in a blink of the cat's eyes.

Joe trudged up the path, hugged his folks tightly and shrugged off the jokes about him being late and there being nothing left to eat. Laughing this off almost totally convincingly, he hared up the stairs two at a time as his Ma excitedly rabbited on loudly from downstairs. Will was away, so he had their shared room to himself as he swiftly unpacked his bits and bobs. Back downstairs, his armful of washing shoved in the big basket, he sat at the table. His tea was a little crozzled from being in the oven a bit too long to keep it warm, but he still chomped his way through it without any hesitation. With endlessly topped up cups of tea, the three of them chatted round the kitchen table for ages, a bit about Joe, a bit about Will, and a lot about Joanne and Glen. Glen's car was talked about even more.

The film had another half-hour or so to go. The volume was turned down as Ma was already in bed. Da had said he was going to join her, several times, but had ended up falling asleep in his chair. Joe was bleary-eyed himself, debating whether to watch the end or just admit defeat and go to bed. It was a repeat he had seen a few times before, so knew what happened, or thought he remembered. It was then he heard the silkiness of the car engine, come to a halt out front. Joe rose, peeked through the curtain to see Joanne slam the car door and yell something at a flustered-looking Glen standing alongside his car. She stomped up the pathway that had previously been her catwalk but was now the steely track for the charging train Joe could see she had become. Glen hovered for a moment or two, wondering whether to follow or not. Joe knew that Glen knew that when Joanne was loaded up with a full head of steam like this, you just stayed well clear until her waters cooled. Joe telepathically told this again to Glen through the part-open curtain. Whether he picked up on Joe's telepathy or not, Glen slipped back into his car and slowly moved off.

The front door only partly slammed. Then Joanne had another go and slammed it shut for sure. There was a muffled, "Is that you, Joanne?" ask from upstairs, with her sharp and short "Yes Ma!" reply. Da remained still zonked out, so Joe rose and went into the kitchen. Joanne was standing with outstretched arms, her palms resting flat on the table top. She was glaring at the end chair, nostrils flaring as she breathed long and hard.

"A drink?" Joe asked as a temperature gauge.

With a slight nod of her head, she answered, "Yeah! Thanks." Joe could tell from her body language she was wanting to talk, but was not sure what to say. He reached for the kettle, relieved she had not let fly with a tirade, and guiltily glad in thinking that maybe she had left all her rant with Glen?

"What's up?" Joe asked casually, sitting down on a seat, at the same time as he sat the two tea-bag-loaded mugs down on the table. There was a nervous moment when he felt the wrath start to build up within her. He waited for her release valve to hiss out at him, but it did not. Instead, she smiled strangely and sat down herself with her anger still bubbling away inside.

"I have never known there could be a bigger pack of absolute up-their-own-arse, self-centred, boastful, patronising bollockses than I have met tonight!" she blurted out, her eyes averted from Joe's. Joe was well used to Joanne's ability to freely express how she felt. That short speech certainly left no grey area about how her night had gone.

"Oh, come on!" said Joe. "You have seen the judging panel on those talent and dancing shows? Were they as bad as that?" He laughed a little as he tried to ease her tension.

She smirked back with a, "Far, far worse than that!" comment. They both sniggered a little, both glad of the ease of tension as Joe poured the steaming kettle water into the mugs creating black tea. In the moment of silence that followed he reached the milk from the fridge and sloshed some into each mug.

"All Glen and I did all night was stand around and listen to ones talking on and on and on about what property they owned where, the shares they had in this and that, private planes... Huh! If we had not left early, I think I would have belted the next one to mention how they were having a jacuzzi fitted to their yacht! Even when they talked about food it was disgusting to listen to. Several of the women were asking why there was no caviar with the canapes? Glen had very tactfully explained that this was Belfast, not Monaco to a couple of them! Some just turned their noses up and ponced off. Then a couple of the men started asking about local delicacies. Ulster Fry's, dulse and wheaten bread did not cut it with them at all! That was the only possibly interesting conversation I had all night! The rest of the time they all just bitched; the blokes as bad as the women. What people were wearing? Rumours about losses on the stock exchange? All sorts of catty gossip, clawing at one another to see who had landed on their feet the best. Then how they hoped they would be knocked over again!" She sighed but Joe remained silent, knowing more was to come.

"Glen hated it too! It is a world he thought he could buy his way into. But it is a nasty world where all they talk about is their wealth, or the things they buy for the sake of buying, just so they can have the so-called 'best of the best.' Glen was ignored like he was some upstart wannabe, several ones asking him how he managed to get an invite to such a prestigious event? Some hinted with sleekedness at standards slipping and letting all sorts come along. He certainly did not meet anyone who wanted to or offered to help his career or his business plans. I felt really sorry for him. I could do so little to help as I just felt so awkward. No-one could talk about normal stuff. It was all about money and showing it off.

"Loaded is what they are and always will be. Loaded onto the Titanic and left to sink with her is what they should be!" Joanne smiled as she said it. She reached into her bag and reached out her tiny mobile phone. "I need to give him a call," was all she said. As Joe left the room, he heard her say 'hi', then 'sorry', followed by 'me too, please don't let's go to things like that again..." Joe went up the stairs to leave Glen and Joanne to their conversation, as they had a load to talk about besides money.

He checked the living room and Da must have woken and gone to bed. As Joe lay on his bed feeling the tiredness creep over him, he thought about money and his personal lack of it. What he would give to buy a car like Glen's. As he thought more, he decided no way would he spend that amount on a target. Such a car certainly drew attention, as all ostentatious things did. A jealous yob with a six-inch nail would make a real mess of a car like that's paintwork. Big houses attracted the burglars with their promises of valuable, robbable stuff. As Joe drifted off to sleep, he concluded that real wealth was not about size or 'how many'. It was about appreciating the simple things in life – like heat and food. Wealth was in the priceless things in life, too – love, family, friendship. Richly-deserved sleep overcame him. Even though he had hoped he had just set his morals high above greed, he smiled contentedly as he could not help himself and began to dream of driving Glen's car...

Lost

He had been lucky. It had still hurt, but not as much as it could have done. It was plasterboard, not brick or concrete block behind the fading magnolia paint. The fist-shaped hole that now studded the wall had luckily missed all of the internal wooden supports. It was clear for all to see, although he was the only one in the dingy room, half-lit from the annoying flickering street lamp outside his window. Unfazed, he simply staggered over and put his shoulder to the side of the bulky and scratched wardrobe that was ancient but certainly not antique. There was not much in it but it was still heavy enough as he shoved it over with noisy grunts and some rippling carpet and muscles. Once positioned in its hole-covering position, he blearily looked behind and saw a huge, strange stain on the carpet, marked with a rectangle frame where the wardrobe had originally been. Floor art, it certainly was not.

After a moment or two's thought, he concluded he had not been responsible for that, hopefully, so he just grunted and threw himself down on his bed. A little blood dripped from his knuckles onto his psychedelic duvet cover but he did not move his hand or any other part of him. His eyes became fixed on the strangely-shaped patch of damp mould on the ceiling above. His head was throbbing, his vision distorted and he could not stop his entire body shaking from the ongoing adrenalin rush. Nor could he shake what had caused his self- and wall-harm, which was with him still. The angry punch to the innocent wall made him feel a bit guilty for the damage. He was left even more frustrated in that it had not reduced his inner turmoiled frustration one jot. The violent attempt at emotional release had freed him of nothing.

"You all right in there?" the concerned shout came from behind the door, over the noise of the toilet flushing in the room next to Joe's.

"Yeah! It's okay!" Joe replied in a loud and distinct 'piss off and leave me alone' tone. He remained lying motionless in the increasing darkness of his room as he spoke.

"Okay!" was the very brief, sarcastic reply, and the only noise that was left was the muffled music and loud, indistinguishable housemate conversations from the living room below.

Normally, he would have created pictures from the slowly and erratically-spreading black shadow shapes on the ceiling. He did this when he looked with fascination at the knots and grains in bare wood too. Gargoyle faces, elephants, flowers and all sorts would have been conjured up in his mind, with his eyes forming and confirming those imagined images. None of that happened now. His mind was in a much darker place than the mould, and the blackness was spreading a hell of a lot faster.

It happened not often but often enough. Even once was too much. He knew he should have control over it. He created it after all, so he had the ability to shape it and, therefore, the right to destroy it, too. In theory he should? It was the means to stop it starting that constantly eluded him. Likewise, removing it took time as he had to build up his emotional strength to confront it head on. He could tell when it was gathering, like blackening clouds before a rainstorm, although no weather presenter could predict the contrasting intense heat and ice-cold of this front moving in to cover his world completely. Sometimes it moved fast, streaming in like a jet, yet other times, like an occluded powerful front, it built up over days.

There were no specific triggers. No bad experience, bad exam result, a bad row with a friend or girlfriend, or bad news that shoved him into this pit. However, these were all thrown in as ingredients to this melancholic mixing bowl when it began. It just seemed to happen, like some demon suddenly or slowly took over his entire being; almost like he was its plaything, to torment and tease as it wished. Then, once it arrived, the hoovering began; every single real and imaginary negative thought was sucked up to feed this growing monster. Everything from slightly burnt toast, to a bus being late, even as petty as the ink in his biro running out, were all blown out of proportion and then added to the ballooning dark mood. The larder of his memory bank would be raided as well, but always the sad and bad experiences of his twenty-one years of life so far. Any sweetness or happiness was ignored and covered in thick blankets of doom to ensure not one glimmer of their light shone through. His body was lying on his bed now, with the light on, but it did not shine into where his mind was now in these deepest, darkest shadows.

He had been here before, way too many times. It happened when he was young but never like it had recently. He still remembered the fear it ingrained in him. His parents' fiery, and sometimes violent, arguments were part of its cause, but there was more to it than that. He was a strong and, in many ways, tough kid, but that was all on the outside. This was the shell and all too often his yolk centre was turned to omelette when he was left powerless to prevent his anxiety scrambling his emotions. Every time it had happened since, he became that scared little boy all over again, feeling feeble in the face of this confusing force. Sure, he had fights, with fists as well as words at school and elsewhere, but these were totally different. Battling with another person standing in front of you is easy in comparison. Winning or losing is irrelevant as you at least know who your opponent is. When you are fighting yourself, it is very different. When you know exactly your own strengths and weaknesses it becomes a war of exhausting attrition.

Every time peace eventually resumes, there is still the rebuilding to complete. However, not all the pieces are every put back together in the exact same way, even if they can all be found in the collateral of damaged debris. It was as if his mind was a fragile dinner plate dropped onto the hard-tiled kitchen floor of life. Bits would scatter everywhere, which he would gather up and stick back together again – eventually. Even when he found all the pieces, and what emotional glue as adhesive he could gather, the result was always different. The major parts would all be assembled and, even if no obvious gaps were left, there were always the dust and tiny flecks that could not be placed back where they originally were. Some of these miniscule bits were seen as unimportant, but others were found out to be essential later. Regardless of their necessity, these would be brushed up along with the other detritus of life and binned, never to be used again and the gaps they left growing in size each time. Even when clear of it, victory was never clean, leaving chips and marks. All the dark, dirty bits seemed to magnetize together, being buried in a mental corner somewhere, ready to burst out the next time and cause the drop that floored him every time.

The raging hormones and discoveries of how much life actually sucked had made this falling happen much more often in his teenage years. Then he had fought it with full on anger but he usually did this alone. He would feel it building up inside him and cycle off on his bike or stomp into the fields. There he would rant and rave, or kick and thump at old tree stumps or decapitate innocent tall plants. He always felt embarrassed afterwards, like he had been some temper tantrum-in two-year-old. It was then the only coping mechanism he knew that worked. He always tried to make sure no one was around to see him and the few times people had, they did not hang about long to watch. If a person is physically hurt, people will rush to help. Joe had seen this and had done so himself. If a person is mentally in pain, people tend to run away, scared of the unpredictability. Perhaps they are scared of their own demons being sparked into action by close contact with such perceived contagious contact. Joe was no different.

Sometimes this had exploded before he had a chance to leave the house, shocking his Ma and sister especially. One time this had happened when his Da was at home. Grabbing his arm, he remembered vividly his Da's concerned and possibly even scared eyes staring into his as he held him. Joe had responded by wrenching himself free and charging off. Da merely asked if he was okay when he arrived back home later in a calmer state, probably unsure what else to say. The atmosphere had remained awkward and filled with unspoken questions for some time afterwards.

Joe and his family knew too well of Da's inner turmoils that, just like Joe's, flowed over the edge at times. Da had told before how his own temper had scared him. Joe had found this hard to believe compared to the pure fear Da's wrath instilled in his wife, kids and wider family. As an older Joe struggled to control his own inner rage, he began to understand what his Da meant, even if it did not help abate or prevent it. All Joe could do was steam off the pressure inside him. This was not a control mechanism, just an emergency release valve. It would work though, for a while. Afterwards, he would be his usual, apparently in-control self, something both he and everyone else were glad off. Until the next time.

As he became older still, it changed again. Releasing a physical blast of teenage angst was no longer enough. Besides, the embarrassment factor of this now mostly obsolete solution was a lot greater. As well, there was the fear he would be so much more destructive, with his extra height and summer-job building-site-gained muscles. He could not use his anger to fight it as the repercussions of it scared him too much, both for himself and those around him. Teenage whacking the heads off docks and thistles would never be enough anyway, as he was now a man. He had so many more pressures and worries. Some were very real, some overthought and some only possibilities, but they all added more heated coal to produce the steam of frustration. He repressed all these, applying more pressure to push them down. He did what the real men of his world regularly did – he balled up all that bad emotion and shoved it deep down. He kept pouring in and pouring in until there was no room left. Not surprisingly, this very flawed psychiatric plumbing system overflowed, leaking all through his body.

He found another cure, if only temporary, in his later teens. As his anxieties about the world around him increased, so did his actively seeking out this ointment for his inner sores. As he poured his life worries into deep mental crevices, so he swallowed pints of beer to dissolve these or at least seal off the entrances. He was suffering the excesses of that medicine as he lay on his bed now. Medics had told him that alcohol was a depressant. Through him voluntarily being a lab rat, he conducted many, many experiments and field tests. The results showed that, after initial euphoric feelings, he could scientifically state this was true.

As he discovered there was a graph-like build-up of happiness and consumption matching each other, this then reached the apex of an almost ecstatic high point, which would appear to totally contradict the depression theory. The sad reality was that, after that high point, the graph would drop vertically. If it could not be stopped and slowed on the way down, then it ended in the pit of despair everyone possesses. What Joe found with this liquid solution was that it made the sides of his pit very slippery. It took a lot of effort to get out. While he was in there, he could easily become lost, whether it was a jungle or even if it was a wide-open space. It was never a nice place to stay, but he would always end up living there much longer than he intended. Even a few minutes was too long a visit. It took effort, concentration and commitment, but he would force himself to clamber out. He was beginning that process now as his knuckles began to seriously throb, guilty embarrassment entering his troubled mind.

After experiencing it so many times before, anyone would have thought he would have perfected an exit strategy technique by now. Cynically, Joe would argue that if he was able to be clever enough to find an easy way out, he should be clever enough to never be in there in the first place! Regardless of his intelligence, that was never the case, either in or out. He had to formulate a new plan every time, trying different techniques until eventually he would be free. Sometimes this took minutes, sometimes days. It took as long as it took, and every time it happened it exhausted him. He was tired of it all but he never wanted to have medically prescribed popping pills to control it. No matter how bad it got, although close once or twice, he had never gone so far down that road that he wished to take as many pills as was needed to end it all. Underneath it all, there was still his sure belief that he had too much of an Average life to live. He dug deep for those reasons now and chinks of light came through as they, so far, always had. He argued with himself, to keep himself as near sane as possible, that everyone went through these bad times and reacted the same way. Didn't they?

The music from below became louder. Probably the living room door left open being the reason, he deduced. He heard fast footstep thumps on the stairs followed by a loud knock at his door. "Here! Joe! You coming down? The pizzas have just arrived. They gave us an extra one by mistake, so there's loads to share. Sure, come on?" the hopeful male voice of Dean rumbled through the wooden barrier.

"Yeah! Sure! Be down in a minute or two!" Joe replied automatically before he had even time to think. His mouth worked like that too much. This time he was grateful for it. More chinks of light came up through him. The blood on his knuckles had dried and he cleaned it up with foamy spit and grubby hanky. The cuts were very small and these joints not red enough for anyone to notice unless they looked closely. He rubbed his face repeatedly, forcing life back into himself. Life was what it was all about and life needed to be lived, no matter what it involved. For now, it certainly involved a pizza and a laugh with his housemates. He could find his way easily to that little bit of assured happiness.

That lifted and enlightened him with the prospect of him appreciating the simple things that made life good. He decided he would keep looking and searching for those. Lost was how he felt when he fell into the darkness but he had to realise he was not. In reality, he was only misplaced there for a while, turned around to face in the wrong direction. He was his own map reader and designer. This would not stop him going the wrong way or being disorientated, he decided, but he was sure he was never abandoned by family and friends. Or he would not and could not abandon them to what was, in reality, selfish moodiness. These were the people landmarks he relied on to keep him focussed on a destination of hope, no matter what the straight and narrow or winding road travelled. They were who brought him back from a wrong, disorientating turn in his life and he always desperately needed these guiding signposts. Lost he may be at times, unable to prevent the cause, but he was never permanently lost and never a total lost cause he resolved and hoped. As he found his way down the stairs, he wished he would find his way in so many other ways.

Lads

"Boys will be boys!" Nan had tutted in a mixture of caring and mockery, unable to supress sniggers. She had stood on the back-door step, well-dressed as always when she visited, providing the unsaid excuse of not helping beyond moral support. Ma had her thumb on the end of the thin hose, black insulating tape covering the worn cracks and snake-like patterning the green plastic erratically. She was trying, with moderate success, to turn the meagre flow into a pressure hose, attempting to reveal her two sons who she knew lay underneath. Ma's initial fury was continually being diluted, as much as the muddy run-off as by the rising laughter. After a few minutes she was chuckling away, shaking her head at the state of her boys and began softly teasing them.

'Only as far as where the rushes start' was Ma's rule, stipulating the area still visible from the kitchen window. He remembered the sense of injustice at Will being allowed, a full year and a half before he had been, to play out in the big field at the back of their house. This was mostly appeased by the older brother responsibility placed, caringly as always by his Ma, on his nine-year-old shoulders. They had obediently stayed within this parentally-designated area but it had still happened within it.

These two young racing dog-chasers had made a discovery, the hard way. The bank at the side of the sheugh when they pounded along, crumbled beneath them, quickly sliding them into the glary two-feet depths of the bottom of the drain at the side of the hedge. Both had landed face first, filling their shocked eyes and gaping mouths with the muddy contents. Spluttering and spitting, they clambered up the soil slippery bank, failing a couple of times and falling backwards into it again. Eventually they reached the solid ground, six feet above. Hindsight is a wonderful thing, and, although at the time sensible, wiping at each other to remove as much of the foul-smelling yuck as possible only succeeded smearing rather than removing it.

Like potters they spread the mud all over themselves, as if making a clay pot that they both resembled. Neither cried, just laughed and laughed, until the prospect of reporting that the mud had won this battle to headquarters caused a slow realisation that punishment for dereliction of duty awaited them. They trudged down the grassy slope, over the rusting gate and went up the narrow path at the side of the house to the back yard. Rex the old dog followed at a distance, suspiciously unsure of what his two human friends had turned into. Small, welly-boot prints left a multitude of signposts to follow, but most certainly it did not need Rex the dog's acute nose to trail the smell of them.

They dared not enter the house and gingerly had part opened the back door, shouting, "Ma!" nervously once. She was there in seconds and, instead of the expected tirade, she was speechless – absolutely and utterly without words. That was probably why Joe remembered this event so vividly, as that just did not happen. Through their blinking, mud-encrusted eyes they saw the anger rise in her face. This disappeared quickly, to be followed by a smile, a disbelieving laugh, then open laughter through the fingers she clasped to her mouth in disbelief. Ordered to stand at attention where they were, Ma moved at a quick march over and turned on the outside tap, its connected hose trickling out water. As she had hosed them down, Nan had appeared at the door and burst out laughing so much she started to wheeze a little worryingly. Laughter proved to be a good medicine as she breathed normally again, continuing to chuckle loudly. Joe remembered the combined laughter as he and Will flicked mucky water at each other. Strangely, he remembered a small ball of whitish frog spawn eggs washing off him and going down the drain. He remembered wishing them well on their journey down the pipe connecting to the small burn beyond the houses, hoping that was where they would develop into fully grown hoppers.

This childhood memory had entered his head as he sat feeling the artificial colours and preservatives burn fizzingly in the back of his throat. Maybe it was this impulse buy that had started him thinking about his boyhood. He had seen the can of fizzy lemon in the shop's overstocked fridge and, realizing it had been years and years since he had tasted it, picked one up excitedly and paid the sad looking cashier, who did not share his expectant enthusiasm. He was probably only nine or ten the last time he has tasted this. He sat on the cold metal bench now, slowly sipping it. His nostalgic excitement had very soon evaporated. The sharp, unnatural taste reminded him of the reason why he had not bought this drink in such a long time! With nothing else to do as he waited, he persevered and continued the torturous consumption. As he finish what had been started by his irrational motive, he watched the two lads with their mum opposite.

They were probably, he estimated, nine and seven, the same ages as when he and Will had retuned as mudmen. This was probably another reason for the vivid memory appearing in his mind. As he watched them, he was totally unobserved, sitting directly opposite them. The two lads were sat intently engrossed in their slightly annoying beeping hand-held computer games. Their mum was equally oblivious to the world around her, with her face and upper body all almost covered by a glossy magazine. Joe snorted a little, not just because a larger swig than before raspingly caught his throat, but pondering if his boyhood with these super advanced computer games would have been better? In comparison to now, those early computer games of his early teenage years were basic in a million many ways more than their computer language. It did not really matter, as the past was the past, but he decided that it would not have. Being screen-free left him to be nature free to explore and wonder at the real world around him, not trapped in a fantasy one. The mudmen day had left them covered in some of what the real world had to offer.

Tech stuff aside, Joe pondered if these two lads, in their bright white trainers and designer labelled clothes, had ever been clarried in muck as he and Will and his mates had often been. *What was it with white trainers?* he often rhetorically asked. The most impractical colour for footwear! The Ditch Day, as it became known in the family, had been an exceptionally messy playtime but others had come close. Had these two young lads ever experienced the pure freedom and joy of being out in the dirty world of innocent play?

He sadly realised, feeling ageist, that these boys were the next generation and he was the one before. Things had changed so, so much. Boys were no longer just boys but future career-seekers, high school mark-achievers, life-planners – or not. Above all they were consumers, aggressively targeted by marketing executives from computer gamers and football clubs. There was so much more to life that that Joe concluded with a little anger and resentment. So, so much more, lots of which did not have a price tag on it. Play often was free but priceless as the same time.

He, rather scarily, jumped to the next generation in his thoughts. Would he be glad if he had daughters and no sons? He had no choice, really. It was not like he would be given receipts and able to take them back to exchange them if they did not fit his perception or circumstances. He laughed this off as he yet had to find a girlfriend with potential to be able or want to stay with him longer than a few months, let alone marriage or children! He recognised that boys and girls are so different at all ages and not just because of their anatomical bits. Besides the planetary difference in descriptions, Joe was just looking for a special someone who did not think him a spacer from Mars or any other planet. Someone who appreciated his down-to-earth attitudes and being grounded, but not as much as him and Will had been on Ditch Day. Someday that was going to happen, and his world would change forever from meeting her. He kept that dream constantly alive, wishing to have this fantasy world become real.

Joe continued to scan around the train station, people watching in his boredom, waiting for his delayed train home. He wondered when he would get his end away as he had been waiting here ages. Almost instinctively, his eyes were drawn to the movement of the two computer-gaming lads' mother. It was perhaps the dramatic throwing down of her magazine on the seat beside her that had caused his eyes to move towards her. The amount of cleavage she had on display as she leant over to rummage in her handbag certainly held them there. A little embarrassment for peeping and the fact that his name was not Tom made Joe look away. He gave into a further temptation and had another quick look back over towards her, smiling sardonically as she raised her magazine again to cover up the display. Joe laughed a little more at the other cleavage on display, on the mag's front cover, not being as much as its reader's.

Not his train nosily arrived and splurged out passengers. Gazing around, he was drawn to two carriage-exiting women with belts for skirts, clicking along hurriedly, balancing on needle like heels. He looked, then looked away as he felt he was peeping again. Arguing with himself that they had dressed like that wanting to be noticed meant that he had one final look before their just-about-covered bums disappeared out the exit doors. The few people off the last train scattered and reached the exit, others reloading the empty seats before the train shot off again. In the ensuing quiet, Joe began to think as he knew he did too much of.

Recent images still flashed in his head, leading him to wonder about the general obsession with certain male and female body parts. There were the very important and, rarely displayed in public, groin parts. Also, of course, as he had just seen more that he would have expected at a draughty train station, there were legs, bums and breasts! Joe was no different from anyone else in that he was driven to think about his own and other people's sex bits more than he probably should. Sex was an obsession on TV, in newspapers, in advertising, in sports. In every aspect of life, sex was shoved in there. Was it because of these that Joe and other lads' and ladies' minds were filled with it? Or was it purely his and their hormones? Was it a pernicious cocktail of both? Was it a purely natural reaction that the media and advertisers exploited to the maximum and far beyond?

Joe had no answers to these questions. He did try to at least attempt to climb up to the moral high ground occasionally. He slid back down far too easily! Regardless of science or morals or whatever – one thing, among many things, annoyed him about this: the obsession with the physical. Everything seemed to be about the image, the look of a person, along with the actual or fantasised act of love with them, based purely on this hype. The what and how had become more important than the who! Joe definitely could not in any way say he had been innocent of never having judged a book by its cover, without even reading the title, let alone a page. It was as if everyone was presumptively labelled on a scale of being a sex debauchee, whether they wanted to be or not. Those who raised their moral voices against this were slid to the scale bottom and aggressively labelled prudes or party poopers. Joe never liked being labelled and thought himself to be variably somewhere in the middle of these extremes.

Everything he could think of was either blatantly obviously sexed-up, or had innuendo, subtle or not, implied to clothes, food and even cleaning products. Words were sexed-up too, with luscious, ravenous, delectable used to perhaps show a better vocabulary on page three than in the rest of those tabloid newspapers? 'Girls getting their tits out' was replaced with their description as 'glamour models.' Whatever they wished or were called they provided the 'tit' in titillation for millions of male readers, and possibly female ones, too. Daily newspapers, billboard posters, TV shows and adverts, without even mentioning the top shelf magazines in newsagents and under the counter videos, all fed into the physical image and lads' and men's lust for it. It was a small, monstrous snake that had always existed, but in modern times it was fed and fed, ironically creating an insatiable appetite for more, until it became an anaconda so large no-one could get a grip of it.

A mother dragged by the hand two young, reluctant, pony-tailed schoolgirls across in front of him. They looked with sad eyes futilely towards him, vainly asking for help. Their mother whickered away as the three of them horsed towards the exit. Joe suddenly thought if those were his daughters. Would he be proud if they grew up and came home to say they had achieved a great career as a glamour model? Or even as adults appearing in so-called artistic movies? What would be his reaction to them revealing cleavage or private parts, or even more, to the world? That scared him much more than he thought it would, actually succeeding in silencing his mind for a few seconds in shock.

His thoughts went off on a tangent, as they often did, and he became angry. It was anger at how lads and men were boxed into portraying them as thinking about nothing else but sex. Women thought of it too, he was sure of that, although maybe not as much. Joe admitted sex did cross his mind several times during the course of a day. Probably more like several times during the course of an hour if he was truthful! He was only twenty-two and currently single, after all! Regardless of his confession of guilt to the thought police, he knew and sincerely hoped there was a lot more to him than that. It was the same for everyone else, male and female. The bits they were born with determined which box they ticked on a form and which of them gave birth to and breastfed the babies in a relationship. Besides that, they were unique human beings who were bigger, more interesting people than simply the sizes of their anatomical manhood or womanhood.

With a snort, Joe knew he was right, but the world was very, very far away from that. Sex sold and sells was the truth. This was whether it was in a capitalist, communist or any other economic world he realised with a shrug of his shoulders. As it was supposedly a man's world, lads and men were sucked into this more and more, which made this grow and grow, becoming harder and harder to stop it. Joe wondered when the day would come, when the much-talked-but-little-done-about, equality of the sexes would actually arrive? Having male strippers at hen parties was, to him, not a way of somehow evening the score, despite the fun the ladies had. There was a lot more to a person than body parts, even if no one really seemed to mind that this was regularly forgotten.

As he shrugged his shoulders, looking over at the two still-computer-game-playing lads, he wondered what the world would be like when they were his age. He wondered himself what the world would be like for him and his hoped-for family in another twenty years, another forty, another hundred? *Would it actually change?* he wondered. Tech and consumerism would undoubtedly change the world, but people would remain people. Before any more melancholy set in, his train arrived at last, making unusual grinding noises that concerned him. He rose to his feet, seeing the ma poke and shout at the two lads to move as she put on a thick coat to ensure her ample chest was kept warm. He noticed it was a big coat.

Before boarding, he politely asked the angry female conductor about the reason for the train delay and wanting to allay his fears for how fit the train was mechanically. All she could say in a snapped reply was, "I am sorry sir, but it has all been a balls-up and tits-up the entire journey." With that she stomped off. Joe smirked as that certainly described his own life journey and probably everyone else's exactly like that.

As he sat on his hard, plastic seat, avoiding the chewing gum on the armrest, he wondered about his mechanics working okay to provide him with sons in the future – or daughters. He truly did not mind which, but decided he would, if he was blessed with working bits, wish to have kids. All he needed to do was find the person who currently did not know she was to be the mother of his children. He looked over at the shapely, black-tight-clad, crossed legs across the aisle. He looked up towards her face to see if she might be the one?

He quickly looked away, thinking he was still that dirty boy standing in the back yard, but without anyone hosing him down to try to clean things inside him as had happened to his exterior back then. Did everyone feel like that at some stage or other in their life, or was it just him? He stared out the window to distract himself. Immediately, the supermodel, almost wearing a bikini to try to sell something Joe did not even notice the name of on a massive billboard, failed in that quest. He looked beyond it, shaking his head slightly, before having a quick look back before it disappeared from view. He half-scolded himself before the train slowed and began to make screechy metal on metal noises. The noise and growing angst on the other passengers' faces certainly distracted his attention back to this real world, real time event.

Two oily, grubby rail workers, the little logo just visible on their greased overalls, came charging up the aisle past Joe. "I dunno what's wrong with her at all! I've looked all over her and inserted all sorts. She just seems to have mind of her own today…" Joe heard the older looking of the two engineers complain as they scuttled hurriedly past. Despite the squeals of protest, the train just carried on.

Leaving

His ma was doing what she always did when she was nervous. She let the words cascade out of her mouth like a waterfall in one of the Glens of Antrim. She was beyond nervous now, and it showed as gallons of vocabulary were dispensed. His da did what he always did when he was nervous: he was silent, nodding occasionally to let his wife know he was still alive as her machine-gunned words ricocheted off him repeatedly. His da was like a rock, his ma a river. Joe was caught in between but his gushing ma was certainly no hard place, and Da appeared more mushy than usual. As Da was driving, concentrating on the road ahead, it gave him the excuse of not really paying attention to try to figure how the sentences coming out of Ma linked up. Neither he, nor Joe, could keep up with the information and anecdotes Ma was over-generously sharing with them both. Joe was in the back seat, leaning as far forward as his seatbelt would allow, staring at both his parents in turn. It was as if he wanted to capture the most detailed memory picture he possibly could, with every single wrinkle, or laughter line, as his ma called them. Both of them had seemed to add more of these every day recently and Joe felt guilt rise in him. The build-up to what they were doing now because of him was no doubt the cause of more of their anxious face-etching.

Although he tried to make it fair, he realised he was looking at his Ma a lot more. He had reached forward and she was holding his hand in her lap. Until Ma reached her peak flow, he had chatted away spring-like to them both at the start of this meandering journey. He had become increasingly frustrated with his Ma going through the list of everything he had packed, numerous times. He had answered 'yes' with increasing difficulty at hiding his growing anger at this pettiness, as his ma kept adding in 'have you brought…?' This check list had taken up at least ten minutes at the start of the journey. Now Ma was voraciously retelling tales about the few times she had been to England, along with friends and family who had been there on holiday and those who were living there now. She was bubbling out words about the city he was going to, obviously having researched it a lot more than Joe had. Joe had only been able to grunt and nod in agreement. The closer they came to their final destination, Ma somehow found another gear to put her mouth into and increased the speed of words yet again. She always hated silences, but maybe she was also trying to fill Joe's head with enough of her words to last him for however long that was going to be before she saw him next. Joe sniggered slightly, thinking he did not need enough of his ma's words to do two lifetimes in this short car journey.

Da had no such qualms about silence. He stared stony-faced through the windscreen, knuckles white from gripping the steering wheel too hard. Joe knew he was not listening at all to Ma, too lost in his own thoughts. However, Da had perfected that enviable skill a long-term partner has of being able to answer with a 'yes!' or a nod, at just the right moment to give the impression he was fully attentive. Joe looked at his da's smooth chin. He had actually shaved for today, it not being a Wednesday or a Saturday. This meant it must be a special occasion. Joe looked at the furrows in his brow that you could grow potatoes in. Although the angle was all wrong most of the time, his da did turn his head often to look back at Joe. Da did not say anything or interrupt Ma, if that would have been possible, but wanted simply to smile and stare at his eldest son. They were nearly there as Joe looked at the side of his wise and tough da's face, noticing one single tear trickle down it. That in itself was a moment. Da's eyes were like the reservoir dam near town and rarely leaked, only spilling out water when it was full to the very top and overflowed. Granda's funeral was the last time Joe remembered that happening. Joe thought that was an apt description of his da's emotions today, this huge wall of a man overflowing. He felt a little saddened to have caused it, but elated with the comfort that gave him. It showed he was cared for deeply and rock solidly, even if his da was not as expressive about it as his ma.

As they queued for the car park, Joe slumped back in his seat. The unexpected wave of his memories hit him so hard then that these had physically forced and pinned him to the upholstery. He knew he would have lots of thinking time over the next hours on the next stage of his journey, but it was as if a sudden panic had come upon him. Although his feet were on the rubber mat on the car floor and not touching the ground, it felt like this was his last time on home soil. That was why a random selection of happy childhood, teenage and young adult memories poured into the vivid cinema screen of his imagination. His ma was still talking, his da still silent.

Joe had, for those few seconds, become caught up in his past twenty-two years of life so far. He smiled broadly in response to the equally broadly smiling faces of family, mates, friends and just acquaintances who all darted to and fro. Emotions rose within him as the breath-taking landscape scenes of the mountains, rivers and fields of his homeland he had witnessed became a flashing slide show. His mates were in amongst all of it, his brother and sister, Granda and Granny, Nan too. Ex-girlfriends, and images of those he wished had been girlfriends, came into his head as well, all provoking mixed reactions depending on who it was.

Suddenly it was as if someone pushed a button on the remote and changed the channel. There had been the still photographs that caught a moment in his history and spoke almost as many words as his ma. There were the moving images of his story that brought back the many things from his personal, individual, unique but average life so far. His happy memories had been in bright, deep colours. Instead of this beautiful, moving life story, it was now the random pictures of news, past and recent, that splattered all over his imagination. These appeared dark and dismal in his mind's eye.

The news pictures in his mind, even recent ones, were all in black and white, grey and gloomy, and changed his mood like it was a coin that had just been flipped. Images of the Dole Office brewed amongst these new pictures. Dour newscasters with dire and dread oozing from their lips sounded again and again. TV recordings of bombs going off provided a base beat. These were the shovers, the drivers, the often-quoted push factors that drove so many to do what Joe was doing. He was leaving this land of loss and limitations. He was thankfully not sailing on a coffin ship like his ancestors, but one of the newest ferries on the Larne to Cairnryan crossing. He was not travelling the thousands of miles many others had, but it was still away. He was still departing to another land to try knocking on new doors to see if opportunity opened them.

It was very exciting for him. His infectious excitement smit his parents. His lack of preparedness, beyond buying a one-way ferry ticket, phoning a friend or two, shoving all his belongings in a holdall and clearing out his bank account, did concern them slightly. Still, they were very encouraging, unable to argue convincingly against his economic and social reasons. Their understanding, their support and above all their love encouraged him to go. These, ironically, also were like wet concrete poured around his feet threatening to have him remain part of his firm family foundations. As the sailing date drew closer, Joe had to jig around a lot more to prevent this hardening solid. It was only his mind that he wanted kept set.

As the jug of his memories poured endlessly into his imagination, the sour milk of guilt spread there too. Although being slumped in the seat prevented him having a good view of either of his parents, he found it increasingly harder to look at them, even if he had wanted to. Them still having close by his soon-to-be-married sister Joanne did little to ease this. Glen easily settled into the Average family but having this soon new son-in-law was not the same as having Joe. His ma had told him this straight when he had mentioned it to her to ease his conscience. Surprisingly, she said the same when he said they would still have his, not-so-wee-now, brother Will. "We love you both the same! But Will's not Joe! And Joe's not Will," was how she cryptically had answered.

"Right! We're here!" Da said croakily, snapping Joe out of his blender of a mind, the noise of which had been so loud he had not even realised the car engine had stopped and they were parked. Ma undid her seat belt and in very unexpected total silence, leaned around to look directly at Joe. She reached over wordlessly and squeezed his arm so tightly Joe wondered if she was wanting to keep that piece of him as a memento.

Da opened and slammed the driver's door, Joe watching him move silently around to the boot. Joe thought he saw his da wipe his forearm across his eyes but he could also have simply been shooing away a bug. The boot opened, letting in refreshing, cool air. As Da lifted out the battered holdall, he giggled as he reached through and for a second or two ruffled Joe's hair. Joe responded as he had done as a kid when his da tried to scare him. He reached up and grabbed the large hand, spinning around to stare at his da's smiling face, noticing how red the eyes were.

Now released from Ma's hold, Joe swung out of the back door and stood up straight. It had not been that long a journey, one small step compared to the giant leap ahead of him. Still, he felt the need to reach both his arms up in the air, stretching his spine. This was the conclusion to the question that had been bouncing around his skull for weeks, months. He had decided to be in a new land and not to be in the hamlet cluster of houses he had called home for so long. Maybe that back-straightening action was instinctive as he symbolically tried to shed his load, throwing everything that had been weighing him down for the past twenty-two years off. If that was what his mind was attempting, he knew in his heart of hearts not everything could be jettisoned so easily.

Da playfully thrust the holdall towards Joe, as if he was going to whack him around the head with it. Joe easily ducked out of the way laughing, grabbing it from him. In tense situations, Da would joke around. He was trying the same now but his face revealed it was not working. Da reached across with his broad arms and grabbed his eldest son. He silently clenched him to his chest, Joe hearing the loud sniff from his da's nose that was positioned right beside his left ear. Although there was still a small amount of air left in his lungs from the fierce hug, Joe was unable to say anything. They parted, holding each other by the shoulders, staring hard at each other. "You take care, son, and never forget you are an Average!" was all Da said before he stood back to let Ma finish off removing the last of the air from Joe. She was silent as she squeezed, kissing Joe repeatedly on the cheek. Then she too stood back and put her arm around Da's waist, his automatically going around her slender shoulders.

Joe had agreed with them that they would say their goodbyes in the car park. That suited Da fine, not one for big emotional displays in public places. Ma had resisted, wanting to see him off right to the very end when the boat sailed. Eventually, she accepted that would have strung it all out too much and it was better for a shorter goodbye. Joe just wanted the very last part of the start of his journey at the ferry port to not torture him any more. He did not want third and fourth thoughts making his mental calculations about this being the right answer even more complicated. With a huge smile, wet eyes and final hugs for each of them, Joe slung his holdall over his shoulder and walked to the entrance. Standing at the swishing glass door, he gave them a final wave. Da gave a large one-handed wave, Ma multiple short ones, in between dabbing her eyes with a tissue.

During his time waiting for foot passengers to be called to board, his mind had remained inexplicably blank, feeling completely overwhelmed by the madness or sensibility of what he was doing. He became distracted by the comic scenario of a small man pushing a mountain of cases along beside an irate and unhelpful wife. He offered and gave them help but even when the call came, and he moved with the rest of the foot passenger herd towards the stairs, he did so on automatic pilot. Crossing over the high-up tunnel to board the ship, he looked a little longingly down towards the car park through the port-hole effect windows. Initially he miscalculated where his da had parked the car so did not see them, causing his heart to sink a little.

Reassessing, he realised the location he looked at was wrong and scanned further along only half-expectantly. Shocked but reassured, sure enough, there they were, still standing in the exact same position he had left them in. He moved his palm side to side in what would have been an impossible-for-them-to-see wave, but magically they instantly responded with wild waves of their own. A tear shot out of his eye and it was as if a cow kicked him in the chest. He took one final look, smiled then walked on. Glancing back, he saw both the people who had brought him into this world give one final wave to send him on a journey to another one.

Luggage

Joe could not help but laugh. When he first saw it, he initially thought the trolley, piled unsteadily high with suitcases, was moving slowly all by itself. Either that or some poltergeist was pushing it along. The buxom, white-faced woman walking along beside it did not seem at all perturbed by this possibly ghostly presence. As it turned to the left and drew closer to where Joe sat, he was able to see that it was being propelled by a slightly balding man who had come up a bit short in the queue when heights were being given out. His face was bright red and sweat stains were growing even more obvious under his arms and across the small of his back. The trolley trundled and its presumed owners came even closer to Joe, so he was able to hear their conversation. He wished he was not able to, as he was struggling to control his giggling. He raised his book up to a few inches in front of his face to try to disguise it.

"Are you serious woman? What the hell have you packed in here? We are going for two weeks! Not bloody emigrating!" he breathlessly and angrily stated, just loud enough for his female companion, and unbeknown to him, Joe, to hear. "I am going to have a heart attack before we even reach the booking in desk, let alone take all this on the boat!" He wiped his sweating brow with the back of his hand as he ranted.

"Well, I did say we should have brought the car, but you said that was far too expensive! We only need to go over as foot passengers and then get the train, you said. It is so much cheaper, you said," the handbag-only-carrying woman snarled back at him.

"If I had known you were going to bring all this it would not have been the car we needed. Frick's sake, a forty-foot truck would struggle to hold all this! It's nearly all your stuff! Only that black one is mine," he yapped back at her. Joe chortled at the increasingly loud confrontation going on. "You could at least give me a hand. A push would help if you are not too busy?" he snarled at her with what Joe began to think was sincere and growing contempt. Still, he could not help but find it funny for some reason.

She flicked her head around sharply and, if her eyes were knives, she would have sliced the small man in half. She reached out with her right arm and pushed the third from top, black canvas case. This one, and the two smaller ones it had previously been supporting, crashed to the ground with dull thuds. "Oops!" was all she said. Then she turned on her heel and stomped off towards the booking-in desk, a broad smile on her face as she reached tickets to the cheerful looking clerk sitting behind it.

Joe stood up straight away, lifted his one battered holdall and went over to help. The man just stood still, obviously fuming inside and, the string of swearwords coming out of him, showed he was doing a good job of showing it on the outside as well. He was just going through all the 'b' bad language words when Joe reached him and picked up the black bag. He thought himself strong enough but Joe failed to lift it with one arm. He had to use both hands to lift and load it back onto the tower of cases.

"Aw, cheers mate!" the man said, as Joe reached for another one and the man lifted the final red case off the floor. Despite stretching up as far as he could, he could not reach it up to the top of the others, so Joe helped shove that even heavier one up.

"No bother at all," Joe replied. "Looks like you are going away for a while then?" he asked with pretend innocence of overhearing their conversation, then realised he was stirring things a bit.

"Don't get me started!" the wee man spat out, his chest inflated and his face bright red from rage and additional luggage handling. Joe could see his reluctance as he grabbed the handle to begin pushing what looked to be his entire encased world in front of him.

"Here, if it's okay, I'll give it a push for you. You could probably do with a breather. I am heading over to the booking-in desk as well," Joe offered with a smile.

"Aw, cheers again. Thanks very much. I know it's only over there but it feels like I have been moving heaven and earth since we got off the train with his bloody pile," he said with a grin and speedily took his hands off the handle. Joe placed his hands on it, trying not to react to the wet sweat on it, and tilted it slightly before starting to push. He almost instantly regretted his Good Samaritan bit but persevered. Once he had started, the tiny wheels trundling it became easier. One of them was a bit buckled, not surprisingly making beads of sweat form of Joe's brow and also making him gain a new respect for the man beside him.

It was only few metres, but a relieved Joe reached the desk, where the sitting cheerful face of the clerk contrasted with the frowning, lemon-sucking face of the lady who had just turned round from him handing her boarding cards to. Her face changed dramatically when she saw Joe, greeting him with a sweet 'oh, hello!' She then resumed her bitter face for the look she gave her husband.

"Hiya! Just saw your husband struggling a bit so I thought I would lend a bit of a hand. I have only this after all," Joe said casually, nodding backwards towards the holdall swung behind his back.

"Yeah! We have had to bring a bit more than that along for our wee trip," she said with a rather sarcastic laugh. "Some people think we have brought far too much!" She glared icily at her husband who returned an equally sub-zero look. "But it is all needed. We are visiting our daughter and our grandkids. We are very excited about seeing our newest one when we get over there. If he doesn't have a heart attack first!" She glared again, finishing off with a cutting, "We can only live in hope!"

Joe felt extremely awkward and powerless to referee, despite the husband being possibly speechless at her cattiness. Or maybe he was too much of a pussy to respond? Or maybe, as Joe thought, based on his ranting earlier, he was too polite to respond in Joe's presence? Or, the one Joe thought was most applicable, the husband having heard it all before, simply could not be bothered to answer?

"Excuse me. Would you like to have someone help you with your bags?" the clerk piped up from behind the desk. Joe was about to respond 'no' but then realised it was obviously not him the clerk was speaking to. He most certainly did not want to deny the wee man help. Joe was sure if he carried on pushing case mountain before him, he would be getting help he did not want. With his wife on his black case and every other case, he would more than likely end up in the back of an ambulance, when his wife's wished for heart attack possibly came true.

"I am sure we can manage," the lady replied rather cruelly.

"Bloody sure we would appreciate some help," the husband loudly interrupted, stepping forward and thanking the clerk several times.

"We are here to help," the clerk replied as he picked up the telephone to ring someone. Normally Joe found that phrase so false and sickly but was surprised that it sounded so sincere and genuine.

Having finished talking on the phone, asking for a John to come to the booking desk, he looked up at Joe and asked, "Yes sir, how can I help you?"

Joe presented his ticket with a smile, saying he was just checking in. He followed this by saying unnecessarily that he just had the one bag and did not need any help. The clerk swiftly checked his ticket, hit quite a few keys on his keyboard and handed Joe his ticket and the yellow oblong card with 'Boarding Pass' embossed across it in black.

"Have a good trip, sir. It might be a little choppy but we have no major concerns at all and there are no expected delays. Our staff will be on board should you need anything," the clerk stated calmly, professionally and, no doubt, robotically, saying this to every passenger.

"That's great. Thanks very much," Joe replied and turned around to see that the couple and their even more unstable-looking suitcase tower had moved a few metres away. He waved over to them with a, "See you on board," which he was not sure they heard, as he headed up the stairs to the departure seating area. They waved back in between sniping unheard comments, with obvious antagonistic body language, that encouraged Joe to leave them both to it.

Sitting, waiting for the call to go on board the ferry, Joe thought about his life in his holdall. There was not much in it, clothes mainly, with a couple of books and some toiletries, including a new toothbrush. It was all he really needed apart from his wallet in his jacket pocket with a good few notes in it, his driving licence and other bank cards. He thought about the difference between luggage and baggage. He thought about need and greed. He thought about having what you want but not what is essential. He knew he always liked travelling light. Maybe lighter than air, on a wing and a prayer too often, he confessed. If bad things happened, he would deal with them when they did. That was what his attitude was, rather than packing a case with oodles of just-in-case stuff that would probably never get used. All that probably did was give hernias, Joe slightly laughed to himself.

The world, to Joe, just seemed to become more and more consumed with consumerism. All the glossy ads, shopping becoming as big a national pastime as football, politicians encouraging the nation to go out and buy stuff to ensure economic prosperity. Joe shrugged his shoulders. What was the point in it all? Spending your hard-earned money on more pointless tat that would either fall apart or break down in a short time to be consigned to the rubbish tip? That seemed a waste to Joe. He was certainly not a skinflint but wanted his purchases to do what they said they would and be useful. He did not buy for the sake of being flash, showing off to pretend how wealthy, even if he had that rare experience of spare cash. There seemed to be so many things bought that people became bored with so quickly and dumped, only to go out and buy something similar and become bored with it. This became an endless circle that just filled the rubbish dumps and the pockets of the shareholders, for them in turn to buy even more expensive stuff they did not need.

Joe shook his head as the stewardess announced that boarding was commencing, smiling and directing the crowd towards the large swing doors. The previously arguing, luggage-jenga couple ended up behind Joe in the queue baggage less.

"All sorted, then?" Joe asked with a smile.

"Yes, they were lovely. They loaded it all onto a little truck and took it on board for us," the lady replied and the normal-coloured-faced, balding man smiled too. They certainly seemed a lot happier, Joe even noticing the man's arm around her waist.

"Been shopping?" Joe asked as he glanced down at several carrier bags in the lady's hands.

"Yes. There was a sale on, and I got a few extra bits, just in case," she replied as Joe let them both past him to go down the aisle first. The wee man just shook his head as he passed Joe. Joe just shook his head too as he followed on, looking forward to buying his fry up and, despite it only being eight a.m., a pint once on board. Now that was essential shopping, he told himself, with no baggage.

London

His head touched the shuddering Perspex. Joe had been staring out the window but not registering at all the scenery rushing past through the downward racing raindrops. He had been so deep in his muddled mind he had not realised his head had been slowing moving towards the window until contact was made. Even the slight, painless bump was only a very brief interlude and he fell straight back into his whirlpool of ifs, buts and maybes, swirling around and around in the same ocean of confusion and memories that he had been for the past hour of the journey. He had remained in that almost laughable limbo for the past few days as he had planned this, he had to confess, mad expedition. There was another hour to go before his station and however long after that to find it. He knew who that was but the what troubled him greatly. Would this be the end of his search after many years? Or would it be the start of a totally new one? This caused his already furrowed brow to be ploughed up even more.

His ma had forwarded the letter from Lizzie. They were geographically far apart now and their previous very close friendship had drifted a bit as well. Her and his intermittent letters, along with her out-of-the-blue and his random phone calls, always felt like they brought music into his life. He hoped his reciprocated with her. However, what she had said in this particular letter, along with what was implied between her rows of neat handwriting, had played an entire orchestra in his thoughts ever since. Had he read too much into those sentences? There were certainly clear facts and messages in the written words. But there were other unwritten, subtle and unsubtle, cryptic messages that he questioned if he had decoded correctly. He was good at spelling words but he wondered if his psychological analysis should have 'sick' at the start instead of 'psyc'? His overactive overthinking was causing him an emotional illness, that was for sure. This journey would either find a cure for it, or cause death. He genuinely was unsure which option he preferred.

Dee had asked numerous times what was wrong over those past few days. Although their relationship was still only months young, his strange silences and distracted responses felt odd to both of them. She knew him well enough to know that was not like him at all. He had dismissed it as work stuff and nothing to worry about. He had tried, when he felt things become a little too tense, to joke around a bit and talk crap as usual. However, he knew these did not have the same motivation and his speech did not come as naturally as it would normally. He hoped Dee had not picked up on this but was unsure. It was after she had left on that Thursday night that he had decided to bring things to a conclusion.

He had rang Dee on the Friday evening at her shared house, saying he was heading down to London the next day. He tried to make it sound casual. An old friend from school and university had been in touch, wanting to meet up, and that was the only day that suited both of them. He did not tell her it was a girl or any other details. The fact about the old friend being in touch was true, the arrangements certainly were not. She was a little surprised, shocked even, and definitely curious about his decision. He had never been to the capital before and she knew Joe's dislike, if not hatred, of the noise and bustle of big cities. But she accepted his reason that it had to be Saturday. Despite the short notice, listening to his desire to go, she agreed although the reluctance was clear in her tone.

He knew she was working on Saturday, so would not be able to come and felt a bit devious about that part of his plan. Her suggestion that she rang in sick and came with him caused him a moment of anxiety. She managed to convince herself, more than his flustered blustering, that she should not. There was important stuff to do at her work, she had said, with disappointment clear in her voice. When she started asking a bit more about who this friend was, the pips on the payphone he was calling from started. This was not pre-planned but a little bonus, the wicked part of his brain thought. It made the guilt for even having such a sneaky part of his brain even greater. Having hastily explained he had no change left, not declaring the few fifty pence and ten pence pieces in his left jeans pocket, the increasing pip speed was a convenient reason for him to say that he loved her, would see her Sunday and hang up.

He did not feel good about not telling Dee the full story. He tried rather pathetically, and unsuccessfully, to convince himself that he had not lied to her. Well, maybe a deliberate lie about the loose change; and about the urgent necessity; and that the arrangements had been made; and there were other things he knew he had probably said with no grain of truth to them.

Apart from all these, he had told her the cropped truth, in its miniscule form and was scared of what he would harvest on this mad journey. But he lied to himself as well as her. He hated lying, as it caused too much confusion telling more lies to cover one lie, as his latest shenanigans had shown. He had given her a very restricted form of the truth, but he was indeed going to London for the day to see an old friend from university. That was all she really needed to know – for the time being, at least. However, he always knew that you do not have to speak words to tell a lie. His silence was lying; his not telling her details was lying; his not explaining why he had to do this so urgently was lying. These lies he was determined to erase on Sunday when he planned to meet Dee. He would tell her everything once he had the complete story to tell. For now, though, he was on this train towards the truth and, when he arrived there, discover if a journey ended or a new one began because of it.

After many years, it was over with Aaron. Aaron had been too perfect, anyway. He was from North County Down, where most of the moneyed aristocracy of Ulster resided. It was a very different world from Joe's, and most of the other residents on the northern side of the border. Many North Downers were a bit uppity, speaking so differently with a refined, real or false, accent. Sometimes there would be a slightly condescending tone. Joe was very aware of that when covered in cement and soil, landscaping a garden for one such 'refined' lady for two weeks with two other equally mucky, student serfs. That was Aaron's higher world but, despite that he seemed so normal and dead on. Aaron was a decent and, despite his upbringing, down-to-earth bloke. That infuriated Joe even more.

He did not wish Aaron to be a drug-using alcoholic who treated Lizzie badly. That would have made things a lot easier, but he genuinely wanted Lizzie to be happy. And she was with Aaron. Or so she had been and that was what had stopped him acting until taking this train south now. But then she was very happy being with Joe too? Maybe more so he thought. Aaron had been training to be a doctor, having gone out with Lizzie since they were fourteen, family friends from they were five. In an attempt at a bit of social climbing, mainly by Lizzie's ma, Lizzie was introduced to Aaron when they were only toddlers. Lizzie's mum worked with Aaron's mother which was where it all began with dinner parties, barbecues and other social get-togethers. As a relationship, more than playing chasies on the lawn, developed in their early teens, both sets of parents approved of and encouraged it. It was a sort of a Northern Irish aristocratic arranged marriage which Joe accepted, begrudgingly. Although Joe thought Lizzie a princess, her family was, at best, at the lower end of this self-appointed Ulster aristocracy. The County Antrim version of this was viewed as lesser by the close knit, southern and eastern elite fringing Belfast Lough. Lizzie's da had worked hard to establish his very successful construction firm but never forgot his roots. He thought the sun shone out of Joe's arse, even giving Joe summer work when he wanted it. Lizzie's ma thought the same and he got on great with both of them. Constantly dismissed as just good friends, Joe never developed it further than that with Lizzie. He thought about changing the relationship often but never did. Too stuck in his ways? Too comfortable with the way things were? He had tried all that reasoning to justify his maintaining a status quo friendship. However, that friendship had also matured and changed over the years, providing new and different opportunities. Now, he had finally convinced himself, this London journey maybe would be the time, or maybe not?

Joe was never shut out at all by Lizzie's family. Aaron, being the perfect gentleman, never did either. He was always chatty and polite with Joe in a frosty kind of way and never truly warm. Aaron being Aaron, Joe could not dislike him, although he had to confess, he did try, more than once. Quite a few times in reality, based mainly on the fantasy of what might have been, if Aaron had not been on the scene. As Joe sat on the train now, he realised that he had been in a kind of purgatory since she had sat beside him on the school bus, on the way to their neighbouring schools in their first-year uniforms. She sat beside him again on the way home. So, it went on over their school years and continued when they ended up, not surprisingly, at the same university. They were always with each other, even when they were apart, their souls together when their bodies were not in close proximity.

He looked at the compact A4 sized map on London on his lap. To him it was huge, Joe estimating it was about the same size as the six counties that made up his homeland. London was in fact a small country within a country he rationalised and, many argued, acted as such. There was as big a, if not bigger, north-south divide in England as there was back home although with a lot less flags, riots, bombs and all the rest.

London dominated everything south of that blurred geographical line. In truth, it dominated above it as well. He had read many stories, facts and figures about the wealth of this place, the enormous capital of the capital. There was great bitterness of those beyond its suburbs when this wealth stayed within the confines of Greater London, only trickling out begrudgingly to the so-called regions. Many had justifiably argued that the UK was governed as follows – London, then London, London again, south of England, middle of England, Wales, north of England, Scotland and then … There was somewhere else? Oh yes Shetland Islands – No! They are part of Scotland. Isle of Man – No! Oh, yes – Northern Ireland! The distant 'region' of Northern Ireland/North of Ireland was lucky to receive anything at all Joe laughed sarcastically. The grand hotels, five-star restaurants, house-priced watches for sale in jewellers and other useless, extravagant bling soaked up and kept the wealth within London's boundaries. With all that wealth came all that power, politically as well as economically. Fairness never seemed to enter into this equation at all, with a rich elite ensuring it maintained this inner circle control that the likes of Joe would never, ever cross the circumference of. The locally impressive wealth of North Down seemed like some drought-ridden desert province in comparison. He was going to see all this for himself to view the money with his own eyes, but his journey was not interested in materialism. He was travelling to seek if something priceless was possible to be maintained or obtained with more than just banknotes. He did not care about his very meagre wallet contents, but was seeking an El Dorado of another kind of enrichment, in this city where the streets were meant to be paved with gold.

His nervousness increased at that thought, knowing he was potentially going to be still rich, potentially wealthy beyond belief – or totally bankrupt – after today. Whatever the outcome, he knew he had to risk it all for either freedom or – what was it the Americans called it? Closure! He thought that those were the wrong words but then… he rethought… maybe they were appropriate. He hoped he would at least still have a friendship after this, maybe not as deep a one as before, but still something to hang onto. There had been too, too many years invested in it to throw it away. But that was what he was risking if he told Lizzie the truth about his feelings. It could totally blow up in his face and leave their deep friendship scattered like a shrapnel jigsaw never to be rebuilt. Scaring himself, he quickly pushed the other outcome into his mind. What if she had the same feelings and had repressed them all these years? Wow, what a jackpot that would be. Then he slumped rapidly into a pitch-black mood as Dee came rushing into his mind.

The train stopped again at yet another station. Joe looked at his little map and panicked a moment as this was his stop. Joe jumped up with a loud scrumple as the newspaper reading man beside him was barged aside, muttering loudly and a little angrily. He was annoyed even more when Joe stood on his foot. Joe's throwaway apology over his shoulder, as he moved down the aisle, did little to ease that pain. Politely shoving ahead and resisting the less polite shoves from others, Joe eventually made it out onto the concrete platform with neat red paintwork. The full flowerpots did little to remove the smell of diesel fumes, or the coffee and fried food aromas coming from the little booth in front of him.

His stomach growled and his throat felt dry, so he stepped forward to the booth. After the four in front of him were served very quickly, Joe ordered a coffee and a toastie with the smiling, Asian man. He turned around and Joe's mouth opened to speak further but no words came. Joe had just seen the price list and had gawped. It was too late to cancel his order so, when it arrived a few minutes later, he handed over the cash. Having spent the money, he thought how much that would have bought him in a supermarket and fed him for a day. Joe never considered himself a tightarse or particularly money conscious, his overdraft proved that. Still, he took a sharp intake of breath at the amount he had just handed over for such small items in his hands. When he turned around and his coffee was sent flying by a fast-running business suited woman, he swore very loudly. The Asian man shouted over to Joe and quickly restored Joe's faith in humanity, by letting Joe jump the queue, as he set up another replacement coffee onto the little counter. Then Joe lost that new faith again just as fast, as the Asian man asked for the price of it. Joe simply stared at him with a gobsmacked frown, said nothing and walked away.

Joe dug out the half-full, lukewarm bottle of water from his backpack and sat on the corner of a crowded bench as he opened his wrapped toastie. He was too hungry to whinge about it any more and scoffed it in three bites. As the unrefreshing water washed it down his gullet, he pulled out the piece of paper which he had written Lizzie's address on. He had it memorised but needed the reassurance. He held it in the same hand as the now empty, tomato-stained toastie wrapper. Joe was unaware that they could move so fast but a plump pigeon that had been waddling around near him flapped its wings, rose up. Its beak grabbed both the toastie wrapper and the address paper in its short beak and fluttered clumsily off. Joe rose immediately, loudly doubting the flying thief's parentage. He sat down again almost as quickly, as the pigeon merged into a sea of legs and other fat flyers looking for an easy meal.

Joe had a strange belief in signs. Neither the small, informative pedestrian ones, nor the huge, brash, neon advertising ones surrounding him now at this huge station. Despite their size, sexiness and sleekness, these in-his-face ads made absolutely no impact on Joe's desires to buy any of the products or services they offered. He was too distracted anyway to focus on any of them, no matter how much cleavage or percentage discounts was shown. No, Joe believed that there were little things that happened that were driven by some other mystical forces. He never knew whether to call them fairies, little people or guardian angels, but he genuinely believed that they sometimes sent messages into the physical world. Was this thieving pigeon one of these messages from that mystical realm? What was it, anyway? That he did not need the address as he knew it by heart, and he had Lizzie's original letter in his inside pocket as well? Or was it much more significant – do not go? He sniggered at this perceived action from another fantasy world and, mostly dismissing it applying this time, he rose to his feet. After quickly giving up saying, 'excuse me' every few seconds, he battled through the expressionless hordes of morning commuters and reached the thronged exit.

There were taxis, buses and people everywhere. He moved towards a stationary taxi and asked the price to Lizzie's address. After the price of the toastie and coffee, Joe was prepared for the need to sell a kidney for a taxi fare. The taxi driver leaned a little further out of the lowered window and surprised Joe by telling him, in a broad Cockney accent, that the address was just a few streets away and, with a 'bloody murder out there!' comment on the morning rush hour traffic, told Joe he would be a lot quicker walking. Joe had known it was not far, but wanted a taxi to make sure he found the right place. The smiling driver, with waving arm motions that almost caught Joe around the side of the head, directed Joe the best route. Thanking him several times, Joe stepped back and faced down the road. A well-dressed businessman stepped up to Joe's helpful taxi driver and promised the smiling Cockney a very large tip if he could have him at a stated address before ten a.m. The close-by Joe overheard their brief conversation and smiled, although not nearly as much as the taxi driver, thinking it showed how good Karma worked. Then he stopped in his tracks.

What the hell am I doing? he asked himself inwardly. *What am I playing at? This is not just mad and stupid, but it is worse than that. I could lose Dee from this, and I could lose Lizzie as well. I know my feelings for Lizzie and for Dee. Lizzie has been a friend for so long, I cannot do this. I cannot risk losing her as a friend completely. She has just broken up with a long-term boyfriend and I am like some sort of vulture thinking I can come down here and whisk her away with my confession of feelings for her. Even if she rejects me and wants to keep the friendship, it would never be the same again. She may not even be at home! I will have to tell Dee about this, as it is the right thing to do. Then she could throw a major wobbler and maybe end it with me as well. I know I love Dee and could spend the rest of my life with her. But I love Lizzie as well, maybe in a different way? Or do I love them in the same way? Which do I love more? Do they love me...* He stopped thinking for a second as he was bumped into by a large suitcase whose owner apologised. It was sharply painful on the side of his knee but nowhere near as painful as his flaming heart shattered and his mind burned.

Joe turned on his heel towards the train station entrance. He turned again to face down the road the taxi driver's arm had waved towards. His mind had gone blank as he turned again towards the bustling entrance. He had a return ticket and he reached into his pocket to feel it was still there, unsure why he did this. Then he reached into his inside jacket pocket, feeling the envelope with Lizzie's letter in it, unsure why he did this as well. He was glad he had brought out the little bit of paper with his wrapping and not Lizzie's letter. If he had lost it, that would have been a lot harder to accept. *But then that would have been a much clearer signal from the little people! Wouldn't it?* he inwardly argued. He turned again looking down the road, then back to look at the still bustling entrance. *Make a bloody decision!* he demanded of himself. He started walking, knowing this decision was life changing for him. He knew then that what he did now would haunt his mind with a 'what might have been?' question forever. Or it could be exactly what destiny, fate or even the spirits had already decided was meant to be? He swore loudly and turned the other way.

Link

"You know the way they say that a chain is only as strong as its weakest link?"

There was a brief suspiciousness of what was coming next from Joe, who begrudged a slightly goading reply of, "Yeah? Whoever 'they' are?" Joe stared at him, unsure if it was anger or mocking, or both, from the man before him.

The man snarled back, "Well, that weak link was you! And it has just shattered into bits all over the place!"

Joe was unfazed, which caught his accuser by surprise. Joe calmly replied, "Well, at least you don't think I am the missing link!" Joe attempted to put on a caveman expression, which, to be honest, did not appear much different from his normal look. The man opposite him frowned questioningly. "At least it means you know I was part of the chain to start with!" Joe continued with a rather bitter smile creeping across his tightly closed lips.

There was a pause as both of them pondered what to say next, each clearly tensing, each attempting to control surging frustration, each trying to psyche the other out. The man standing opposite him sighed loudly, glaring intently at Joe. He was trying to figure out if Joe was accepting guilt, formulating a defence, or, as it increasingly appeared, just simply did not give a shit. "You know what I am talking about, don't you?" he asked Joe directly.

"I think so!" was all Joe said quietly and intentionally misleading, his concrete face betraying nothing of his inner emotions. The man opposite would have more chance trying to intimidate the ridged cement and stone yard they were standing on, than penetrate Joe's exuded hard exterior. This solid outside cocooned an emotional mush of anger, nervousness and worry that slopped about inside Joe.

"You don't seem to realise how serious this is! And the impact this is going to have on the team," the man replied sternly.

How it impacts you, more like! was the instant unsaid thought that went through Joe's mind as he smiled sarcastically sweetly back, making sure his eyes betrayed nothing. Joe nodded his head at the man, who skellied a vulnerable look back that showed he felt Joe's silent counter accusation.

"This will have repercussions, especially for you!" the man stated threateningly, his inner anger going up a few degrees Celsius as Joe just apparently coolly shrugged and pouted his lips. The man sighed deeply again and breathed out very obviously. "If you have nothing else to say, it means I am going to have to take this upstairs!" the man said. It was a last-ditch attempt to drain some reaction from the blank faced Joe facing him, but nothing flowed at all as the conversation stagnated.

"If it's heavy, I can help you carry it up!" was Joe's smart-arse reply that he was quite pleased with. The returning hard-eyed stare showed Joe had hit a weak spot in the man's projected authoritarian armour that he thought was providing his power. Joe smirked as his mind tallied up another point on his imagined scorecard.

"If that's your attitude, I will leave it for now and I am sure the ones upstairs will want to talk to you," the man gave as a departing thrust that he hoped would have broken Joe to, if not beg for mercy, at least show some remorse. Joe's repeated shoulder shrug and lip pout was not the response he wanted. Feeling cornered and, with no other options left, the man turned on his heel and walked away muttering.

Joe turned around and walked back, in the opposite direction, across the weed-strewn storage yard mumbling 'what a first-class tool!' to himself. He added, with a little laugh, "And not the sharpest tool in the box, either!" He was not bothered about the uneven, sharp stones he walked on, thinking more about the stony ground his job appeared to have ended up on. After that curt tit for tat tete a tete, Joe could not decide if he was bothered more about being setup to be upset, or being upset at being set up? As he slowly walked, Joe reached his hand up to the top of his chest. His heart was beating fast but there was no pain there. The man he had been speaking to was more of a pain at the complete opposite end of his torso! Although he had given Joe some heartache in the past, Joe had managed to match it in return. That was what had happened previously, but Joe was unsure if he was still going to be able to do it this time around. He swore out loud about 'f'ing office politics!'

Joe felt the thin, gold chain. He had worn this since his eighteenth birthday, fumbling with it through the thin cotton of the striped shirt his ma and sister had given him, and below his twisted tie that his da had bought him. He twiddled it between his thumb and two fingers. The chain was valuable to him, far more than the shirt and tie, far more than anything he could think of at that moment. It was not for the fairly small monetary amount he could have sold it for, but for its spiritual wealth. At times like these he would rub at it, linking back to his parents who had bought him this adornment to mark his adulthood. The habit had become more and more ingrained as he faced more and more stressful situations, as his work and family life became more complex and challenging. By rubbing each link like they were beads on a rosary, it was as if they brought coolness to him to cope with heated situations, like had just happened. It was not proper praying but in reality, was. With each rub he would mumble asks to God, the universe, the fairies, whoever was out there, for help. Sometimes they answered, sometime he had to wait, sometimes they remained silent. The fact that silence was still an answer to a prayer was something he found even harder to accept than a 'no!' It left him feeling not listened to, alone, even, which was far worse than having his demands, often asked for like a spoilt child, being refused.

He asked for his father's strength, determination and humour to see him through. He likewise asked for his mother's patience, kindness and gentle authority. This had now become a common chant of Joe's. Although both his parents were still very much alive, Joe still felt able to reach out to touch their spirits, as he hoped they could with him. Joe always thought the spirits of the living were even more important than the spirits of the dead. The dead spoke from past lives, the living for the now. He did not have any speed dial list of live or dead ones on his mobile, or a special spirit phone to contact them with. In fact, he had absolutely no evidence of any kind that he had ever successfully achieved linking up in either realm. But he had inexplicable feelings, tingles and shivers, that calmed or tensed him for no reason. These were two main sorts, a relaxed happy feeling, which he currently did not have. Then there was the 'be alert, hairs rising on the back of his neck' one, which he had oodles of walking across the yard. Even just being made more alert certainly made him feel so much better, reassuring him someone always had his back covered, even if he could only feel, not see them. Whether people thought him a bit mad or not, anyone would be totally and truly off their heads to refuse a guardian angel's help, was Joe's view.

Understandably, he told very few people about this ability he was still figuring out. He was worried others would take his da's, sometimes brutal but always with harmless intent, mickey-taking to another level. A couple Joe had told mistakenly about this. Then he had walked away quickly. From their reactions, it had been too easy to be able to imagine them putting more cushions on the walls to make his potential new cell abode ready. This had put an urgency in his stride away from them. Others were okay with it, dismissing it as a bit weird and left it at that with an 'each to their own' resolution. Some even embraced the whole thing enthusiastically. One girl was way too enthusiastic, almost wanting to sit down to have a séance there and then. This prospect had scared Joe off very quickly, well before any fingers connected on a table to do any dialling, let alone spirits answering the calls or the seancers (if that is what they are called) having to leave a voice message if they were out.

It was a kind of faith he supposed, but church folk would more than likely not agree. He justified it by simply asking how did they link up with their God, or gods? They prayed and asked and felt a non-visible presence. *Why was his so different?* he always wondered. It provided him with the confidence to face life and the advice shovel to deal with the brown stuff he increasingly encountered. That was a good thing, surely? His ma said she did reach out the same to Joe, although he wondered if she was just humouring him. His da always just laughed and teased Joe about being 'not right in the head.' But Joe knew his da secretly did give it a go, though. After all, it was his da who believed in the fairies and never messed with ghosts. He was probably more in touch with the spirit world even more than Joe was. So, it was not surprising he felt his da's large presence beside him often, even when miles apart in body. Boy! Did he feel the need of that now.

His parents had passed on their genes to him, so he knew that genetic chain link of all these powers were already in him. Knowing which to use, when and how was something he was still working out, wondering if he ever would. As he walked his mind revealed no answers, despite his chain having heated up from all the subtle rubbing he had done. He pointed his face skywards, threw his arms out by his side and threw a 'huh! Now you decide to abandon me!' look at whoever was up there, supposedly in control.

Joe entered the main office block, disappointed in his failing to slam the softly-sprung glass door behind him. He was desperately trying not to care, but anger was taking over and dominating his thoughts entirely. Joe felt victimised. He let out a little bleat of disapproval as he concluded he was being lined up as the scapegoat. Sure, he was the one that had started this ball rolling, but it had gathered a thick layer of moss authorisation on the way from his boss and other senior managers. From that recently-finished, brief conversation, it was obvious that the stone was now being slate-like wiped clean, using Joe as the scourer. Joe was being left holding it alone, feeling the heat of the friction it had caused as it had moved through the work system. As happened so often, if something became a hot potato, no one asked for the butter and salt. Instead, they passed it on to whoever, not caring who that person was as long as it was not them. When the hot potato actually turned out to be cooked to perfection, then these same people shoulder others out of the way to have a stab at it with their own fork and claim part of the prize. "F'ing office politics!" Joe muttered again.

It was a chain of events that had led to this spat in the yard between Joe and his boss. The chain had started off very strong, everybody linking together to pull it through. Then it had snapped. Possibly, someone should have seen the weakness earlier, but Joe had looked hard and not found any. He or someone else could have welded it or reinforced it, or tried at least to do something before the break had happened. It had happened further up the chain from where Joe happily pulled his length along, still strong in the naive knowledge that everything was holding together. He had just been told it had not and the anchor at its end was falling down, about to make a big splash that would soak everyone involved. From his boss's recent rant, it would pull Joe under too.

Joe raced up the back stairs two at a time, the neurons in his head failing to make any connection to help make a plan to deal with this. He was confident the accusation of him being the weak link was completely wrong, but doubts still persisted and his confidence waned. He found his cluttered desk and slumped into the seat. As he swung ninety degrees this way, then ninety degrees back, staring at the strange brown stain of unknown origin on the ceiling above, he had a thought! What if he was right and there was no inherent weakness in what he had connected together? What if a hacksaw or an angle grinder was involved? What if it had been deliberately sabotaged, hoping the chain would become a rope for Joe to hang himself with? He shuddered as he started joining those dots together. The more he did this the more the large arrow formed, pointing more and more at the man accusing Joe of being the weak and broken link. Now he had done it, the answer was obvious and easily found. If he had done it after only a few minutes of focused thought, others with more decision-making power and intelligence would see it too, surely? He dared to smile and felt a hopeful relief. He rubbed at his chain, thanking his da for determination and his ma for patience.

His eardrums painfully rattled as the tannoy squealed like an air raid siren. It ended as instantly as it began. As Joe blinked and poked his fingers in his ears to dig out any remaining reverberating noise, a very pissed-off female voice was heard through it. "Would someone please fix this bloody tannoy link, for pity's sake? Pete, that's your bloody job, isn't it? Oops. Sorry did not realise I was on transmit." She swore loudly and apologised again before eventually letting go of the button, but not before she no doubt heard the raucous laughter coming from all the differing departments. A few moments later, with a much lower decibelled screech to begin with, she had another go, nasally announcing, "Apologies for the tannoy problems. Peter is now sorting that out. Would Joe Average please report to the Managing Director's office immediately please. That's Joe Average to the Managing Director's office immediately. Thank you." There was another louder screechy squeal and a muffled swear from the announcer before it went quiet again.

Joe let out a muffled swear himself. The penetrating, suspicious stares from those around him cut to the bone. He tried hard to ignore them but only manged to avoid eye contact, as he looked around anywhere but at their eye-borne questions and teasing accusations. His boss had obviously been true to his word and had managed to take it upstairs. He swore again as he gathered his frantic thoughts. Grabbing a paper pad, he scribbled down some notes from the dots he had just joined. He knew he should really have a proper typed-up document, but his handwritten drunk spider notes would have to suffice. It was not much protection. Nor was it a cutting-edge offence, but at least it would give him something to fight back with, to parry anything they swung at him. He sniggered, trying to remember that quote about the might of pens and swords. He was unsure of where his short, inky stab sat within that aphorism and fought hard to dispel the doubts as to his asking if there was any point.

He half-ran into the toilets, splashed his face with cold water, straightened his tie, pissed remarkably easily, flushed, washed his hands, gave up quickly trying to straighten his hair then fixed his tie again, before he left and bounded up the stairs two at a time. Although he knew where it was, he had never been in the MD's office. It was as if it was a company shrine that such a mere mortal as Joe would corrupt with his presence in such a sacred place. He walked past his boss's office on the way. As he quickly peeked in, he was confused by what he saw. It was only three o'clock in the afternoon but his boss had his coat on. More than that, he was clearing his desk entirely, placing his personal items in a plastic carrier bag. His boss had his back turned and did not see Joe, nor did Joe make any attempt to be seen or heard by him. Joe tried not to think about it too much, wondering if his boss had received a promotion or was just moving offices. Nevertheless, this lingered confusingly in his thoughts.

Knocking firmly three times, he heard the permission to enter granted with a muffled but surprisingly friendly-sounding 'come on in'. As he closed the door behind him, feeling sweat trickle down his spine, he smiled nervously as he spoke. "Hello, I'm Joe. You wished to see me?" He never knew whether to add sir to the end of such sentences. He certainly did not know the man behind the huge paper strewn desk well enough to call him by his first name, and calling him Mr Bell did not have a good ring to it.

"Hello, Joe. Glad you could come. We have been having a look at your recent project. It appears that it should have worked, but didn't. This was very disappointing, as I had high hopes for it. I asked accounts and technical support to look into it and it appears it should have worked. We have found the weak link and, as you may have seen as you passed, he will no longer be working for this company."

He paused and peered closely at Joe, unable to figure out Joe's reaction. Joe was aware that his flinty face was probably in caveman mode as his brain chipped away with a stone axe trying to figure out what the hell of a ding-dong was going on. To break the awkward silence, Joe replied, "Oh! okay, sir," thinking Mr Bell was possibly pulling his chain, but that was not his style.

"This means that there is now a gap in our organisational chain and we would very much like you to apply for that position. There will be stiff competition. It will be advertised internally…" Mr Bell chimed on about this and that. Joe was not listening. All he could think of was the fact that the supposed missing link had been found, but it was not there. The link had been broken deliberately and he was not responsible. Sure, it often felt like every day was another day on the chain gang at this place, but he felt great for being free of those shackles of guilt and worry. No doubt, this other more senior job would have all sorts of hyped-up benefits and privileges. The advert would probably have gilded words, but these just covered up the fact that there were still glitzy corporate chains. However, Joe thought very seriously for a moment about these golden chains. Whatever the financial rewards, the price he would have to pay was that these would be even stronger and heavier ones to carry than his old ones.

He was deep in trying to link his thoughts together some more, when Mr Bell suddenly finished speaking. Joe nodded vaguely with an even vaguer smile, frantically trying to remember what exactly he had been told in those last few minutes. Joe's brain rattled and clunked around but he had no chain reaction in his thoughts. He stood up and thanked Mr Bell, reaching across to shake his hand. The elderly man rose from his seat slightly, shook Joe's hand once and let go. As Joe turned towards the door, he heard Mr Bell mumble.

"God, I am so glad to be finally rid of that ball and chain..."

Little

A little bit of honesty with himself was needed. Just a little, to stop himself denying it. It may have only been a little crush, which he may have stopped growing, but it was still there, awaiting regrowth opportunities. The fact it remained meant there was always that possibility that he would act on it. He had convinced himself he never would. Almost! This was, after all, only a wee thing, a bit of fun, a bit of banter with a work colleague. It was tiny, miniscule, he knew, in comparison to his feelings for Dee, his new-found English love. She had kissed him on the train when he arrived in this new-to-Joe country and had been the only girl he wanted to keep on kissing for the rest of his life. What he felt for Dee was simply so much larger than this. Whatever this was?

"Her from HR!" was how the others he worked with spoke about the person Joe had ended up spending most of his lunchtimes sitting beside. It was as if they refused to mention her name in case there was some industrial tribunal about it. The fact they never mentioned her name did not mean they had not accused her directly. It would have been a piss-poor layer of defence even Joe's sparrow, rather than eagle sized, law knowledge could have legally cut through.

He was still new to the job and she was still helping him settle in, he justified to himself. That had been twelve weeks ago now, he reluctantly admitted with a little guilt. On day one, 'Her from HR' had been the one who had shown him around his new job and offices, explaining everything as they went. She confessed to him that inductions usually only take an hour. His had taken four.

He had bought her a coffee and a dodgy-looking iced bun the following day as a 'thank you' in the work's eating area. They had been sitting together every lunchtime since. The others' little winks, head nods, smirks and stares had combined to herd the two of them into the furthest chair corralled corner of the canteen that had once held three times the numbers of current employees. It was as private as they could get, away from the noise and jibes of the other conversations, but still not out of stare range. After several weeks, the stares had stopped but the little innuendos still swarmed midge like around Joe constantly. It was the same for her, she told him. Yet still they continued.

'I love your accent' was what had really started it all off on that first day. From this cue, Joe had just kept on talking ever since. She, at the start, simply smiled and listened intently and likewise had done so ever since that first day. The more they met the more they both talked. Little chinks appeared in their personal protective armour as the lunchtimes passed by. Each let the other peer in, initially for a little while. Then, little by little, for longer and longer, until they trusted enough for those burrowing little holes to become caverns. Both their partners had been told about their lunchtimes together, their suspicions and a few snide comments being divulged the following lunchtime with no guilt or regrets.

It was how he said things as much as what he said that she loved. It was how often he said 'wee'. How she never managed to totally replicate what he said in his local accent, laughing together when she did. How his accent was so gentle and almost sang to her. Joe knew this, simply because she had told him, many times. Maybe this stuck in Joe's subconscious, as he realised it was all true. She did not have enough phlegm for his Ulster Scots Irish. He supposed his accent did sort of sing-song along. As for 'wee' he said this word more and more in front of her without realising. Thirty-two times, she had counted, unknown to him, one lunch hour. He felt a little embarrassed by that, but she just laughed at her wee joke. They had spent many a lunchtime as Joe explained how the word 'wee', like little, may mean small. However, in his homeland it had a range of meanings far, far beyond that.

'Her in HR', Joe found out early on, had studied English at university. She was intrigued by the use of English words in different regions. Linguistics had been two of her modules at uni, so Joe intrigued her from the start when his accent stuck out as he waxed lexical to her. There was a French fella, Frederic, from Fismes and a big bloke from Buenos Aires everyone called Ben although that was not his christened name, working at the same company. Neither of these seemed as foreign as Joe to her. It had sparked her interest in how the Queen's English was so right royally bastardised when it was delivered in an Ulster voice. She picked his brain as he became her personal pronunciation project to keep her sane amongst job descriptions and equality law. Joe was keen to be her wee guinea pig so he gave the meanings of the words he spoke as cutely and squeak free as he could.

'Wee' itself took several lunchtimes. Wee, Joe explained, mostly meant little. Joe gave the example of 'a wee cup of tea in your hand', which remained a well-used phrase back home. This initially caused her some concern about cup and mug availability in Northern Ireland/North of Ireland, along with potential scalding. Joe clarified things and used a different example, 'a wee cod' which meant a little joke. She was very fishy about that one too. Third time lucky he explained how the word for a child 'wain' had come about from 'wee yin', yin meaning one. This set her off asking about yang, confusing Joe a little and he felt his patience melt away a bit, but her smile brought that back easily. This had been her first wee lesson and he braced himself for what was to come.

The next day he tried to talk about other things, but she insisted on more wee stuff. A little reluctantly, he began again. This time, he explained the difficulty he had in choosing examples the day before. This was mainly due to the fact that wee is often used paradoxically in his homeland. A wee man, can be of short stature, but just as easily be a giant. Tone of voice, he educated her, was so important to pick out the sarcasm. 'A wee bit of stoor' could be only slightly dusty or a fog filling a room. This sort of stuff was what she loved, scribbling down notes that she would never let him see. He caught a glimpse of one note saying 'wee means small but can also sarcastically be big.' He was happy with that description and pleased with his teachings.

So, their wee lunchtime get-togethers continued until, in his fifth month in the job, on his ninety-third day, she came over to what had become their table that lunchtime. Instead of sitting, she stood, her hair a hash, her face white and her eyes telling that she had just tholed something she did not want. Joe held his wheesht and said nothing. He was nervous but curious at the same time, knowing something was very wrong.

"We have a wee issue," was all she said. "My so-called workmates in HR, have raised a complaint about us two meeting at lunchtimes."

Her eyes saddened and Joes burned with mild anger. "What the hell has it to do with them yins who you spend your free time with?" he barked at her, unable to hold back his frustration. He knew there was desperation in there too, as he felt the real threat of losing her. There was remorse afterwards as he realised, he had shouted this at her when it was not her fault.

"It is unbecoming conduct for someone in HR to be fraternising so closely with one particular work colleague. It could possibly mean the whole HR department faces accusations of favouritism." She read from the scrumpled letter in front of her, her eyes not angry but sad and anxious. Joe had not received any similar letter, making him feel even worse for her. Nor had Joe any formal, quasi-disciplinary meeting to discuss this. All he had had was the usual gossiping comments and pissing-off probing questions ribbing him to request a progress update. These varied from snide 'how's it going with – you know?' to crude 'have you stuck it in her yet?' and everything in between. None of these he answered beyond a scowl.

Joe backtracked, bringing his anger under control. He knew from what she had told him the ones she worked with were a bunch of thaveless gulpins. (She had been taught that these were 'useless fools' on lesson five.) That description was now too polite for them, he decided, so added a few new adjectives and nouns, English, Irish and Ulster-Scots. "Look, if all this is getting you into trouble then we just leave it at that. The last thing I want is for you to be caleeried. I dinnae want this thing to be made a whole styachie of!" She stared at him, questioning. He looked back at her perplexed then realised she had not learnt the word. 'Confused' and 'mess' he nodded to her, glad to see it made her smile. It was so strange that with her he was able to talk normally, his accent coming through, unlike with the others with whom he had to pronounce properly and slow. It was not just because she wanted to learn his dialect, either. There was more to it than that. A seed had been planted, sprouted, and Joe felt it was budding into an unknown flower. This HR letter and meeting planted a size ten on this, stomping and crushing what they both had treated as a delicate, precious thing. It was now gone as she clearly did not wish to fight for it, nor did Joe, to cause either of them more hassle. It was what logically and arguably had to be done, but neither of them had to like it.

She nodded ever so slightly. Then she did something she had never done before. She kissed him on the cheek before shaking his hand. "I'm sorry," was all she said. That was the end of Joe's wee lunchtime escapes. Times when he could bring a wee taste of his homeland's Ulster Scots into his new English job. Her from HR had started off as someone he spoke of as being 'just a wee friend at work'. It changed as it progressed and, in a way, Joe was glad it had ended before this wain of a thing between them grew up. It was a delicate and precious thing to them both, but they were young and felt powerless to fight for it in the face of this officialdom.

He hardly saw her over the next weeks, just a brief 'hello' in the corridor or seeing her racing into the canteen for a can from the drinks machine. Awkwardness had descended on, between and around them both making them avoid each other as much as possible. This made the intensity they had shared previously even harder for them both to cope with. Joe knew he certainly did and would have been very surprised if she had not. It felt like the eyes of every single other employee of the firm was on them even more. It freaked him out but he quietly worked away, deflecting the still ongoing 'bits of banter'. He kept his head down to ensure as low a profile as possible, waiting and waiting for the rumours to go away. They did not and, if anything, got worse, instead wondering what had happened to break them up and creating all sorts of rumours to fill the gaps Joe would not fill in.

Then he heard she had gone to a new job. He had been looking himself but nothing so far. He felt strangely numb when he heard that, not regretful, not relieved that she was free, nor sad. The day he heard that, he walked home from workkicking a few things on the way, but this gave no relief. While she was still in the same building, he had still had some little hopes that they could meet up, if only infrequently when this had died down. Those hopes had been small to start with but ended up vaporised. Joe was never a big thing person as he knew it was little things that made people happy. At work it was not just what you did for your job, but those chats with colleagues, burgers on a Friday, jokes and craic. Her in HR was gone now. Although only knowing her for a short time, he knew she had definitely left a wee friendship hole in him.

The following week Joe was sitting alone in the canteen. He often did recently, when it was raining hard like it was and he could not get outside to escape. He sensed someone coming close to him and looked round. The smartly-dressed young man about Joe's age sat down without being invited, reached out his hand and shook Joe's vigorously, saying, "Hi, I'm Samuel." Joe began talking, telling him who he was. "I'm the new guy in HR," Samuel replied. Joe chatted a bit more, asking Samuel what he thought of it so far. Samuel interrupted him after a wee while. "I love your accent. Tell me more about it…" So, Joe told him a wee bit. The following day he told him a wee bit more. And so, it went on, little by little.

Lagan

"Brain…" He meant Brian! "Are you having the usual?" Joe said, yet again reminding himself he had to get used to that and keep using his proper name. They were most certainly not at primary school together any more. That was over twenty-five years ago, Joe slightly shockingly realised! Brian… Joe and Joseph were having their almost monthly regular Saturday morning fry-up catch-up. It was the same wee café, at the same time, or thereabouts. It was the same menu, which all three looked at, as always, before ending up ordering the same food as before; and the time before that: and the time before that. It was all part of the same enjoyable, relaxing with a couple of mates, routine.

This Saturday they were briefly slightly irritated that four laughing lads had taken their usual table. There had been a moment, Joe had seen looks clearly on Brian and Joseph's face, which silently asked the questions *Why are they sitting there? They should know it's our table. Why do they not know it was our table? Should I tell them…?* Joe's face had probably been saying the exact same, before they shrugged their shoulders and shuffled over to the last empty table in the place.

It felt a little strange being over by the wall instead of the window. All three of them had fumbled about a bit, not sure which seat to take. They were sat now, had already looked at the menu and each ordered the same as before – Brian and Joe two full Ulster Frys and two teas; Joseph a vegetarian fry and a coffee. Brian was Joe's oldest friend from way back. Joseph had moved over from England to work at the same bank as Brian. That was nearly two years ago, Joe was surprised to calculate in his head. He dwelt in his thoughts a second, the speed of the years passing scaring him a little, before he tried to remember where Joseph was originally from. *Was it Hampshire?* Joe asked in his head. *Definitely south of England, somewhere.* Before Joe had settled that annoying detail Joseph asked a question, as he was prone to do, still trying his very best to get to grips with the complicated uniqueness of Northern Irish life. Brian and Joe waited as Joseph swallowed the last of his well chewed fried tomato that had left little drizzles of bright red in each corner of his mouth. It made him look a little like Dracula after a feed. Joe pointed to his own mouth corners, nodding towards Joseph, who received the message and swiped a napkin across, leaving it streaked bloody.

"I heard the weirdest phrase today. I have been trying to figure it out but have no idea," Joseph stated, building a little suspense. Brian and Joe's eyes urged him to carry on and stop faffing about. "My department were in a meeting and Thomas asked if Sylvia thought he had 'Come up the Lagan in a bubble'!" Joseph shook his head, eyes wide as he stared across enquiringly at the other two, his fork and knife armed hands spread out in front of him ready to dissect their answer. Brian and Joe looked at each other to decide who went first, as both of them worked away with their own knives and forks at the vegetable roll on their plates, which was definitely not suitable for vegetarians like Joseph.

Brian went, as usual, "It is simple enough, really. It means, 'Do you think I am naive?' Or maybe 'born yesterday' might suit better. Basically, it is a Belfast way of asking if someone thinks they are stupid and do not understand the real world."

Joseph nodded and ahhhed, obviously seeing the context of it. Joe had nothing much to add so chipped in about the river itself. "Well, you know the way capital cities have rivers – London has the Thames, Paris has the Seine, Dublin the Liffey? Well Belfast has the Lagan! It is not that big a river, not big at all compared to these others. A wee river for a wee capital? It is less polluted than people think but still a lot more than it should be, and has some really nice river walks long it. I have dandered along it a good few times, but can honestly say I have never seen anyone in a bubble on it!" Joseph smirked at that and Brian gave Joe a little nudge with his elbow.

"Hey, that would be a great idea for a wee business down by the riverside. Brian's Brilliant Bubble Breakaways!" Joe became quite excited as he continued, before Brian's dead eye curbed his enthusiasm. "There might be a few problems, though!" Joe continued, unfazed. "The saying is only about coming 'up' the Lagan in a bubble, so how would you bring Brian's Bubbles back down again?" Brian's dead eye look remained the same, despite Joe's giggles as he cut through the pork sausages on his plate.

"There are some really strange sayings, aren't there?" Joseph continued sipping his coffee. "What's that one about pots and kettles and black? I've heard that a couple of times, over in England too, and still not sure what that's all about. Our kettle is white plastic and our pots are grey steel with copper bottoms!"

"That one's sort of the same as throwing stones and greenhouses. You know the one I mean? In Victorian times they swung black pots or a kettle over the open fire to cook with, so they both ended up black." Brian continued. "You would see them up at the Folk Museums."

"Have you ever heard them arguing when you have been up there? Maybe they want to be other colours too?" Joe asked. Brian went back to his dead-eye look, knowing Joe was building up to something and dreading what. Regardless of where Joe's tangent was going, Brian gave Joe a 'go on then' stare, to get it over with. "Well! Have you ever heard the kettle calling back to the pot that it is black too? Have either of them ever actually stopped for a moment to ask if it is still politically correct for kettles and pots to describe each other's outer colour? In the modern world, it is not just about what is on the outside but what is on the inside. That can apply to kitchen items as well as everything else, surely?" Joe grinned broadly at his newly cooked up philosophy. Joseph laughed a little, Brian just groaned, both thinking the scourge of racism having spread to kitchen appliances a potty concept.

"Then there is the most famous ship saying of them all!" Brian announced, keen to change the subject before they started debating racism in kitchen utensils. He dismissed Joe's suggestion of 'land ahoy!' then had to dismiss Joseph's 'ahh harr! Me hearties!' as well, although he did laugh at Joseph's hand over one eye as he said it.

Likewise, he said no to Joe's rather alien suggestion of 'clingons on the starboard bow!' Joseph had almost finished 'fire one torpedo…' when Brian mildly lost his cool and uttered a firm, "No! Listen! It is the 'She was all right when she left us'!"

Joe swung back in his chair nodding as he swigged from his mug. Joseph just looked blank as he mopped up the last of his sauce with potato bread. "Titanic?" Brian said towards Joseph. Joseph was still thinking. "The big ship that sank! The most famous ship ever!" Brian continued but Joseph still did not get the connection. "It was all right when it left Belfast, meaning it was not our fault!" Joe looked hard at Joseph, as Brian did. Despite them both having their ears tuned in, they still did not hear the penny drop to signal that Joseph had connected it together.

"Here!" Joe butted in. "There have been thousands and thousands of ships. Maybe even millions if you include all the canoes and wee ones. Thousands and thousands of these have been sunk, especially during all the wars in history. Harland and Wolff built hundreds of ships at the mouth of the Lagan in Belfast Lough. There was also Workman, Clark and Co who built ships in Belfast too, did you know?" They did not, and Joe continued, proud of his little-known fact. "So did Glasgow's shipyards and all the other ship builders across other countries. So…" He paused for suspense. "Name me ten ships?" Joe lifted his mug of tea and took another large swig as he swayed back on his chair to see how they fared answering that question.

Brian and Joseph stared at each other. They thought silently for a moment or two. Joe added cheekily "Doesn't matter if they have sailed up or down the Lagan or not. Or if they did it in a bubble or not!" They all smirked and thought hard about Joe's question. Joe realised he was struggling to name ten too, and glad he had not said twenty.

"Well, there is HMS Caroline, down in Belfast docks, for one." Brian paused after he said this. "Do the Stranraer and Cairnryan ferries count?" Brian said with a twinkle in his eye. Joe just glared at him. "So, the Strangford Ferry is out as well, then?" Brian asked. Joe nodded sarcastically, giving Brian two fingers on one hand and a middle digit on the other. Brian touched his own thumb for Caroline to start their list.

"Oh! Oh! Victory! Nelson's ship at Trafalgar! That's one for sure. Then there's the German Bismark warship that they made a film about hunting it down," Joseph excitedly said. Joe nodded as Brian pointed at two of his fingers in turn. "Oh! The one with no one on board, Mary-something! See More? No! Sea something? See less. That's it. Mary See Less, and it is great that when you're speaking you do not have to spell things correctly!" Joseph said, becoming even more excited and Brian touched another three fingers.

"Mary Rose!" Joe added in casually. "Henry the Eighth's ship." Another of Brian's fingers was touched.

"Hindenburg?" Joseph chipped in. "No, that was an airship. Do airships count?" Brian and Joe shook their heads in sync.

Joe nudged a surprisingly silent Brian in the ribs. "Come on, youse are bound to know a few more?" Joe encouraged, deflecting from his own lack of suggestions.

Brian spoke up. "Well there is the Mayflower that dropped the first pioneers off in North America." Joseph and Joe were both impressed with that one.

"What was Charles Darwin's ship called? It had a dog's name?" Joseph continued, staring at the table for inspiration.

"Rover?" Joe joked.

"Beagle! Beagle!" Joseph blurted out and Brian touched off another two fingers.

"QE2," Joseph said and earned another finger. "Is there a QE One and a QE Three?" Joseph asked, joking. Brian and Joe hummed and harred for a moment as there possibly should have been but decided not to include these. There probably was but they were not sure. Although both thought Joseph should get an extra point for effort, Brian and Joe both gave him a thumb's up.

There was silence at their table for a minute or two, as the other customers' chatter and cutlery clatter continued all around them. Brian tutted and flicked his last three fingers with, "Stranraer Ferry, Cairnryan Ferry and Strangford Ferry. Those are the last three so all done!" All three laughed with relief, all thinking they should have been able to have said more famous ships than that.

Joseph snorted a laugh. "We actually did not mention Titanic!"

"Aw! I am fit to be tied at that!" Brian said with clear frustration and his face reddening.

"Wind yer neck in Brian and catch yerself on. It's only a bit of craic," Joe replied, nudging his elbow with his own, before setting his knife and fork on the empty plate before him.

Joseph stared blankly at them both, feeling self-conscious. Joe and Brian looked back at him with confused 'what's wrong?' expressions. Joseph obviously wanted to speak, but was not sure where to start. He did speak after a moment or two. "So, what's fit to be tied where? And the neck winding thing? And that catching yourself? Both sound painful. Who was it told me about yer man being drunk and zipping up too fast after a piss…" Joe and Brian both smiled at hearing Joseph say, "Yer, man," a localism beaconing out amongst his still-very-English accent. It was as if they were taking pride in their pupil's achievement understanding 'Norn Irish' as locals call it.

Joe and Brian both interrupted to stop hearing that leg crossing, arms folding, squirming story again. They explained the first bit, saying it was about restraint and not getting angry or frustrated. Winding your neck was not to be done physically, with any sort of turning handle, but was again to do with calming down. Catching yourself, they told Joseph, was basically wising up and being sensible. Joseph seemed well pleased but a little overwhelmed with yet more newly acquired knowledge of local sayings. He hoped his *It's still a very strange land* thought was neither sneaked out, spoken, nor could be seen on his face. Looking at Joe and Brian's reactions he was not sure.

They were all finished up in devouring their food and Brian sank the last of his second cup of tea. They stood up, about to leave, chattering about their plans for the rest of the day. Brian had been having a bit of car trouble and had left it over at Builder's for him to fix. He needed a lift to collect it that afternoon. Joseph said he would love to help but he was taking his wife and kids out that afternoon. Brian was grateful that Joe jumped in with his offer of help.

"I can run ye over no bother at all!" Joe said cheerily. Joseph's face just dropped in stunned silence, his brain doing a little horrified loop at yet another one! He thought he was closer to mastering the art of localisms but they kept throwing new ones that made him feel far away. Joseph sighed, Joe and Brian looking at him curiously and wondering what was wrong as they left the cafe. Joseph put a smile on his face and muttered, "Fine, fine!" to let them know everything was okay. Joseph was in fact deciding if he should go down to the Lagan and step back into his bubble. At least he was safe in there and did not have to think. It would also be nice to float away and to see where it would take him. A scary little thought came into his head about returning to England due to being unable to steer a bubble! He smiled that thought away, as he realised, he could do with one of Brian's Bubble Breakaways.

Lineage

Will called her 'His Princess' with a new sincerity ever since he had found out. They had been going out for over a year now and things were getting pretty serious. The fact that she had told him showed just how serious she was about her relationship with him. He had felt very honoured that she had, given that Will was a complete sieve. She knew that. Everyone knew that. In fact, even sieves knew that and, if they had feelings, they would envy Will's ability to let so much through. Because of this, she had set strict telling criteria. She insisted that he swore on everything precious to him, especially his testicles, that he told his immediate family only. Da, Ma, Joe and Joanne were the only ones to know. She had repeated, "Only ones!" numerous times to him in her explanation, Will in turn had explained to his family. Absolutely no one else was to be told! No one! Not his mates down the pub, not his workmates. No one else but his immediate family, and they all had to swear to tell no one else either. Not even husbands and wives were to be told. When Will had jokingly asked, "You'll be wanting us to sign the Official Secrets Act next?" her hard, more-serious-than-cancer stare wiped his smile off and stopped his nasal laughing immediately. All he could do was meekly respond, "Oh shit! …You're serious!" secretly unsure if he was ecstatically happy or terrified at this right royal brain melt that he had gotten himself into.

Will did as he was decreed to do, fearing that his head might end up on a spike outside Hillsborough Castle if he failed. She might also have had special punishments for other important body parts. He had read some cherry-picked bits of history. His former rather comical fascination with the gruesome ends traitors met did not seem so funny now. Will was genuinely stunned and disbelieving at first when she told him. She never had any airs and graces about her to start with. Now, though, he looked at her slightly differently. He saw in her an authoritative quality that seemed above normal people, somehow. He wondered if he should have suspected sooner?

Will, as instructed, told all this only to his immediate family, after a nervously excited start on his arrival at his urgently-called family meeting.

Joe and Joanne had burst out laughing over the phone, when Will had called an Average family conference. He had never called one before and they thought he was taking the piss. When he demanded it, they thought he was taking the piss even more. But he had been serious. More serious than he had even been in his life before! Neither Joe's wife Dee, nor Joanne's husband Glen were to be present at Will's family gathering. Will had insistently insisted on that. Dee had met Beatrice several times, Glen at least twice. Neither had seemed that bothered about being left out, thinking it was Will going to announce his engagement to his family first and they would hear about it all later.

On the specified following evening, exactly at the specified time the four of them all sat around the kitchen table waiting on Will's arrival. Joe had arrived five minutes early amazingly, so made Will's lateness a little ruder. Average family conferences were always held at the kitchen table for some reason, never on the comfy sofa or armchairs which Joe would have preferred. They were expecting, like Dee and Glen, the news that Will and Beatrice were engaged, or going to be. They were all a bit surprised and slightly suspicious when it was just Will that turned up, a bit late as normal, without Beatrice. Being alone they immediately changed their meeting's raison d'etre, all thinking gloomily he was going to announce Beatrice and him had broken up. Ma had asked where she was. Will dismissed this with a sharp and nervous, "She's fine." Ma, Da, Joe and Joanne were still left confused but glad they had come to a now strangely intriguing evening.

Will started off waffling on a little about the length of time Beatrice and him had been going out. Everyone nodded, with an ever increasing 'get on with it' or 'cut to the chase' look in their eyes. They knew he was desperate to announce something big. They were desperate to hear it and get on with the rest of their evenings. Then he told all four of them about the build-up and Beatrice's precise instructions, before saying, somewhat anxiously, "You must swear never to tell anyone outside this room. Swear it!"

Four heads nodded and said, "Yes. Of course!" even before they knew what they were swearing to.

"Not even Glen or Dee!" he nodded at Joanne and Joe in turn, leaning slightly forward to each of them to stress his point. They nodded enthusiastically, muttering 'of course!' keen for Will to get on with it and becoming slightly annoyed at his apparent drama queen tactics.

"Beatrice is one hundred and ninety-fourth in line to the throne!" Will announced in as grand a matter-of-fact tone as he could muster. Will stopped speaking and looked at them in turn with a slightly smug look on his face. There was a silence for several rapid heartbeats, as if the other four in the room had been zapped by electricity. They were all stunned. *Was this one of Will's wind-ups?* They were asking themselves. Then they studied Will's intensely serious-looking face and knew it was not. Even Da could not hide his reaction. This! This was something totally out of the blue! The four of them did not know what sort of blue it was, certainly not having expected a royal one?

"Which throne?" Da quietly asked, genuinely interested in confirming. Ma let out a little scream of amazement and thumped Da lightly on his extended bare forearm. "The big one! With Liz on it!" Will answered cockily. Da nodded silently, pouted his speechless lips and looking as astounded as it was possible for Da to ever look behind that hard but kind face. Joanne excitedly clapped her hands, bent over and kissed Will sloppily on the cheek. She let out girly screams of delight as she kissed Ma, then Da and even Joe in the end, twice, caught up in the moment as she was. Ma just quietly cried. Tears of happiness, Joe hoped. Da went very quiet, staring hard at the kitchen table top, not even appearing to be blinking.

Joe was not really sure how to react. He did reach over and hug Will, more to reassure him than anything else. Joanne clearly thought it was something to celebrate. He was not sure about his Ma's view on this. His Da certainly seemed to have gone into worst case scenario mode, or was very distracted by something else. Joe was struggling to figure out why. Joe just thought about Will and Beatrice's kids. Where would they slot into the royal succession tree? Joe's reaction was, as he often found himself, somewhere in the middle of this very unique, aristocratic Average family dilemma. Joe's family had a mixture of views on royalty and they all came flooding out now. Not so very long ago they had been having a half-jokingly, half serious argument come debate about whose head should go on the coins and stamps, if there was no royalty. They easily came up with very viable and some very not so feasible contenders, along with ridiculously funny ones. What Joe remembered from this was the fact even the members of this average family could not agree on who to choose, which gave a tiny taster of the wider national dilemma if no royalty existed.

Da's voice stopped Joe's thoughts. "That's amazing, Will." There was a pause before, "We have our own royal roots... but they are not Irish... or Scottish... or even English... but French!" Da said quietly but loud enough for everyone to hear. A hush descended as this was front page family news as well. Joe laughed a little, wondering, the way this evening was royally progressing, if the Queen was going to turn up at the front door for a cuppa! His da gave him a slightly scornful look, thinking Joe was mocking what he had just said. Joe shook his head with a smile and his da carried on. "It was just before Louis the Sixteenth lost his head at the end of the 1700s. And I dinnae mean just ranting off on one!" Da chopped the back of his neck with the side of his hand. "Just before this happened, our ancestors ran from France, knowing things were getting too politically unstable and violent...!"

"So, they came to Ulster for a rest from all that?" Will joked. The rest of the family sniggered sadly and ironically. Da smiled broadly too and silently waited a moment or two to let it sink in. In this brief time, Joe, like the rest of his gathered family, were grammatically incorrectly putting adorable acutes into their names. As well, they placed the much-more-serious-sounding, two-thirds of a triangle graves in as well. They were Frenchifying their first names as well as their surnames. Joe, hearing the others doing it as well, mumbled, practising saying Average in a lightly floating French accent. It seems so much more appropriate than the sometimes nasal, sometimes phlegmy, Ulster way or pronouncing their surname. The local pronunciation of their surname made it sound so... well... average! From what Da, was saying it gave it a whole new classiness, with even royal connections they were beyond curious to discover more about.

Joanne was practicing saying it out loud under her newly discovered, non-garlic smelling French breath. She was really taken with the whole French sophistication concept of this. She looked like she was already figuring out her newfound French chic to accompany her other, also newly-discovered this evening, potential future royal connections. Joe wondered if she was wondering if that made her a princess too!

Da continued with his own version of a history lesson. "There were Protestant Hugenots from France already here in Ulster from the end of the 1600s, starting their own businesses and really expanding the linen trade. There were families of Gastons, Molyneauxs, Goyers, Bouchers – all scattered about County Antrim and Down, mainly. The Averages had connections with many of these important families through marriage. With

France falling apart, what was left of the Average French clan took off on a boat, with a pile of other emigres and escapees, and ended up here." Da paused, realising that he had in fact never told his wife and kids the full story of this, only snippets. They sat transfixed as Da continued his demonstration of previously-hidden history teacher skills. He had mentioned a vague French connection to their family history a few times before but that was as far as it had gone. No one had really paid it that much attention before, thinking it was just another of Da's joking about wind up stories. He was certainly delivering the punchline now.

"So where does the royal bit come in then, Da?" Joanne asked excitedly. "Are we connected to the French monarchy as well?" she added hopefully.

"Well…! That's where it all gets a bit… well… like a long-ago conspiracy theory!" Da replied a little sheepishly and shyly. That was totally out of character for him. Da never ever had any sort of woolliness about him before when he spoke. Ever! He was always so sure of what he said, even if it was well thought out or just an angry rage. It was no surprise then, that his wife and grown-up kids stopped there bleating and listened intently to this new side of the big man sitting at the top of the table, the uncontested king of their wee three bedroomed house. Joe sniggered silently. He briefly pondered if the paving slabbed area out front and the fenced off twenty feet square grass bit out the back now qualified his family as landed aristocracy?

"I am sure the story has been added to and added to over the years, until I am not entirely sure I believe it myself. That's probably why I have never told you all before. Not to take away from Will's big announcement, but now seems a good opportunity." Da went quiet, second thoughts almost appearing like a neon display board on his forehead, possibly regretting having started all this. The family sat silent, arms reaching quietly and often to remove the chocolate covered digestives from the plate in the middle of the table for silent munching. As Joe munched, he said 'le chocolat' and 'biscuit' under his breath as suddenly everything now had become French!

"Louis the Sixteenth and his family found that the revolution in France was literally a serious pain in the neck. It meant St Peter did not have to warn them about the 'mind your head' sign on the top bar of the Pearly Gates when they visited. Louis' eldest son, heir to the French throne, died in prison. Or so everyone was led to believe! From what my da told me, that boy who died was one of Louis's many… let's call them… unofficial sons. The real one was on the same boat as our ancestors…! Supposedly!

And I mean supposedly! He ended up here in Ulster and married one of my great, great, great whatever aunts. They became Bourbon-Averages." A vision of his distant ancestors, dressed in period clothes, munching small rectangular chocolate-coloured biscuits came into Joe's imagination before his da carried on. "They bought a large farm with their smuggled wealth from France and had sons and daughters of their own over here. As things heated up even more in France, Napoleon spreading across Europe, they removed the Bourbon from their surname to keep the secret. They kept an Average surname on its own to blend in more. That surname has lasted until today."

"Holy shit!" Will blurted out and then repeated it. Joanne's eyes took up almost all of her face and Ma looked like she would never close her mouth again. Joe frowned, then frowned some more, silent in his regal and not-so-regal whirring thoughts. This was a brilliant story. It was up there with Monte Cristo and Iron Masks. But Joe knew his Granda was an amazing storyteller, both fact and fiction. Which side of that coin was up in this case was anyone's guess? Possibly both, knowing Granda, and Da? Joe desperately wanted to believe it. Like his da, Joe was struggling a little to swallow it whole, choking on hard to chew chunks of it. It was so very tasty, though!

"There is a lot more to it than that. There was a family tree going way back centuries. Your Uncle Jimmy should have it, I hope, although I haven't spoken to him in years since the big row we had before Granda died." Da went silent again, his face showing relief at telling them but also embarrassment in case they did not believe him. There was the usual flash of angry regret as well, as happened every time his Da's and then his brother's farms were mentioned.

"Wait until I tell Beatrice this! What does that make this Average family? Are we directly lined up to the French throne, then? Would that Average family tree prove it?" Will could not get his words and questions out fast enough. Da just shrugged his shoulders and sighed.

"Beatrice and my kids would then be in line for both the French and British crowns! Wow!" Will went quiet for a change, and Joe could almost see the steam coming out his ears from his overheated brain.

"There are going to be quite a few others in between before your kids would get crowns on their heads for either!" Joe mocked as he looked at Will. "What was it? One hundred and ninety-odd on the British side! Who knows how many hundreds on the French side! That's even if they reinstated the French monarchy which is a long shot to say the least!"

"Who cares how many?" was Will's response. "What is it they say? If you're not in you can't win?"

"It's not a lottery!" Ma joked. "I am sure Beatrice's side is all official and recorded at Buck House or wherever. Besides, some Average family tree that your uncle might or might not have, there is not much else to prove the French side." Da smiled and tilted his head knowingly, causing Ma to do the same but instead questioningly. "What? Is there more?" she asked, the confused look on her face showing her brain was nearly at exploding point.

"Well… My da did pay to get a couple of those genies… not the ones in the lamps … but the other ones? What do you call them?" Da smirked as he spoke.

"Genealogists." Joe replied. Joanne whispered to Joe, asking if they were not something to do with mountains and stones. Joe corrected her that the rock people were geologists. Joanne nodded, accepting her world was being rocked enough tonight, without her adding any more hard-to-understand or believe what they were hearing, far-from-down-to-earth, facts or fables.

"That's the ones! Genealogists!" Da said loudly. "They came up with some very interesting stuff!" His eyes twinkled, before he added grumpily, "But your Uncle Jimmy has all that stuff as well!"

"Well, let's go see uncle, then!" Will almost shouted, rising from his seat, all set to go visit.

Joe butted in with, "Do you really want to do that? Jimmy is more of an angry uncle than a croissant! Cross aunt – get it?" Family groans and laughter were emitted in equal measure.

"No! No! Just content yerself!" Da replied a little sadly. "Your uncle never believed all that. Even when the fellas drew up an accurate family tree, with copies of birth certificates, church records and all the other evidence, your uncle still thought it was all crap and made up. He has probably binned it or burnt it. I haven't seen it in years, so I don't know. All I have is the story." Da stared at the table again and Ma reached over to grab his hand supportively. He smiled back at her with a look of crushed hope in his eyes.

"Here, I have to go! I have to tell Beatrice this! This is awesome! This surely makes us equal in the royalty stakes! Maybe we should have a royal wedding!" Will babbled. He received intent, excited stares from Ma and

Joanne. He shook his head. Muttering, "No, not yet!" to silence the wedding bells ringing in their eyes. Before any interrogation began, Will turned to everyone. "Remember. Not a word to anyone else about Beatrice's royal lineage. Please! Do not let me down! Please! She is too special to me, whether she had blue blood in her veins or ordinary red stuff like us. Or maybe not? Is French royal blood still blue as well? Let's see!" Everyone at the table chortled nervously, as Will pretended to stab his wrist with half a chocolate coated biscuit. Then he was gone, the front door slamming behind him and his car starting up almost immediately afterwards.

Ma cleared the table and Joanne shuffled up right beside her Da. "Tell me it again. Tell me the whole story. Please, Daddy." It was as if Joanne had become eight years old again, begging for a bedtime story. Da put his arm around her and she snuggled into his chest, grinning a bit manically. Joe looked at the two of them as Ma eased down onto the hard chair close to her husband on the other side. Ma just sat happily, deep in her own thoughts. Joe tried to figure out from her distant looking face if she was really that bothered about royal connections or not? She had a contented look of simply being glad to have all her family around her, rather than her expectation of receiving any invites to palaces or Heads of State banquets. Or maybe she was already picking out a hat in her mind for such a heady occasion? The appearance of a twinkle in her eyes and a sweet smile made Joe wonder if she had found one.

Joe sat quietly as his Da began to tell it again. Joe listened closely, wondering if there were any new bits his da had just included or if this was the original version. He smirked at the fact his da had never shown any French preferences. His da detested wine and garlic, for a start. Royalty or not, it was still one hell of a story, even better second time around. Joe concentrated as he heard the words, memorising them. He knew for sure he would be telling this same story to his children and grandchildren, regardless of its authenticity. He decided he would call them princes or princesses whether they were real ones or not. His mind drifted as he wondered if it was true, how would it change his life? His family would possibly certainly not be average any more if it was? He snorted a laugh, realising it would not change one thing, as his family bond was too strong. Or at least he hoped it was, to survive this test as it had so many others before. Nevertheless, he would still like to see what his Uncle Jimmy had stashed away. Just to be sure. *Mind you*, he thought, *Average is still average in French the same way it is in English!*

Lesbian

Not that he had a stopwatch handy. Maybe he had just imagined it. Maybe he had wished it. Nevertheless, those elongated seconds or two lasted too long to be… What was the word he was looking for? Appropriate did not seem appropriate, but it was all that he could come up with. Joe inwardly knew he should not have, but still he had savoured every split and full one of them. He could taste and smell the sugary mixture of Southern Comfort and cherry lip balm from her mouth. It left a sweet residue on his own lips that stirred other sweet residual memories he thought had long gone. The gaze of his own blue into her happily-glazed, grey-blue eyes, silently lasted too long, too. As his eyes widened to encapsulate her whole face, it looked as warm as the feelings filling his body and mind. Her cheeks had a slight alcoholic glow and those hypnotic eyes were as welcoming as they always had been.

He may not have known how long the kiss was, but he certainly knew the chances of anything romantically happening because of it were up there with Hell becoming Antarctica. Perhaps it was this reality creeping in, perhaps not? Either way, before he had time to fully savour the completely unexpected elongated moment, it was over. She broke the seal of their lips and the intensity of their stare as she stepped back and simply smiled at him. These simple actions left Joe feeling his glass-like emotions had a spreading crack, like a stone had chipped the window pane of his fragile feelings. Her moist mouth opened and she spoke something about how happy Joe must have been today. "Uh-huh!" was all he could mumble in reply.

She threw one arm around Sorcha beside her, pulling her close and muttering into her ear. She kissed her with a flourish and noisy 'mmmms' before her lips left her cheek. Sorcha gave a short smile and nod in response but carried on with her intent gaze at Joe. There was no warmth in Sorcha's look. It was something she always did the few times he had met her. It seriously unsettled him. His secret nickname for her was Shriveller. Every time they met, he always felt she withered him, leaving him prune-like and also mildly fearful. Sorcha's deep, brown eyes would have been beautiful. That was if he could have seen beyond the sharp daggers of which she seemed to have an endless supply, saved up especially for him, he paranoidly often thought. It was always the same vision that came to him in her presence. He was spread-eagle, vulnerable parts of him covered with multi-coloured circles for easier targeting, on a spinning, upright, circular, wooden table. Unlike in the shows, instead of the flying knives missing him by inches, every single one hit where it was intended, piercing, cutting and trying to remove bits of him completely. He overcame this intimidating, unwanted and unnecessary pointed wall image to feebly utter a, "Hi, Sorcha!"

"You hate me! Don't you?" she sworded with a slight slur at him. She thrusted this in for a killer stab, whilst he reeled from the shock of this sudden steely question.

Carol pulled at Sorcha's firmly gripped shoulder a couple of times saying, "Course he doesn't? Why would he? Why would you say that?" She looked with concentrated concern at her, but Sorcha's face remained fixed on Joe's. "You love her, Joe. Don't you?"

Joe looked around trying to think, totally aware of failing to hide the desperation Sorcha always instilled in him. He could not answer neither any of Carol's questions, nor especially the Sorcha love one, as he knew that was certainly a step too far. He tried to find Dee, or his ma or da, Joanne or his, as of nine hours ago, brand new officially signed paper Brother-in-Law Glen. Anyone would do. Anyone! Even a great-aunt or neighbour, someone to give him a reason to leave. No one was close to the three of them, all busy chatting at the metres away bar, sitting around at the tables yards away or strutting their half-drunken stuff on the even further off dancefloor. Knowing he had no other option he replied softly and directly to Sorcha, "Hate is a very strong word. True there are things I do hate in this world but you are not one of them, Sorcha. I can assure you of that!" He smiled reassuringly but knew it was so thin it was anorexic. He held back deliberately from answering the love question, not sure what word he would use to replace it.

"Well, you don't like me then? You cannot deny that?" Sorcha verbally lunged again. Joe stepped back to attempt to physically avoid it and, although feeling nakedly unarmed, tried to conjure up some way to parry it.

"Whoah! Whoah!" he stuttered out, raising his hands in front of him, the one holding his pint managing to slosh some of his beer onto Sorcha's shoes. Neither his word, nor the accidental spillage, did anything to quench whatever heat was boiling up inside her. "Where are you getting all this from? What have I done? Or not done?" he asked deliberately defensively with an interrogating tone.

Carol swigged the last of her straight-up sweet spirit, then stood, still clinging tightly to Sorcha's shoulder, mouth agape. Joe could see she was exasperated and stunned at how her believed sweet Sorcha's spirit was gone as well! Before Carol was able to pull healing words together, from her fuddled mind, to try to calm what was rapidly turning into a fever, Sorcha erupted.

"You are jealous! You always have been! You can't deny it, can you?"

Joe scanned around desperately again, looking away from Sorcha's accusing, hard eyes that gave him only the very briefest of moments of release. He silently radiated a plea for help but no one was flashing blues and twos to come to his rescue. Adrenaline pulsated in and, mixed with the alcohol in his bloodstream, kick started a revving up surge of anger which he only partially manged to contain.

"What...? Where...? How...?" was all he was able to mumble out.

"You cannot face the fact that not only is Carol so far out of your league, she is not even in your sexuality category! She is with me, and you cannot handle that! Never could!" she spat with vicious vindictiveness at him, He could almost see the sizzling acidity of her words. Joe swore loudly and in genuine shock, but Sorcha carried on. "You have always had a thing for Carol! You cannot deny that either, can you?" Joe felt a chill run through his veins as he inwardly could not deny that truth.

Carol had been Joanne's best friend from school. Joe knew her as well as any brother could a sister's best friend. Sure, he sometimes had had some silly, teenage, hormone-driven feelings for her but never, ever did anything about them. These remained hidden in the shadows of his mind, where he knew light would never penetrate to release them. That was just something that he accepted was never going to happen, although he could not stop the wishing, even if he had wanted to. She was three years older than him, for a start. Being two entire school years above him was almost a generation gap romantically for both schoolboys and girls. If, and it was a Titanic-sized if, he had gone out with Carol, it would have been seen by his classmates as akin to dating one of his ma's friends! That would have been a colossal iceberg that would have sunk without trace the little credibility he perceived he had amongst his schoolmates. It would have been even worse for Carol's cred. Plus, she was his sister's best friend, and he would never do anything to embarrass her by word or deed – at least outside their family. Family first was the Average family motto engraved in all their organs and limbs, as they did not know if that had a family Coat of Arms to put it on.

That friendship had remained strong through all their teenage years and early twenties. It had drifted a lot when Carol started work and Joanne went off to university, but they still kept in touch meeting up for nights out and coffee chats. Joe had not seen Carol in years before the huge family event of Joanne and Glen's big day that had happened without a hitch. Standing in his ill-fitting, hired usher suit, trying not to fidget at the front of church, he had seen Carol come in. He had felt a bit strange and awkward as he had slowly watched Carol take her seat in the pew, looking amazing in an azure, cleavage-showing, snug-fitting dress. Sorcha had sat beside her in an expensive-looking, tight-fitting trouser suit and blouse looking almost as radiant, if she had smiled just a little bit more. Or even just a few times more than she did. Carol did not seem the slightest bit annoyed that she was not one of Joanne's bridesmaids. As sometimes happened, family topped friendship at such big events as this. Joanne had been partially forced into having two cousins, who she had been bridesmaid for, as her immaculately presented dress and flowers helpers.

During the quite quick church service and endless photographer fussing afterwards, he had not been able to communicate with Carol beyond nods and waves until now, late on into the reception. Socialising with long unseen relatives, neighbours and friends was a required duty of the brother of the bride. He had introduced his fiancé Dee to everyone, repeating the same old line about not having set a date yet but soon. It had taken up too much time which he could have spent beer sampling, but the generosity of a wedding celebration ensured he never went thirsty for long. He was dearly wishing now that he had not made the conscious effort to come over and chat to them. Carol, he had so wanted to, but Sorcha's security guard aura had deterred him. He felt moth to a flame drawn, even if it was just a slight burning desire to show that he was not avoiding them, but fearing his residual spark for her would set things alight. If he had left it at the flying past, brief nod stage, he would not be seeking an escape route into the wings left or right. He had to face the fact of where he was now and had to act like a man, whatever that meant, and deal with it.

Joe's inner, semi-drunken rage bubbled over. He could contain it no longer, faced with this Sorcha onslaught. He had to find a way of turning this off. A few drinks the worse for wear never, in his experience, helped provide the clarity of thought and reasoned responses such situations as these needed. He was proved right yet again. Overcoming his sheepishness, he let fly a flock of facts that he really should have brain filtered before releasing into the wide blue yonder of the darkened, disco lit room. But he had to say something. He could not stand and be gobbed off at like this for absolutely no reason.

"You are talking through your arse as always!" was not a good start, and he could see Sorcha tense to breaking point. That was, nevertheless, how he started and prepared himself for things to go downhill, the only way they could, from there. "You have no idea what you are talking about! You have never taken the time to get to know me or given me the chance to get to know you! Have you? I have tried to be polite but you have always given me a cold shoulder the Artic would be proud of! You are the one with the problem! Not me! It is you who are the jealous one! Not me!" He made a show of swigging his beer, to dramatically let his expressed worthless pearls of angry wisdom sink in. He could tell these had only stung the skin and not sunk any deeper. Before he could sharpen any of his blunt points, he certainly felt it.

It was not the slight pain that shocked him, it was the fact that she had done it at all. It was to the receiving Joe as full-blown confusing as Ulster politics, as Carol had reached rapidly over and slapped him across the cheek. The force of it would have been enough to have his eyeball pop out swing ball-like to look at the heated red hand mark left on the side of his face. His eyeball thankfully remained where it was with no horror-movie repercussions. The rest of his body did remain almost motionless too, only slightly wobbling onto his left foot as he absorbed the blow. He jibbled another skoosh of beer onto Sorcha's shoes which he shrugged off, knowing that additional spill could surely not make things any worse than they already were. He glimpsed the redness of Carol's assaulting palm as she clasped it over her mouth as she stared wide eyed at Joe. "I am so sorry," she said. "I do not know what came over me." Joe could see Sorcha smirk vengefully. This quickly disappeared as Carol lent upwards and Joe was able to briefly taste the Southern Comfort and cherry lip balm intoxicating mix again as their lips met.

Sorcha stormed off, snorting. Bar bodies moved swiftly and fearfully out of her way, a mother frantically grabbing her doll-like dressed daughter, all obviously not wanting to be involved in the potential train wreck as Sorcha steamed through. Joe watched her go with a little relief but also with a small feeling of unfinished business, which he easily dismissed. Carol looked briefly at Joe, shook her head and mouthed 'sorry' again. She swished off after Sorcha, forgetting to hold up the hem of her dress as it swept the spilt drink sticky carpet. Joe looked after them and could not help himself from smiling. This puzzled him but not enough for him to worry about it. He took another short sip of his beer and started to slowly walk to the bar. His legs gave a slight unexplained wobble, stopping him in his tracks while he figured out if alcohol or emotion had been the cause.

Then he felt an arm lock into his and was drawn into those loving blue eyes of Dee who now walked beside him, as he hoped she always would. A tiny spark of anger flared in him as he inwardly chastised her for not being there to help him through what had just happened. He blew it away instantly and gently snuggled his shoulder into hers.

"It really is a small world!" she happily babbled away to him as he relished the sound of her soft voice. It was heavenly compared to the hellish hatred that had happened minutes ago. "I have just met a friend of mine from my school who is friends with Joanne from working along with her. Have not seen her in ages, so it was great to catch-up. Come on over so I can introduce you. She was my very special girlfriend. Now we have met again I suppose she still is. We will need to keep in touch and meet up. She has invited me to stay over with her sometime…"

Joe could feel his face freeze as very weird thoughts came into his head. Dee looked at him realising something was wrong but not knowing what. "Don't worry, she is the sweetest person! But I should tell you, before you come out with something stupid, she came out! She revealed a few years ago that she is a lesbian and is not a big man fan, if you know what I mean? Bad previous experiments and all that…"

Joe fell into a sort of trance as she led him along, knowing he was certainly not the perfect example of a man to influence her to change her mind. Trying to overcome his fear of saying the wrong thing again, he filled his mind full of all sorts of questions he felt totally unable to answer, and possibly never would. Women were enough of an enigma to him without adding all this into that weird and wonderful part of his reasoning. He swallowed hard, kissed Dee softly and dug up his courage to face what lay ahead. As they walked smilingly over, he reached up and gently touched his slightly tender cheek, then his lips. He had been slapped once and kissed twice that night already, but was confident that the laws of chance would prevent that happening again on the same night. Pausing, he nervously thought fate or destiny can always throw up some strange surprises.

Lanced

Joe waved to his ma from the green gates at the entrance as she drove off to her nine a.m. hairdresser's appointment. She sped off, almost forgetting to wave to him. He was not annoyed, as she was probably too keen to make sure she was not late for a much-awaited treat. She was probably still debating with herself about which follicle style she favoured which caused her distraction, although she would probably end up choosing the same one as always.

Joe walked with a very slight limp up the short, tarmacked driveway, seeing two blackbirds hopping and fighting on the ground before him. Although both pure black, one looked older and was certainly wiser, almost predicting the moves of the other. It was giving a good account of itself until Joe's encroaching presence split them up. They fluttered to the neatly-trimmed shrubs nearby, before returning to start round two in the same spot, almost as soon as he had passed. He quickly reached the large, wooden front door with huge brassy handles and pushed the left-hand side open. He turned and entered the room on his immediate left, as everyone else did when they visited here.

It looked exactly the same as every other time he had been here since he was a baby. The acrid, hygienic smell was the same too. The paintwork on the walls was a new colour, but that was changed every year so did not really count. As he quickly scanned the room, he nodded and recognising the same hard, wooden chairs all around. He laughed a little as the one with the dodgy looking leg was still there. No one had obviously sat on it to firewood it out of its continuing pointless, purely ornamental existence. There were the same two strange horse pictures hanging on the walls at either end which had faded slightly. They still had those same, crazy eyes looking out from the canvas that had a slightly disturbing effect of anyone who saw them. He wondered if the handful of magazines piled haphazardly on the little table were the same ones from his last visit seven months ago. Probably he thought. Apart from paintwork, why bother changing if you do not have to, seemed to be the building's owner's motto.

It had probably been the dining room of this large Victorian house. There were certainly a lot more chairs in it now, but Joe was fairly sure, even if the magazines were moved, only three dinner plates could fit on the little, possibly antique, coffee table. He looked over at a very old lady huddled in the corner wondering if she remembered living through the Victorian times? Beside her sat a balding man, coughing incessantly. This caused the concerned frown of the blond-haired woman immediately next to him, who was possibly his wife, Joe guessed. All the other seats were empty at that moment so she could have moved away from the projected germs if she had wished. More people started coming in. A screaming baby had a face almost as red as the embarrassed mother trying desperately and ineffectively to quieten it. Then another mother bustled through the door with a teenage lad with a major sulky face. A bearded man was then followed by a girl from his old school class whose face reddened, waved over nervously and sat in the farthest corner from him without saying a word.

As he sat, leaning heavily on one buttock, as he had been doing for several days now, he began to think about what lay ahead. Not the reason for his visit here, but the end of his last two hard years of ordinary school. He had done a lot better than he had expected in those final exams and would be starting A-levels in two weeks' time. He disliked calling them advanced level as that sounded far too intimidating, wanting to keep everything on a level, average footing.

He was glad to be distracted by the smart tied and suited man sticking his head through the gap in the partially open door calling for 'next round'. The old lady eased out of her chair and hobbled over to the smiling face who greeted her with a friendly smile and a, "How are you today, Mrs O'Leary?" She mumbled a reply Joe could not hear and carried on shuffling through the door. Joe went back to thinking about his chosen subjects for going back to school for a little while longer. Then he started to worry if Frank was picking him up at seven or half-seven in the morning for Joe to help him with that roofing job on the other side of town. The storm had made it urgent that the leaking roof was repaired but Joe's priority was being here to have himself fixed first.

The same head came through the slightly ajar door again, several minutes later and repeated the 'next round' call. The coughing man and the blonde-haired lady both rose quickly from their seats in response. "Hello,

Mr Connolly. Not often we see you, so it must be bad!" the smiling man joked, causing a repetitive cough, laugh, cough, laugh from the man. Joe saw the blonde lady roll her eyes. She remained silent as they exited the hushed room, apart from the still screaming, almost traffic light red-faced baby.

As he waited again, Joe thought of the three brothers who owned and ran this essential community service, all three having followed in their father's footsteps. However, it was questioned if the man who had raised and educated them so well was indeed their father. All three of them looked very different, which still, after all these decades, had the gossipers in the town talking. Their mother was known to be 'very loose with her affections' was how Joe's nan had put it. The fact that she was a doctor's wife caused it to be a big, if local, scandal.

Regardless of their parentage, they had a thriving practice and the system worked really well. Hidden away in the back room under paper files were two cheerful sisters than did all the medical admin. Morning surgery, which Joe was contributing to now, was from nine a.m. to midday, afternoon surgery from two until four-thirty and evening surgery was from six-thirty until eight-thirty. They never expressed the slightest tinge of resentment when essential house calls were needed. If you needed them on a Saturday, you could call the golf club, and if it could not wait until Monday, a trip to the hospital was needed on a Sunday. Locals just went along with whatever ailment or affliction they had, sat on one of these hard chairs (not the broken leg one) and saw the doctor after a few minutes wait. On his few visits here, Joe always described it as like sitting at the barbers waiting for a haircut. He ran his fingers through his thickening hair and thought he would do that this morning as well. Joe always thought this thriving General Practice had perfected a system that generally worked to keep all the locals healed and patched up.

The smiling face entered the room again and it was Joe's turn. "Good morning, Mr Average. How did you get on with the 'O' levels? I am sure you excelled yourself," he said over his shoulder.

Joe muttered, "Okay, I think." As he followed him across the large hallway into the room opposite. Joe did not really have time to answer more fully before he was offered to take a seat by Doctor Sinclair.

The doctor stood leaning against his impressive and neatly arranged mahogany desk and asked, "What can I do for you today?"

"I have hard wax in my right ear and this really painful big spot on my backside. I cannot get rid of either of them." Joe replied simply.

Joe had had his waxed-up ears sorted out before. He had no idea what its proper medical name was, but he sat still as the doctor steeped forward after producing a handheld light from his suit jacket pocket. Joe flinched a little as the coldness of it touched his lughole, definitely not a proper medical name for an earhole. Dr Sinclair then checked the other ear, letting out a little 'aha' before saying, "Right, trousers and underpants down so we can have a look at this spot." Joe stood up, did as he was asked and turned around. Normally he would have felt extremely vulnerable in this position, with his hands resting on the back of the chair, slightly bending over, his bare arse exposed. However, the doctor very quickly looked closely at Joe's backside and told him to dress himself again. The doctor sat behind the desk briefly and wrote some notes. Lithely, he moved over to the now covered up and one-buttock seated Joe and asked if he had any headaches or any other pains. He moved over with a large wooden lollipop stick and asked Joe to open his mouth and say 'aah'. He peered closely into Joe's mouth, shining his little torch into the back of his throat. "And those stiches healed up okay?" he asked, and Joe pulled up his left sleeve to show the fading white scar left from the deep slice, made from a broken slate on his last labouring job seven months ago. The doctor briefly held Joe's forearm, closely examined the previous wound, nodded contentedly and strolled over to the other door in the room.

"Okay. Let's go next door. You know the drill for syringing your ear. But that is not just a spot, but a boil on your gluteus maximus. We will have to lance that. We will do that as well today. Any questions?" He rapidly went through his diagnosis and prescriptions. Joe just nodded silently and followed him through to the other mini-operating room. Joe had been in there before to solve his ear problems, have injections and be stitched up in a good, healing way. As a kid it had always intrepidly intrigued him and it still did. It had steel sinks, chrome taps and huge glass fronted bookcases full of all sorts of bottles and packages. Its drawers were equally full of sterile trays of gruesome looking implements.

It was an indescribable sensation. The warm water skooshing into his ear making Joe not really wince, but certainly not showing happiness on his face, as he leaned over the large metal sink. He was starting to wonder if any of his brain was going to be washed out when it stopped. "All done," was the brief response from Dr Sinclair as he turned off little taps connected to the hose and its pointed metal end. Joe peered into the sink and saw the large blob of yucky stuff.

"Right, trousers and underpants down. Lean against the bench for me, please," he continued. Joseph obeyed and nervously assumed his buttock baring stance, trying and failing to not think about prison showers. "There will be a short, sharp pain and then it will be over," Dr Sinclair briskly stated as he reached into one of the metal trays. Joe deliberately did not look round but still managed to catch a glimpse of the glint from a large scalpel in the doctor's hand, which did make him tensely wince. He smelt the nasal overwhelming strong antiseptic and felt a slight sting on the boil as wet cotton wool was dabbed onto it. "Okay, I am just about to…" The doctor began his sentence as he touched Joe's backside with his fingers but did not finish the sentence. Before Joe had even had time to brace himself for whatever was about to happen – it did.

There was an intense sharp pain and, as he was about to grit his teeth for more to come, Joe felt the stinging soothing sensation of antiseptic. The doctor calmly and efficiently spoke again. "All done. You can dress again." Joe felt more wet cotton wool being stuck to the pain area, applying more of the unpleasant, tingly sensation antiseptic before a large sticking plaster was swiftly smoothed on. "Your other ear is totally clear, and you can take the plaster off the boil in three days' time. Any questions?" Joe shook his head as he hoisted up his jeans and buckled the belt. The doctor opened the door and asked if Joe was doing A-levels. Wishing him all the best he walked with Joe as far as the waiting room door, where he opened it and stuck his head in again, calling his familiar, "Next round…" followed by, "Oh dear! Oh dear! What is up with this little chap today…" as the baby's cries quietened.

As Joe was about to open the large entrance door, he paused a moment to savour the now baby-screaming-free silence of outside. With a smile, he nodded a silent congratulations to Dr Sinclair before he left and walked, with much less of a limp, down the tarmacked driveway. He rotated his jaw, delighted not to be hearing that annoying popping noise any longer, adjusting to hearing clearly from having a non-bunged-up ear. He reached behind to his behind and touched where the big spot, or boil, had been. It was a little painful but in a relived way, nowhere near as sore as it had been. He realised his slight limp was even less than it had been, the bulging ball of puss no longer rubbing against the cloth of his underpants and jeans. He smiled with relief and looked at his black strapped watch with the chipped glass. It was half past nine.

He ran his fingers through his hair and decided to walk down to the barbers to have his own crew cut hairdo. He knew that sort of cutting would not be painful at all. Correcting himself in his thoughts, he remembered that time when the point of the scissors had almost accidentally went through to make a lobe hole big enough for an earring. He, almost entirely, dismissed this as a one-off exception, which was apologised sincerely for, with the accepted offer of a free haircut an unexpected compensation that he had not expected. Afterwards, ears intact and with no earring options he hoped, he would still be in time to meet his Ma at her hairdresser's next door. She would still be ages. She always was, spending more time talking than having her hair worked on, to make the most of her trip to town to treat herself. He felt good and a lot lighter, the blob of earwax and ball of puss had been small but heavy loads to bear over the past few days. A haircut would make him feel even lighter; he smiled.

-

It had not ruined his thirty-first birthday, but it had not exactly helped him celebrate it either. His bunged ear was really bugging him and he was puzzled as to why it had happened to him now, having not had any ear problems since he was a teenager. He had tried olive oil and hoked about with cotton ended sticks. He had even dug out those useless drops that the chemist had given over a year or two ago. It was for one of the kids when they had waxy ears, but they created such a fuss it was only used once and their ears sorted themselves out leaving yuck blobs on pillowcases. It had taken a while to retrieve the bottle from the back of the medicine cabinet in the bathroom that was even more bunged up that his earhole. He had rummaged for ages amongst the half full bottles and packets of uncompleted prescriptions. These were all well out of date and probably never, ever would be used again but kept, as in most people's houses, for some very vague 'just in case' reason. This was one of those such occasions. He had been squeezing the liquid out of that brown glass bottle for four days now, squirming as it very slowly flowed down his ear and ended up with an awful taste in his mouth. Still, it did not make any difference, not stopping the sticky sensation and only starting to really increase his grumpiness.

As if that was not enough to contend with, the large painful spot on his right buttock was seriously depleting his happiness reserves as well. He was over thirty now and mystified that this large spot had appeared. His body was physically well beyond the pimples of puberty stage, even if his mind was not! He had even tried his own bit of surgery on it, sticking a large needle painfully into its centre. Only a tiny bit of yellow puss had slowly oozed out and, if anything, had made it even more painful. His hips were becoming sore from his increasingly sitting lop-sided to ensure this bulge of pain did not make contact with a hard seat surface.

Dee had been telling him to do it persistently and he now had to face up to the reality that he was reluctantly going to have to. He was in work and so, personal calls being not really allowed, he went into the toilet cubicle. He sat with the lid down, in his now customary and annoying one-buttock down, one hovering position, and rang the doctor's surgery. This was the fourth time he had tried. He sighed and held his mobile to his currently good, wax-free ear. The hold music irritated him even more this time, but only slightly, and nowhere near as much as the repetitive, nasal, 'we are very busy at the moment. Please hold and we will be with you shortly' every few minutes. He was half dozing off, wondering if he did need to use the toilet while he was here, when an actual human, female voice awoke him from his stupor and spoke to him.

He explained the ear and buttock problems as the reason for his call. His joke about the receptionist not thinking he was talking out his backside provoked absolutely no response from her either way. He could hear her typing away on a computer keyboard as she went through her standard list of name, address, age, smoker, non-smoker and other seemingly pointless questions that Joe answered in an increasingly disgruntled tone.

"Yes, we can arrange an appointment for the eighteenth, Thursday at two ten p.m.," she answered eventually.

"But that's almost two weeks away!" Joe replied, failing to hide his surprise and frustration.

"That is the earliest appointment we have, sir. If your condition becomes too painful or deteriorates, please go to your nearest Accident and Emergency," she said in a polite rebuke.

"Okay then, if that is the earliest, I will take it," he replied with a heavy sigh.

It had been painful, Joe like a limping bear with a sore ear and arse for two weeks, but eventually the fourteen days passed. He arrived at the swank, fairly newly-constructed Health Centre fifteen minutes early for his appointment, just on the off chance they might take him sooner. He sat in the bland waiting area, balanced on one hip, shaking his head as the popping in his ear was intense now. He also wondered if he should have brought a cushion as the red plastic seat was uncomfortably hard enough even for a boil-free butt. The receptionist sat with her head down behind the large counter, only raising it when someone entered and came forward to tell her they had arrived. She routinely merely smiled, asked their name and tapped away on the computer before telling them to take a seat. She also explained that, "We are very busy so please be patient and we will be with you shortly." Joe received this same monotone instruction when he had arrived. Her frequent repetition of it now, even when he was only half able to hear it, was growing increasingly annoying as he became a less patient. He really wanted to approach her and ask her to talk like a normal human being to other people, rather than sounding like some machine. But he did not, as it bothered him but not enough to make a Medical Centre scene. Instead, he just sat staring around unable to hide his boredom.

As he looked around the crowded room, he played a little game with himself, trying to guess the illness. There were many elderly people that would have been impossible to guess. Several of these had small, white bags with green crosses on them, filled with many little plastic bottles and tablet cartons. Joe unkindly described them as mobile chemist shops. There were several screaming babies whose mothers did not seem to be that concerned. They just chatted away to the mother beside them and made the odd, 'sssh, there, there,' waving a soft toy randomly in their face. Joe wondered if the weird, pink and rather freaky looking furry alien one mother waved, might have been the reason her toddler was screaming so loudly? There were builders there too, one obviously with back problems. Two others had large wet looking bandages on their hands and arms. There were middle-aged women trying to bury themselves inside copies of glossy magazines. All of them, including Joe, looked up when there was a sharp beep and the neon strip above the reception desk displayed a name, a doctor and a room number. This system felt very impersonal Joe thought, like a production line of pain being processed. Then that named person would rise and trudge off, leaving everyone else to return to their toy waving, magazine reading, grimacing in pain or whatever else they were mind-numbingly doing to while away the unknown time it was going to take to be seen.

At fifty-three minutes past two, Joe's name was displayed. He resisted the urge to jump up and cheer like he had won some competition. His left butt cheek was totally numb from sitting slumped, meaning he doubted if he could have jumped up anyway! He limped off to find the room and doctor as the machine had ordered him, feeling like some defect product on the production line. As he hobbled along, he realised he was not even sure of who his doctor was. He had one named on his medical card but had not a clue when the last time he had seen him, or even what he looked like. To be fair, he did try very hard to visit the doctor's as infrequently as he possibly could. He was certainly not a regular, definitely not regular enough to be on first name, or even surname terms, with whoever had been allocated to deal with Joe's medical issues. The last three times he had been in the past possibly six or seven years, he had had a different doctor each time. This caused him confusion and a bit more frustration when he had to talk two of them through the short sick list under his name on their computer screen. In hindsight, he should not have been annoyed at that, because at least it showed they were professional and above all cared.

His heart did sink down a bit when he walked in and saw the female doctor sitting at her desk in the cramped room. There was still a childish bashfulness about exposing his bottom to an unknown woman, or to any stranger for that matter. He said 'hello' and took a one-buttocked seat.

She looked at her notes and then at her computer screen before she spoke. "Mr…" She looked again at her screen, Joe catching sight of the wry little smile that shot across her face. It disappeared quickly and she assumed her professional demeanour. "Mr Average. What appears to be the problem?"

Joe explained about his ear and his boil. She stood up and shone her surprisingly warm, handheld torch in his bunged ear and into the other one as well. "Yes, it is quite blocked. I can prescribe some drops for that." She sat down and began scribbling on her prescription pad.

Joe was a bit disappointed and knew he should speak up to ask for something more substantial. He muttered, "No syringing?" to which the doctor simply shook her head. He said nothing more, as the prospect of mooning his arse at this lady doctor was playing on his mind.

"And what about the boil on my behind?" Joe asked. He nearly said arse but stopped himself in time, thinking that using 'behind' was much more polite and refined.

"Yes, if you could pull down your trousers and lie face down on the couch, please." She smiled impassively as she indicated the couch with a slow movement of her hand. Joe did as he was asked but meekly asked about his boxer shorts before he lay. "No, just leave those on, please." He was relieved about that retained partial modesty.

He lay there awkwardly, trying not to drool on the tissue paper-covered pillow, as she very briefly looked at the butt boil. "Yes, you can get up now and dress," she replied in a professional tone. "That does look quite painful." Joe raised his eyebrows in agreement but did not say the 'you think' words that had sprang into his mind. "I will prescribe you some cream to ease the pain and will refer you to a dermatologist for them to decide further action."

"Why is that necessary?" Joe asked impatiently and with restrained calm. "Can it not just be lanced off? It is really sore and I really want rid of it as soon as possible. I've waited over two weeks to have this looked at."

"That would be the decision of the dermatologist. It looks to be infected and that is why I am referring you." she replied with a firm politeness as Joe's guilt about his needle piercing swelled up in him more than his boil.

The prescribed drops for his ear were the same as the old ones he had found in their medicine cabinet and had tried futilely. So, Joe was enormously surprised that, although it took ages, they worked. He was in so much discomfort that he made a conscious effort to specifically follow the number of drops and timings of them. This was something he was not very good at with taking medicines. After the second or third day especially, his tablet-taking would become random at best, if he even remembered. Now, after two more weeks of drop torture, he was able to wax lyrical about being wax free simply from following instructions. He would try to not be childish and do as he was told more in the future he resolved half-heartedly. He had no problems with the childish bit, which meant he was halfway there.

Sorting out his other medical issue was becoming an even bigger pain in the arse, in more ways than one. It had taken nearly seven weeks for him to even achieve seeing the dermatologist. Then they had stuck a syringe in the boil and sent it off for analysis, as well as taking blood tests which also

200

were sent away. He had waited another week on the results coming back. The dermatologist had rung him and prescribed some more creams, asking Joe to trial these for five days. She hoped it would remove it completely but asked him to call her to let her know. With his new-found obedience he did as he was asked, spending five days slathering cream on his even more inflamed cheek. He amazed himself by following the jar instructions exactly. It did ease the pain a bit but the larger bulge was still there. When he reported back, she said that, as this had not worked, they would need to surgically remove it. She had gone silent a moment and then her voice came back on the phone to tell Joe that, as he was an urgent case, the earliest available date for this minor surgery was in three weeks' time.

Joe had really wanted to loudly express how pissed off he was at having such a trivial but painful thing dragging on for so long. He provided a milder form of his displeasure to her, knowing it was not her fault and not wanting to make an even bigger arse of himself. So, he waited another while, actually thinking his skeleton had shifted because he had been sitting and walking funny for weeks and weeks. Then the day eventually arrived, Joe pessimistically waiting on news that his appointment had been cancelled or rescheduled, as often happened, but was very grateful it had not.

Dee dropped Joe off at the green gates of the minor surgery clinic, after they had delivered the kids to school. She, like Joe, had taken the day off work for this. Joe assured her it was not really surgery at all and was nothing. Rather than waste an opportunity, Dee had booked herself a nine a.m. hair appointment. After they kissed, Joe reassuring her again he was okay on his own, she almost forgot to wave to Joe as she sped off to try to beat the traffic and not be late. Joe limped, as was becoming scarily normal for him having done it for so long, up the tarmacked driveway to the large, four storey glass and concrete building in front of him. The building may not have had much character but it gave Joe a cold and unwelcoming feeling he could not fully explain. He felt like the building did not really want him, tolerating his coming as an inconvenience it had to put up with. *Maybe it will be different inside?* he hopefully optimistically thought to himself.

Two cats were hissing and one clawing feverishly at the other in front of him on the grass, away from the constant toing and froing of people on the entrance path. Joe paused a moment to watch, realising that one looked older and more experienced than the other. The younger one looked nervously flustered, jumping here and there, not seeming to know what to do, its fur dishevelled. The younger one pranced this way, trying and failing to attack. Then it danced another way and again failed to make any sort of contact, its claws missing their target widely. It flew around and tried from behind but yet again nothing. During all this, the older one had stood circling and watching every strange movement the other made. Joe thought he could see laughing disbelief and a little bewilderment in the golden rings of the older one's eyes. Then, more than likely fed up with this pointless faffing about, the older one moved forward. With one quick and powerful swing of its paw, the older one acted, smacking into the side of its opponent head.

It was not that vicious, Joe thought, more of a hard slap than a claw ripping blow. Whatever it was, it was very effective and the younger one took off, bounding away with its tail limp behind it. The older one looked almost smug as Joe moved on and caused it to move on too. The old cat had a strut that Joe hoped he could imitate after today's so-called minor surgery. Joe admired the fact that it may be old but it certainly had showed there was plenty of fight left in it yet. Maybe the younger one had learned something from it as well. Joe hoped it had had a bit of a wake-up call as to how things should be done to achieve success. Joe hobbled on up the path, limping along and taking much longer than it should to walk along the path. He wished he felt more confident as to where this path led.

"...So, you are telling me that you did not receive the letter advising that the appointment had been rescheduled? And no – one contacted you by phone to advise you of this either? That is our procedure and would have been carried out, which is why I cannot understand how this has happened..." Joe had no qualms about making a scene on this occasion as the boiling heat of his anger erupted for everyone to hear...

Labyrinth

There had been job interviews. There had been the times when he was about to sit exams and impatiently waiting to almost accost a postman to get the results. There had been a few times, quite a few, when he had waited on headmasters or teachers, or parents, sometimes all three together, dishing out punishments for some, what Joe always considered, over-reactions to misunderstandings. There had been the build-up to the 'we need to talk' previous relationship talks, which had sometimes ended up with neither of them speaking afterwards ever again. All of these combined and more could not match how he felt. He was so absolutely, totally and utterly kacking himself that, with so much inside him, Joe had to check occasionally to make sure he had not physically pushed anything out. Nervous did not even touch the sides of where he was, even though he was so tightly clenched it would have made it easy.

Dee's brave attempts at calming words of 'they are only my parents' brought inner boil rather than inner peace to Joe. 'They are lovely people and I know you will all get on like a house on fire' made him feel even worse, with a repetitive flashing image of him watching Dee's parents' house burning to the ground due to his clumsiness with a cig butt somehow! He was not grateful to her for planting that thought in his head. Despite his frazzled nerves pressing the nicotine reload button repetitively, he decided he was not going to smoke at all during the entire visit, just in case Dee and her parents' faces were lit up in a way he most certainly did not want.

Dee was driving, not just because they were travelling in her car, but Joe was not sure if he could remember how to! His mind was in such a state. Dee had been patient at the start when it had been first planned three weeks previously. Back then, Joe was a bit anxious but coped okay when she announced that she had arranged this. After all, they had both agreed it was time to meet her parents. Despite his growing cloud of regret at that agreement, Joe reluctantly knew he could not rain check this meeting any further. However, as the time drew nearer, the pedal of his angst was pressed harder and had accelerated.

As they drove along, his palms were literally dripping sweat, his tie was almost choking him. It was as if his was brain was being fried as he imagined the roasting, he was going to receive from Dee's interrogating parents. The ability to speak seemed to elude him, not sure what to say. That was very unlike him, especially when it was just the two of them together. Maybe he felt a little intimidated after her patience had eventually broken. She had sworn loudly at him, several times, sergeant like demanding him to 'pull yourself together!' He was trying to do this but failing, feeling his joints loosening and like he was trying to catch live eels in a jelly and oil-filled pool. Her nerves had obviously started to show, as they had arrived at the day of reckoning. He was trying not to be selfish, but was too busy with his own apprehensions to help with hers.

By the time they pulled up on the driveway, Joe was as cool as a gherkin for some reason. He was not quite there with the cucumber yet, but was in a much better place than he had been. Perhaps being at the destination meant the dread of it was now gone. The acceptance of 'we're here' focused his thoughts, as there was no going back. His heart was still pounding a bit, but he had at least stopped sweating and his deodorant had held out impressively. Also, he had removed the tie altogether, going for a more casual look instead. Dee was happy with that. Rather her grunt at him, when he had flung it off, he had taken as an okay. Besides, he felt more comfortable when he had not some length of cotton or silk, or whatever it was made of, trying to strangle him. His fast-beating heart had been doing its best to deprive him of oxygen and that was enough to deal with. As he closed the car door, he psyched himself that he was ready to do this – to meet his girlfriend's parents! He was at least ready as he ever would be, still feeling like he was only wearing his boxer shorts no matter how he confidently tried to dress that up. Looking over at Dee, as she very forcefully slammed her door closed, he realised she was maybe feeling more exposed than he was. He had a very brief moment picturing that, but the upcoming possibilities of the now moment instantly removed that image from his thoughts. He made a mental note to return to it later when this was over.

Joe strode over, grabbed her by the hand and kissed her hard on the lips. She smiled and clutched his hand tight. He said nothing, just stared at her, conveying messages of, "This will be okay! I will watch what I say! I will not make a dick of myself. I repeat – I will not make a dick of myself!"

She received these loud and clear, sighed before they walked swiftly over to the begonia-potted front steps. Dee touched up her lipstick quickly en route, before she rang the church bell chiming doorbell twice. As they both waited with nervous smiles glued to their faces there was no answer. Dee tried again, a moment of concern on her face, checking the date and time in her head. The door opened smoothly.

Joe's homeplace would have fitted into this house at least twice, maybe three times, and they had a huge, beautifully kept garden as big as the field out the back of Joe's family home. Despite its size, it had a homely, not-ostentatious feel about it. It all radiated sensible investment, hard work and saving, which would have been very much in keeping with Dee's dad's high-up-in-the-finance-world status. Her mum worked as an independent accountant for a long list of local companies and self-employed contractors. Maybe it was Joe's 'I'll always muddle through somehow' attitude to his finances, along with never really having had a pleasant conversation with bankers or accountants previously, that made him a bit apprehensive. He hoped both of them would want to talk about anything else besides what they did for their day-job. No doubt they probably would at some stage, but he hoped this would not happen. He attempted to block out other possible topics but inwardly knew that there were even more complicated conversations awaiting him.

Sat in, rather than on, one of the very large comfy living room sofas, the talk was small in comparison. Safe topics of the weather, gardening, traffic congestion on the way and familiar jamming bottle necks were mentioned. It was as if Dee's folks did not want to appear too nosy, talking generally to avoid any awkward silences. Then Dee's folks began talking about interest rates, and inflation, Joe's mind groaning as they did. As Dee took her foot out of her sandal and reassuringly rubbed Joe's ankle with her big toe, hidden under the coffee table, her dad began talking about the extremely important but very dull FTSE! Dee's foot was re-sandaled and, disappointed at that, Joe felt the urgent need to end that conversation topic before his brain fell out. When her dad mentioned construction, Joe leapt in to begin to tell them both a bit about his da's work, his folks back home, his sister and his brother. They nodded and thanked him, hoping they would meet them someday and wished them well. They were polite and courteous but Joe knew they were stalling and holding back from asking bigger questions. He knew what he did not want those questions to be but was warily prepared in case they were.

As the four of them sat around the dining table, Joe felt he was not really coping well with what he probably imagined was the maze of mind games going on. He felt the urge to try to relieve this presumed pressure a little further and began to tell them a bit about himself. He succeeded, he thought, in being factual rather than boastful. Again, they nodded and thanked him, wishing him well and he dared to think they might actually have been impressed, even if only a little bit. They told him they already knew quite a bit from what Dee had told them. This made him feel slightly scared as to how he matched the image that Dee had portrayed of him. Had she told them the truth, the whole truth and nothing but the truth? Joe inwardly shouted, *So help me God!* Or had she presented carefully selected evidence before the judges? He knew a little about what she had told them but made a mental note to check with her on the way home, for cross referencing. It was as they tucked into the very succulent and tasty Sunday roast, a huge helping even for him, that Joe sensed the elephant in the room was put in its very large envelope and addressed. It was about to be delivered.

One of the main reasons he, and probably Dee, had been nervous about meeting Dee's parents was the dreaded question of sleeping arrangements. That was what hung over everyone he was sure when meeting a partner's parents. They still had their own flats but were back and forth quite a bit. It was a very personal area that he was sure parents wanted to know about but dared not ask, so they were in as awkward a situation as the boyfriend or girlfriend. His own parents never asked or even hinted at asking. It was just a totally avoided subject with innocent assumptions probably made but never stated out loud. That was another maze of unanswered, and in truth unanswerable, questions that no one wanted to ask or answer. However, there was, no doubt, curiosity on both sides. Sons and daughters wanted to know if their parents knew already or suspected, approved or disapproved, or 'they're adults now... own decisions' neutral. In return, parents probably made assumptions, decided to try not to pry or just avoided this subject all together. There was also, certainly in Joe's da's case, a bit of unsaid non-malicious glee taken in watching their off-spring and partner squirm in this limbo world of unknown that was far from funny. Although Joe's ma or da had not met Dee yet, Joe had seen this happen when he had brought a girl home for tea, with his sister Joanne's boyfriend Glen. Will, his brother, never brought any of his girlfriend's home, probably for that same reason,

Joe tensed, although he kept reassuring himself that there would be no direct questions about how intimate he had been with Dee. Unlike on those occasions, he had not brought any protection with him for such probing. Questions like that would verge on being an invasion of privacy, even if they were the parents of one of the people involved. However, he was half expecting a question from her dad or mum along the lines of his intentions with their only daughter. He swallowed hard and failed to make it unnoticeable, basically because he had no answer at that particular time. Joe sensed Dee's dad was building up to a big question and Joe began to prepare himself as best he could with a pathetic sounding 'beds are just for sleeping' defence if asked. The question when it arrived was not so dreaded personal but was much bigger both in what it asked and the repercussions it insinuated.

"Northern Ireland really is a complete labyrinth to us. We do not fully understand all that is going on there," Dee's dad stated as he cut to the chase as easily as he sliced through his Yorkshire Pudding.

Joe could not help but laugh with a little relief and reply, "No one really does, so don't feel bad at all."

"It's all the acronyms, political parties and organisations we hear on the news. There are so many, and they are so confusing!" her dad continued.

"Yeah! There are loads," Joe replied, looking over at him and registering from his facial expression that he wanted Joe to continue, so he did. "First off you need to understand the difference between Nationalist and Republican and Loyalist and Unionist. Nationalists want a united Ireland by purely peaceful means. The SDLP, the Social Democratic and Labour Party want this. Then there are the Republicans who are very, very different from Republicans in the USA. They are mainly the IRA, Irish Republican Army, who use guns and bombs to, in their view, fight for a United Ireland and bring the North of Ireland back within the control of Ireland. They are represented politically through SF, Sinn Fein. The current IRA began life as the IRB, the Irish Republican Brotherhood, in the nineteenth Century before it became the IRA, which then split into the Official IRA and Provisional IRA. In more recent times another main Republican group, the INLA, Irish National Liberation Army, was created. It used bombs and bullets, to further its cause, the same as the IRA, as well as dipping into politics as well. With me so far?"

Joe looked at their mazed, rather than amazed, faces. He had kept it as simple as possible, he thought. In reality he knew he had lost them already, even after having only told one half of the story, realising both Dee's parents appeared as green about Northern Irish politics as those groups he had just mentioned. Nevertheless, he had started so he had to finish, as he had only given one side of this multifaceted acronym story. "Then there are the Unionist political parties, who want Northern Ireland to stay part of the United Kingdom. There is the UUP, Ulster Unionist Party, which was, for a long time the only Unionist political party, also called the OUP, Official Unionist Party. Then the more radical DUP, Democratic Unionist Party was created in the Sixties. Then there are the loyalist organisations that, in their view, fight to defend Northern Ireland from Republicans. The Ulster Volunteer Force was created as a British Army regiment in the First World War.

"This name was taken by a loyalist paramilitary organisation as it used guns and bullets and bombs in its defence of what it believed in. It went into politics as well through the PUP, Progressive Unionist Party. There has also been a splinter group from the main UVF, which if the LVF, Loyalist Volunteer Force. There are also the UDR, Ulster Defence Regiment created during the Troubles which was part of the British Army, along with the long standing RIR, Royal Irish Regiment. The UDR and RIR are not terrorist groups, but that depends on your views of the British Army!" He gave a raised eyebrow look to follow on from his last comment. Their faces remained blank, apart from a slightly smouldering look as their brains burned with overthinking. Joe had started this already overloaded with fuel fire but he still had to carry on. There was still more he had to add, to ensure he gave the complete picture, despite that this risked causing total burn out.

"Then there is the largest loyalist organisation called the UDA, Ulster Defence Association, which is not in itself paramilitary, but this is often disputed. They have a political wing too, the Ulster Democratic Party UDP. However, there are more violent loyalist organisations associated with the UDA, including the UFF, Ulster Freedom Fighters and RHC, Red Hand Commandos which again use guns and bombs against what it sees as Republican threats. Finally, we have the RUC, Royal Ulster Constabulary, which are the police force in Northern Ireland/North of Ireland." Joe paused and took a slightly gasped breath, He knew he had to end this list as soon as possible, his audience listing like a rudderless ship battered by an acronym storm. "There are a few others, including the LOL, RBP, AOH and Apprentice Boys lodges, but those are the main players. There you have it." He finished off with a little relieved smirk. Joe could see 'more?' beaconing from both Dee's parents' three letter overload, probably restraining themselves from letting a few four-letter words loose in response. "I do not know why people think that it is so complicated?" Joe added with sarcasm as thick as the gravy on the half a roast potato he shoved into his mouth.

He was still being greeted by stunned faced around the table. Even Dee looked stunned, Joe realising there were previously untold 'acros' in amongst all that spiel that had taken her to the height of confusion. Joe, thinking he had covered the entire alphabet in his listings, inwardly laughed at himself for trying to think of 'acros' with Q and Z in them, knowing he had missed these letters for sure. "I think I have done the best I can to be like the Alliance Party and stay in the middle," he was about to say to conclude but thought that might have been the final straw of confusion to the camel-faced parents, so he held back.

There was silence. Dee laughed fakely to ease the situation a bit, while reaching over and grabbing Joe's, poised-to-stab-carrots, fork-holding hand very tightly. Although only touch was involved, all of his senses, including his sixth one sprang to attention to try to decode what Dee meant. Was it a 'shut up' grab to stop him talking? All senses agreed this was most likely. Was it out of love, with the higher the level of tightness, the greater the love? Possibly, his senses questioned. Was it a 'wait 'til I get you home' hand clutch that had only argument, not romantic, likelihood? All senses tingled at this being very likely. Was it to stop him eating? None of his senses could see that one being a serious contender, as with a food full mouth he would be unable to talk. Finally, all of his six sense votes were democratically cast and they jointly agreed it was just to ease her own nerves.

"I am still figuring it all out myself," she stated, hoping her parents would say something, apart from just stare blankly at Joe. "I am hoping to go over soon for Joe to show me around and meet his family," Dee added to try to start a different conversation. Joe saw her mum just look at her silently with a face that silently broadcasted 'are you mad, girl? Visit that seriously messed up place?' Joe could not help but unspokenly agree with her. He still wanted Dee to meet his folks, family and mates at some stage as their relationship was getting serious. The fact he was meeting her parents proved that point. They were both so OTT about each other they were starting to make LTPs – long-term plans, both excited about these and reassured how easily these seem to come together.

Dee's dad cleared his throat and then spoke. "As I said, it is a labyrinth, and I hope you do not feel offended when I say that I still struggle to understand it all. When you mention that very, very long list of letters it, truth be told, has fried my brain a little! Or a lot to be truthful!" He laughed as if he was joking but Joe, and probably everyone else at the table, could tell that it had in reality. Dee's dad's eyes betrayed his increased but unadmitted confusion. "And then there are the colours as well?" Dee's dad added casually, half wanting to know but half reluctant to melt his brain further, his face showing he instantly regretting having asked.

"That is a lot easier to explain," Joe replied, receiving questioning looks, with a hint of terror, from both Dee's parents and Dee as well, who actually sunk her fingernails into his still held firmly fork-hand. He had tried, several times, to explain his homeland to Dee. She was certainly not stupid, despite going out with him, but she did struggle to comprehend it all. She was getting there, a lot better informed about Northern Ireland/North of Ireland than many other mainland UK residents. Joe began and Dee's grip eased. "Well, it is basically green and orange. Green is the Nationalist and Republican side from the green of Ireland represented in the green, white and gold of the Irish Tricolour. Then there is the orange which represents Unionists and Loyalists, who are red white and blue for the Union Jack of the United Kingdom. Northern Ireland is part of the United Kingdom and, although many people describe themselves as British in Northern Ireland, it is not part of Great Britain, which is only Scotland, England and Wales. You probably already knew that." Dee nodded along with her dad. Both nods were neither in agreement, nor confirmation of understanding. They were more nods of disbelief that this had been described by Joe as an 'easy' explanation! Dee's mum just stared across with a perplexed look, as her loaded fork of gravy dripping beef hovered mid-air half way up to her mouth.

"How does the orange fit in?" Dee's mum asked softly as the gravy dripped onto her plate, Joe glad that it showed she had at least been listening.

"That's from William the Third, Prince of Orange, who was Dutch and a Protestant. He, with his army of course, defeated the Catholic James the

Second at the Battle of the Boyne in 1690, to establish a Protestant British monarchy. That is where the Orange Order originated from, wearing orange, purple and sometimes burgundy sashes when parading. There is also the RBP, Royal Black Preceptory or also called the RBI, Royal Black Institution, which is above the Orange Order in terms of rank and wears black sashes when parading. Then there are the Apprentice Boys, who commemorate the Siege of Derry/Londonderry which happened two years before the Battle of the Boyne. They wear crimson sashes on parade. The AOH, Ancient Order of Hibernians, are the Roman Catholic lodges which started in USA in the 1830s to promote Irish Catholic rights and came back to Ireland form there. They wear green sashes when parading." He sighed heavily, knowing he had provided far too much information for his audience. He had been nervous and rushing so could hear his own accent thickening the more he talked until he ended with a porridge-like statement. "Lots of colours back home as well as the forty shades of green of the landscape!"

After a long pause that had not just verged but mounted the pavement of awkward, Dee's mum spoke. "Thank you for that, Joe. It is very complicated alphabetically. And colourful too! I may need to ask you again about this sometime as my head cannot take it all in," she replied, clearly baffled beyond belief but not wanting to show it. Joe knew she had resigned herself to never ask again.

"Anytime!" Joe replied as, with his hand released from Dee's grip, he scooped up the last bits form his plate and forked them into his mouth. He could not resist laughing to himself, thinking his bombarding them with the complexities of his homeland had diverted them completely from any intense relationship questions. Yet again he was wrong.

"Just before I bring in the dessert, and to move on to a simpler topic – so, are you planning to live together soon?" was the sledgehammer of a question Dee's mum pounded out, without neither sweetness nor sugar-coating. She mischievously gazed like she was at a tennis match between Dee and Joe's faces. Joe looked at Dee, and Dee looked at Joe, goldfish open-mouthed and obviously gasping about in their fish-bowl brains for any sort of answer. Neither could look at the questioner.

Joe eventually looked at Dee's mum and saw her grinning broadly. "I am only kidding with you both. Life is even more complicated than Northern Ireland!" She gave Joe an understanding stare. "It is complicated enough without parents sticking their noses into your personal business. You are both adults and can make your own decision. Just please make sure, whatever you decide, that you keep each other healthy, happy and hurt-free. That is a big enough mystery to try to solve. I will get dessert now."

Joe felt like a part deflated balloon, that bit of tension released at least. He looked over to Dee, seeing in her eyes the same expression he felt. She reached both hands over to her still food remaining plate. Joe could not see what she was doing in that quick flurry of her hands. Then she pushed her plate nearer to him. In green peas and orange carrot slices she had spelt out, as Joe read it, ICU. Ominously and fearfully, Joe mouthed, 'Intensive Care Unit' back towards her. She shook her head dramatically mouthing 'No! No! No!' She quickly moved several small carrot pieces across to where she had originally had them, before the plate moving had shifted their location. She placed these in the right and top right of the C, making a heart shape.

Lilliput

"Hiya Lilliput. You've been busy. The wee ones aren't mine, are they?" Joe asked gently and jokingly, reaching over to tap her on her upper arm as she passed by amongst the other shoppers on his hometown high street.

She turned immediately and stopped, looking up at him, a little shock showing as he had disturbed her from her daydreaming or worrying or both. After two seconds of confusion, her round face changed, with the brightness of recognition shining from her eyes. "Did they teach you nothing about biology at school, Joe?" she retorted as a cheeky smile worked its way across her lips, exposing perfect, white teeth. "These take more than kisses and only nine months, not ten years to produce!" She laughed a little before adding excitedly, "Good to see you! It has been a long time."

With a laugh and a beaming smile, Joe nodded his head and stated equally enthusiastically but a little sadly, "Has it really been that long, Lily?"

"Yep! And I don't even know if they are still running the Youth Club or not!" she replied, her brown eyes penetratingly fixed on Joe's blue ones, the warm smile equally fixed on her mouth.

Joe looked caringly down at her, in a physical not condescending way. She was, after all, well short of five feet tall, her head and shoulders just above the top of the double buggy handles she had been pushing almost effortlessly along the pavement. Joe bent his knees and haunched his six-feet-two-inch frame down in front of the buggy. He noticed the square heels on her black shoes that boosted her upwards only slightly. He peered in, looking paternally and wishfully at the two sound-asleep, little, rosy faces. They peeked out from the elephant patterned blankets and blue, woolly hats that keep them cosy against the biting October breeze. "Wow, they're wee belters! I hope you haven't called them Peter and Paul, because they will only end up robbing one another?" Joe commented softly with a smirk. Then he had an anxious moment, thinking that was the wrong thing to say; disastrous even, if she had chosen those two names? He really had to sort out installing a filter, making words pass through his brain before he blurted out stuff like what he had just said out loud.

She leaned over and, with a slight laugh, pointed in turn. "This is Samuel and… this is Sean! They certainly keep me from getting bored but have been sleeping and feeding well thankfully, so far."

"Those are grand names. Hello Samuel! Hello Sean! And they look nothing like me, which is a very good thing!" Joe replied quietly, looking at each cute face then up at her even cuter one, still smirking. There was a hint of sadness in his tone, that he could not really explain, and hoped Lily had not picked up on.

"Mark and I were married two years ago. I don't think you ever met Mark? We have been together since college and we've got a wee house down the road from my parents," she said, almost as if she wanted to change the subject, although still with a happy look on her sparsely but neatly made-up face.

Still crouched and watching the babies, marvelling at them twitching as they dreamt, Joe replied in a loud whisper, "Just got engaged myself and about to get a house. I met Dee when I was working over in England and she, fool that she is, decided to come back home with me. Big changes going on for both of us!" Lily nodded in agreement as Joe continued to look back up at her, encaptivated now as much as he was when he was a spotty, gangly youth. To Joe it felt like he had time warped back those ten years. Their conversation felt stilted somehow, like it was all just small talk between them. He sensed unspoken messages being sent to and fro that seemed to make them both feel slightly uneasy, scared even. He felt a huge surge of repressed feelings that he was struggling to contain. It was a whole fruitcake of emotions being held back, with large slices of anger and regret. Both these were covered up by his reenergised feelings of young love that iced over everything else from seeing her again so unexpectedly. They were talking about the present as a way of blocking what they really wanted to discuss – their past together. It was as if they both wanted to say so much more but were waiting for the right time, not really sure if there ever would be a right time. In the middle of the high street, amongst busy shoppers, was definitely not it.

She had not changed that much since he had known her. She was certainly not any taller, even with the small heels on her shoes. Her facial features had matured but had the freshness of youth still clearly visible. He doubted she would say the same about him, but she would hopefully notice that he was at least not still wearing blotchy brown NHS specs. It felt like a lifetime ago when they had gone to the same local youth club that ran every Saturday night from September to June. Depending on the crowd, some nights were better than others but it was always busy and popular. There was the odd expulsion, sometimes by the scruff of the neck, and membership cards taken off those causing fights, or bringing in booze, or generally being lippy and disrespectful to the formidable and truly admirable club leaders. Upsets like these did not happen often at all and it was generally a fun place to go. When Joe started hanging out with Lily, it made his Saturday nights even better. Those times together had been intensely brief but he still had a special, valuable place reserved for them in his memory bank. A first is a first after all, and worth remembering.

They had to put their names on the scattered sheets on the table in the entrance hallway at the start of each Saturday night. These were for whichever activities they wanted to take part in that night. There was a new girl straight in front of Joe in the sign-up queue. He had seen her arrive and had found himself drawn and pushed towards her emotionally, as well as physically. A few of his friends that egged him on made sure of that. He truly felt the awkwardness of his fourteen years, although secretly delighted that he stood directly behind her, over a foot taller, in the queue. As they waited, he so wanted to talk to her, really wanting to say something funny, to catch her attention and let her notice him; but his shyness took control and words did not come. Then she put her name in one of the tiny boxes on one of the sheets. He remembered how it amazed him how the leaders managed to interpret some of the squished and shortened scrawls! Christopher McGillicuddy had no chance whatsoever and always just put C McG instead! Another of Joe's friends, Phil McCracken, equally struggled to fill in a box. Joe, having an average length name, was usually able to fit it in okay.

Joe easily saw over her shoulder as she minutely wrote in the box. As he slightly misread it, he blurted out, "Oh! Lilyput! That's a name I haven't heard anyone called before! But at least it is small enough to fit in one of those wee boxes!" She sharply turned with a scowl and Joe cringed, waiting for the cutting remark or physical slap, truly regretting what he had said. He had been reading Gulliver's Travels at school which might have explained it. It was still a very random and possibly embarrassing thing to say, and there was also the real potential he had caused her offence. That was something he dreaded, her thinking he was a stupid eejit and cold shouldering him for ever, based on a couple of words. Back then he had an even worse lack of a filter for what came out of his mouth. He wondered if he ever truly would be able to control his words or if he was always destined to speak too freely.

"I may be wee, but I am not that small!" she had replied, the scowl gone and a questioning, smiling face in its place. "I'm Lily Potter, but I could not fit it all in that wee box. Could not even fit in 'er' at the end! The teachers tell me off about my handwriting and I suppose the 'o' does look like a 'u'. They are tiny boxes, aren't they?" She had unexpectedly formally reached out her elegant hand, very politely, as she rapidly spoke. As relief had flooded over him, Joe had taken it in his twice as big hand, feeling such a surge of delight at being able to touch her. He had been in a moment of stunned silence and held onto her hand longer than he really should have. She had looked up at him saying expectantly "And…?"

"Sorry! I'm Joe. Joseph Average!" he had replied in a rush, knowing he looked a bit gormless staring into her beautiful and remarkably spot-free face. He remembered having reached up, trying to be casual, using his left-hand palm to cover up the left side of his reddening face, where a couple of bright red blemishes beaconed out.

She burst out laughing. "Seriously! What's your real name?"

"Joseph Oliver Average is my full name," he answered with a laugh, well used to having such a response. He dug into his back pocket and produced his Youth Club membership card which he handed to her.

"Any chance?" came a snarling remark from behind. They had not realised they were holding up the queue for signing the sheets. Joe glanced round to look Matt in the Hat in the face. There were a few at the club had bets going that Matt wore that weird hat even when he slept in bed, as he was never seen without it on his head. There were even bets he was bald underneath! Neither bets were ever claimed, as neither facts were ever found out. Joe apologised quickly to him and scribbled his name beside one of the activities on a sheet. Having a moment of doubt, he looked back at the sheet as he moved aside, and realised he had put his name on the craft sheet instead of football. He genuinely did not care, and, grinning, he suddenly felt fate had worked a little bit of its good stuff, as LilyPut was written above his name for craft too!

Holding his card, she nodded. "Okay, I believe you Joseph, Oliver

Average. So, tell me, as this is my first night, I heard this is a good club. Is it? Or does everyone here make fun of small people?" He had been very unsure how to reply, her tone joking but with a hint of heightist tiredness. Then she had unexpectedly held his hand. Together they both dandered over to some of the empty chairs, at the edge of the hall. Joe had felt like he was floating and could not keep his eyes off her. He had babbled away about all that they did at the club, who the leaders were and funny stories involving puking from too many marshmallows and silly injuries. As they had sat, it was easier, as they were more at eye-level, talking more about themselves than the Youth Club. They chatted and chatted, bought orange juice and crisps from the tuck shop, then sat to talk some more over the noise of the energetic shouting as the games got under way and endless conversations of the others.

They forgot about the craft completely and nobody came looking for them. Or maybe they had but had decided to leave the two of them alone. Either way, it had been a night that had stuck in Joe's memory ever since. That was when knowing Lily had started. There was, however, another experience with Lily that had always been in his top ten memory chart ever since it happened. It came flooding back to him now as he stared at her twin boys, then up at her, wondering if it was still in her memory too. He hoped, a bit smugly, that it might even be in her top ten? He tried to read the expression on her face but, although it was beaming and beautiful, he could not. Did she remember? He most definitely did.

Joe had fumbled about several times before, trying to achieve it. Heads had been butted, noses bumped and even once a lip had been split. He felt the pressure of this rite of passage and, in his nervousness and naivety, had made a right mess of it when he had eventually reached that point with girls. As a young teenager, he could not understand why it was so difficult to do. Granted it was not on the lips, but he did kiss his ma and Nan, so he knew roughly what was involved. He had seen it lots of times being done on TV and in films. It was just a matter of co-ordinating lips together, so why did it seem so difficult? Maybe it was the significance of lips meeting that caused his jittery flummoxing, as this physical act had so, so many meanings and repercussions. Now, ten years later, although he was no master at the art, or felt he had any qualifications in it at all, he was at least able to kiss properly.

Back then, by the time he was fourteen, he had only tried a few times before with girls. Each embarrassing attempt delayed the next try. It took that bit longer to gather up his courage each time after an embarrassing failure. He remembered waiting and waiting until what he thought was the right moment and then hashing it up. Either they were not ready, or he was too ready, or they were both ready and just could not make it happen like it did in the movies. Once, it even resulted in him being kicked in the shin, after his forehead bounced off one girl. Her anger had flared instantly, almost as quickly as the large bruise on his shin; inflicted on him by her shoe whilst she rubbed her head. Those clumsy early attempts had left him on two occasions kissing the girls and making them cry. He did tell his ma about these when he got home, the girls telling him to leave them well alone. Telling his ma was a mistake and only made things even worse, providing even less of a personal confidence booster. His sister found out. She especially took delight in taking a hand out of him so much that he did not know if he was doing left or right. Will, his younger brother was a lot more supportive, learning a lot for when it would be his turn. Da just told him not to worry and it would happen when it happened which, although true in the end, at that time brought absolutely no comfort or encouragement at all.

He could not really remember the girl's involved in these dummy runs, dummy being the perfect description for him in these cases. Then, he was maybe too hard on himself as it was just messing about, really. It was really older kids playing a slightly different version of Kiss Catch to what younger ones did. Joe had never been very good at that game anyway, no matter what his age. He was good at the catching, with very little kissing happening for some reason. However, Lily changed that, and would always be remembered by him for it.

It was after school the following Monday after their long, long Saturday night chat at Youth Club. They had met up on the short High Street and wandered aimlessly past the shops in town, wondering about what was the best thing to buy with the forty-seven pence they had between them. They kept their money, too focused on each other and ended up at the park. It was not much of a park, to be truthful. It only consisted of a well-mown, expansive grass area; two large sorry looking trees; one old slide that had seen better days and one set of rusted swings. A lack of recreational facilities aside it was a good hang out spot for local kids. There were two paint-peeling benches and the furthest away one was empty. Other school kids, still in their uniforms, played football, which sometimes looked more

218

like rugby, with blazer goalposts on the grass. Others sat or stood half-watching the football, half-nattering and teasing. Others messed about, creaking back and forth on the swings. The sun was shining, the birds singing, the exams were over and life felt pretty good for Joe. He had not planned for it, but it was going to be an even better day than he had thought.

Chucking their schoolbags on the sun-shaded damp concrete, they sat down together at the farthest away bench. They were still holding hands, as they had been the entire time they had been drifting about. She stared into his eyes and he into hers, neither of them speaking. Their faces moved closer, some magical magnetic force working overtime. Joe's nervousness was non-existent, giving him a brand-new experience of inner confidence. He remembered it feeling so natural and with no hint of any teenage angst or worry. Their heads tilted automatically, both to their respective rights. His eyes closed as his slightly chapped lips met her moist ones. There was a tingle that surged through him like he had been electrocuted in a sensual way. Time stood still and he had no idea how long they stayed in that moment of pure bliss, wanting it to last forever. It was beyond anything he had ever felt before.

"OOOOHHHH! Smootchy! Smootchy!" was guldered across and snapped them both out of their shared, hormone-rousing encounter. They slowly moved apart and briefly glanced over at the four kids standing a few feet away, laughing and spouting other teasing words that Joe and Lily ignored. They reluctantly rose from the seat, slung their bags over their shoulders and walked off back into town. Neither of them spoke, just stared at each other, still in silent awe with each other. Their eyes tried to express something much more than a totally inadequate 'thank you'. Their audience of four younger kids followed them, sniggering and chuckling, until they reached the park gate. They turned down the street and the younger kids stopped, shouting a few things that neither Joe nor Lily even registered hearing or remotely cared about.

They walked holding hands, even tighter than before, Joe feeling like he was somewhere in the sky on number twenty, way beyond cloud number nine. He remembered Lily looking to be sharing that same fluffy ball of moisture, or maybe that was just his wishful thinking. Regardless how she felt, he knew that beautiful moment was tattooed into his inner being then. It still was with him all these years later. This priceless picture vividly glowed in his mind as he looked up at Lily now. An unfaithful, adulterous question came fleetingly into his head that he dearly wanted to answer and act on. He shook this curiosity away quickly. Realistically, he knew neither of them should or could take that risk. It had been a very special moment, but it was the past, and they had moved on with their lives.

That image blurred but the question remained hanging as his thoughts became darker. He felt the reminiscent sadness and regret again from way back then. They had met every day after school like that for the rest of Spring and at youth club on Saturday nights. Summer came and, when neither of them were not working, they would be together. Whenever possible their lips would meet, their hands would caress and that tingle would surge through Joe again, although nowhere near as electrifying as that first time in the park. Then they were back at school. Two weeks in and then she was gone! She was ripped out of his life, leaving only the memories and a gaping emptiness that never went away. It was a burning hole that cooled over time but remained intact. Joe had just become used to having it but it felt like flames had started sprouting from its edges as he looked up at her. He felt like he was being scorched again and that pain of his fifteen-year-old self-felt as real now as it did back then.

Lily's da had been threatened because of his work. Joe never knew what he did but the police had told her da and given him the advice to go, as quickly as possible. Joe had heard the rumours that a short letter of explanation had been written to Lily's da by those who wanted him to move on. They had even enclosed a gift inside, which would never be on anyone's birthday or Christmas list, and the bullet made the letter's instructions impossible to ignore. Within a day, Lily and her family had been whisked away to another town, another school and to another life without Joe. She had written to him soon after and had tried to explain. He had read that letter so often he was sure he could still, even these many years later, recite lines from it. It was a letter he still had somewhere, buried in a box of papers in the attic. She had not given her new address and no other letters ever came, making this piece of paper even more uniquely priceless to him. It was a letter he had no plans to ever show his fiancé Dee, even though they had talked about their first kisses. As he looked up at Lily behind her twin's buggy, he felt scars in his heart open and begin to weep.

Joe rose to his feet, still staring at her. He frantically tried to compose himself and force himself to put on a happy face. The memory of that first kiss made that so easy and overrode the sadness of her loss. The thoughts of what might have been were harder to shift. Her eyes were still fixed on his and he still struggled to read what they said. He knew what he wanted them to say but was not sure. Then she spoke.

"Isn't it strange how life works out? Who knows what might have happened if things had been different?" she said rather dejectedly. "But really glad everything is working out for you."

Joe's spirit soared when she said that as he mumbled 'likewise!' in reply. Maybe he was hearing what he wanted to hear, but that did not matter. There was definitely a wish in there, or at least evidence that she had thought about him as he had done her. They could have been together! It could have been their twins in that big buggy. He could have placed that ring on her finger. They could be living near her parents. Fate, destiny or whatever obviously had had other plans for them. Joe was totally unsure how this meeting made him feel. Was it a warm, rekindling of young love or reigniting the fiery torment? He really did not know. He knew, and possibly Lily did as well, that it should be cold cinders and ashes between them, but their faces revealed that it was not. Sparks were flying and both of them seemed to be trying to stop anything catching alight. Joe gave her a smouldering look which he hoped would help. She missed it as Samuel gurgled and caught her eye.

He remembered so clearly back then, and occasionally in the years since, how he had planned Lily and his life together. First love and first kiss are never forgotten. Even long after she was gone from his life, he fantasised about going on missions to find her, sweep her off her feet and whisk her away. But he never did try to look for her. Instead, he waited for the same fate or destiny, which had failed him before and taken her away, to help him to live out his dream. Both had failed him these past ten years. Now fate, destiny or divine will had decided to reunite them, almost like they were playing some even crueller trick. Joe imagining these three forces, for good and bad, enjoying a drink together. He pictured them having a real good chuckle at what they had each done to tear at the emotions of Lily and Joe yet again. She was only a small person in stature but had been a big influence in his life. Seeing her again showed that she was still the same as his lasting, but distant memory, of their brief time together. This ballooned in his mind and heart. It felt like fate was really having fun torturing him and, as Joe waited for the pins to come out, he increasingly savoured every second being near her before this bubble burst.

A kiss is only a little thing in reality, he admitted to himself. Thousands, millions of these happen every day. But every single one is special. There are those quick pecks on the cheeks of family members to show an enduring love and respect. There are the attempted face swallowing ones of overwhelming passion. There are all sorts of kisses but that first proper, special one leaves a lasting impact beyond the physical lip contact. It can always remain in the top ten of everyone's smooching chart, only superseded by the first kiss when that life partner soulmate is found. Joe had read his sister's magazines that hyped all this up beyond belief. He had thought, and still did, that all those articles, books and films made it puffed up, romantic, oversentimental guff. However, everyone has real personal experiences of it, or, despite the potential for pain, should have. His was as real now, kneeling before her and her children, as it was when he was a fourteen-year-old lad in that park. His first kisses with Dee were so, so special too but in a different way. Maybe his face had dropped a little when he thought guiltily of Dee but, whether that was the reason or not, Lily decided she had to move on.

"Sorry, but I really have to go. Great seeing you and maybe we will bump into each other sooner than in another ten years' time?" she said with that captivating smile she still had, but with the brightness of her eyes noticeably fading.

"Me too. Great to see you as well. Yeah, hope to see you again sometime too," Joe replied, shaking himself out of his over thinking. He found it really strange that he did not want to give her his phone number and address. He thought he should but a greater force prevented him, making it feel inappropriate somehow. Likewise, she had not given any contact details. Neither arranged it but they were both left things hanging in the air, hoping for the hands of fate, destiny, divine will, or the gods that had all made it onto the cricket team, were all good catchers. It was as if they both realised their lives had changed too much, looking to the future not the past. They were not going to force themselves into each other's future and let whatever will be in the years to come happen. Joe certainly was, and Lily's face betrayed she might be as well. Both were perhaps a little scared that meeting up again would rekindle those longed-for teenage feelings. It would be throwing a spanner into the workings of their current lives, causing complications and possibly more pain. It was too big a risk for either of them. Life was normally complicated enough, without adding extra weight to its daily load he rationalised. Lily would have to remain a memory only. *What a memory*, Joe said to himself with a huge grin. Lily saw it and smiled back with a questioning sweetness.

He said goodbye to the still-sound-asleep twins. He leant over towards her, about to kiss her on the cheek but stopped after only millimetres of movement. Although his legs started to walk away, he could not remove his eyes from looking at her, with her steadfastly returning his gaze as she too began to roll the buggy forward. A little bit away, he turned to face the direction he was going but felt compelled to turn for one last look. He thought it only happened in the movies, but she turned at the exact same moment as him. Their eyes met through the other pedestrians on the pavement, creating a personal microsecond in time. Joe felt everything go in slow motion. An urge to rush down and embrace her, like in the movies, came over him but he could not act on it. Staring at her he wondered if the same thoughts were going through her mind, picturing their re-enactment of a scene from some romantic film. A very tall man walked between them and broke their eye connection. When he had moved past, ducking to avoid a yawning from the greengrocer's shop, she had turned her back to him and was walking. He stopped and watched her go, savouring the moment that at least this time he could watch her leave with his consent, rather than have her taken from him.

He realised that she had taken a little bit of him with her this time and he guiltily cherished what she had left with him. The height difference had never been a factor when they had gone out together, Joe always feeling a bit of neck ache was well worth it when stooping over to kiss her when they walked along. Now, as the distance between them grew he felt an awful lot taller. He was not as big as the face of the Giant on Cave Hill in Belfast that inspired Gulliver's creation; but he grew larger, more sure of himself with every stride as he moved swiftly up the street. He may have joked about Lily being in Lilliput, but it was as if she was there and he was in Brobdingnag, travelling to their separate lands.

As he walked, he talked to himself. That small in stature girl had tied Joe up tightly in emotional bonds back then. Even when they had just met on this shopping street, he realised how these had still left a few rope burns. He rubbed his wrists innocently as he sighed with relief, glad he had not pushed things when they met. That could have ended up with him making a complete yahoo of himself, or both of them doing so. He was left with his memories and, much as he may have fantasised in the past and even presently about what might have been between them, it was not to be. Lily was in a little bit of his scarred heart but he thought it was spacious enough to accommodate her, in a little special corner. He was able to make room there for all the others who he loved and cared for. He thought happily of Dee and knew she was starting to take up even more of his big heart. He wondered if he was going to need to have a giant's heart to store it all. He entered the shop he had come into town to visit and saw the 'Giant Sale Now On!' signs plastered across its front windows. "Maybe they sell giant hearts here and I can buy one!" he laughed to himself. "No storage issues if I had one of those!" Maybe he had one already, he wondered. He hoped he might.

Leadership

PLEASE EXPLAIN HOW YOU MEET AND EXCEED THE FOLLOWING ESSENTIAL CRITERIA: -

EXCELLENT TIMEKEEPING

Joe rubbed his eyes for the fifth time in the past ten minutes. Or was it the tenth time in the past five? Whatever the number, he knew he was half-past dead tired. The cold shock of the freezing tea in the back of his throat, when he downed the dregs from the mug beside him, did nothing to wake him up. He looked blearily at the chipped glass on the shiny new leather black strap on the watch on his wrist. Was that his fifth or sixth new strap? Or was it more, on this time link to his childhood he obsessively kept? He rubbed his eyes again to dispel going off on yet another brain weary tangent. It was twenty-past-one with the study light becoming even more blinding in the darkness of the room. A slightly disgruntled, dressing-gowned Dee had brought him a cup of tea and a biscuit before midnight. *What a wife she was!* he had thought at the time. That had felt like an age ago, when she set the hot tea beside his keyboard, asking if he would be much longer. "Only a couple more questions to check. Another five or ten minutes, tops!" he had over-optimistically replied. That was an over an hour and a half ago.

Midday tomorrow was the deadline. Or actually midday today, he realised in panic. He read over what he had written about always meeting deadlines and laughed a little manically. He read over about his capabilities in prioritising things. That he realised he had listed this as number five in the section, causing him to ponder a moment, thinking he should prioritise prioritising more and move it up this list. Unsure, he left it where it was, possibly prioritising this for later. The simple, or not so simple, act of finishing this was his top priority.

Having missed the post by two days, he was going to have to hand deliver it before going to work in the morning. He knew exactly where the company was but it was a bit of a detour. It meant he would have to set his alarm for silly o'clock, to make sure he was still at his desk for seven a.m. That would work, he had decided as he planned the route in his head. It was, after all, finished now.

Well, almost! All he was doing, and had been doing for the past hour and a half, was checking it over, adding bits in, deleting bits, filling in answers to a couple of questions he had missed and generally becoming more pissed off with this task. Eventually he admitted tweaking defeat. It would have to do as it was, so he hit the print button and as he did so, snorted sarcastically. "Timekeeping?" he tutted out loud.

HIGHLY ORGANISED

He anxiously hoped there was enough ink in the chuggy, second hand printer that almost needed a geriatric walking aid to help the sheets come out. His rapid breathing stopped when he was able to exhale with relief when it started to labour and give birth to the paper hardcopy of his creative creation. *Had it enough paper?* he panicked. He sharply took in a breath at being unable to answer this question, just as the printer beeped the answer that 'Paper Tray Empty'. Where was the extra paper? He knew the kids kept nicking it to draw on, despite being told not, causing a little more panic to rise. With a sharp exhale, he found half a ream that had fallen down the back of the desk. Straightening a couple of crumpled corners, he fed the fickle printer. He had used other 'f' words to describe it before, but fickle was most apt this time. Like an ungrateful cat, it scratched his finger when he closed the flap, possibly annoyed at the feeding delay. However, it then purred contentedly as printed words on sheets were produced.

Had it enough ink? This was his next cause of angst. Rummaging in the stuffed desk drawer, he found the spare ink cartridge he suddenly remembered he thought they had. With a welcome sigh, he half-congratulated himself on being sort of half-organised, at least for solving the potential ink problem. Smirking a little he knew that was nothing to do with his planning ahead. Pure luck, and probably more so Dee, were the more realistically likely reasons it was there. Hopefully he should not need it but backup was always good.

He had been organised, sort of. He had filled in all the easy bits – name, address, qualifications, work experience, etc five days ago, just to have actually made a start on it. Then he had been too tired from work the following night, not worried as he convinced himself there was still a load of time. The night after that, little Ava had a bit of a temperature. This cooled after she had puked up hot, milky white gloop out of the blue, requiring a red-faced angry clean-up. This had been followed by a couple of hours of anxious new parents baby watching. Ava, with her sister Bella in the small bed beside her, both slept contentedly and blissfully unaware of their traumatised guardian angels watching over them. The night after that he simply could not be arsed to do it, starting to have second thoughts about even sending it in. He did do some more blurb writing in the never-ending boxes the previous night, leaving, what he wishfully and misguidedly thought, was just a bit of tidying up for tonight. The tidying up had been a lot messier than what he had planned.

As he watched the third sheet crawl out of the printer, he felt like driving his size eleven up his own backside. Calling himself several names that he muttered out loud alphabetically, he saw to his horror that he had written of his ability to organise that 'I orgasm work plans to ensure total customer satisfaction.' It was even more frustrating when he saw he had written 'cuming' in the next sentence. Laughing in disbelief he saw that he had 'cum' again in the third line after that, instead of 'sum'. Overcoming the shock, he laughed as he thought about how funny it would be leaving them as they were, to give his future employers a laugh. Reality kicked in and that was not an option. He flicked the screen back to life, scrolling down to have another go at inserting things correctly. A reprint was going to be necessary. "Organisation!" he tutted out loud. He spotted he had had not spelt this word neither accurately nor correctly. He tutted some more as he corrected them too.

EXPERIENCED IT USER

"No! No! No!" he yelled in a whisper, so as not to wake Dee, Bella or baby Ava. It must have been after a late-night snack as the printer began chewing away on the jammed paper. Swearwords dripped continually from him as Joe tugged and tore to remove the blockage to the flow of paper. Tiny chunks kept coming off as the printer kept on whirring and spluttering as it tried to push and push with no release. Without switching it off at the mains, he grabbed a large metal paper clip. As he was bending this into a hook, his guardian angel let out a loud cough as a reminder. He reached over and unplugged it before beginning his hoking about.

Joe was sure he was as sane as anyone else, but he firmly believed in the spirit world. There was a big spirit above all the rest that included ghosts, fairies and all those other-worldly creatures which Joe concluded we should all learn to leave in peace. Why is this relevant to a computer printer? In this other world there are evil spirits, as well as mischievous ones, Joe believed. When it came to technology, Joe felt he was the victim of such forces. Every time he used this printer it was as if he could feel the six-inch nails going into his doll effigy. It always messed up. It was the same for the one at work. The photocopier there as well seemed to go into poltergeist mode when he went near it. Maybe it was his wariness that alerted the bad fairies to his plight and they decided to have some fun when he went anywhere near such machines. Whatever it was, almost every single time he printed something at home it went wrong. When Dee, or even the kids, printed something – absolutely not a bother at all. It was the same at work a lot of the time. Joe even feeling guiltily glad when these machines messed up for work colleagues, meaning it was not just him the bad fairies had it in for.

Joe was of an age to remember when home computers were in their infancy. They had reduced from wall to TV sized to hand-size in mobile phones. It was the speed of this change Joe struggled to keep up with. It was probably as much his own nervousness about being forced to become more aware of new software, hardware, malware… and stop himself from constantly being aware. The days of permanently deleting things were gone they kept saying, although Joe had proved that theory wrong a few times. It was not the making mistakes that frustrated him, it was the constant, constant changing and upgrading, and his constant, constant failure to keep up. One constant was that IT was in the sprint and Joe was in the 800m race. He did always finish but by the time he reached the line five other races had been completed for him to catch up on. It left him in a state of constant exhaustion. Nevertheless, according to this section of the application he was 'fully competent in all aspects of IT and keeps up to date with technological advancements.'

With sarcastic laughing, he managed to remove the last of the sticky jam. He gave it a little thump on the side as chastisement, rather than trying to butter it up, before switching the printer back on to have another go at spreading the word about his job suitability. The nasty spirits must have become bored and moved on to torment someone else as the paper flowed out smooth as silk. "Why did it not do that the first time?" he asked out loud for only himself to hear, swearing he could hear a snigger he did not make in the empty room.

VERY HIGH STANDARDS OF DETAILED REPORT WRITING

As he read again the final sheets spewing out of the printer, he gave an embarrassed little laugh. It was not a complete work of fiction. It was all, or almost all, based on facts. Creative was a much better word than fiction to describe it. He had honestly and genuinely shown at face value his career details to date. He had, however, taken these and applied some lipstick here, mascara there, splodged on foundation creams to cover any blemishes, removed a few out of place hairs… He generally enhanced what he had, without the need for him to make-up anything else. As he read, he felt like a sixty-year-old prostitute, slapping on more and more to cover up, before touting experienced wares to compete with the younger, more talented ones. He stopped himself going off on a thought tangent of everyone having to prostitute themselves to some level, selling themselves for a job. It amazed him how much some people would indeed sell – souls included!

There were bits he was sure he smelt, as well as seen with his eyes. He left them unchanged, hoping the readers of it would think them sweet, and also, he was just too tired to be bothered to change them. He may have stretched the truth somewhat but not so far that its bowels opened and the whole thing stank. A job application is, he accepted at the end of this very long day, a report on yourself. It is not only who and what you are, but how you have reached where you are at and how you got there. Within all these whys and wherefores, there are parts of everyone's lives that stink. Whether they want to share these with others is up to them, only opening themselves up when they choose. Joe had chosen to only reveal a little of these in the words on the pages, mainly because he himself still struggled to explain why he was where he was at in his life. How was he meant to tell that to a future employer?

Then there are the bits everyone wants to or loves to share. These can include the boastful possession obsessed things, salaries and job titles. There are also the simpler, priceless values and experiences of family, friendship and community. These last three were Joe's focus when he tried to summarise his life report before him. As he read, Joe thought it was still average, not just to match his surname. It lacked huge salaries and any flamboyant job titles that could be made to sound a lot more glamorous than what they really were. What it did have, he hoped, was character and commitment. He wanted to show how he had survived life's struggles through working hard, watching out for and giving to others the luck and help that is always there but we all sometimes miss or do not ask for. Joe wondered if anyone would ever achieve an 'A' for those sort of life reports. He gave himself an 'A' for effort but knew he would still be a 'C' average middle grade.

HIGHLY DEVELOPED INTERPERSONAL SKILLS

The smutty teenager part of his brain always seemed to come through when he read this word. Interpersonal always seemed vague, and therefore, open to a potentially crude interpretation of it. While at a joint interview skills tutorial at university, he had asked the English student sat beside him, possibly not as innocently as he tried to sound, if she would like to see his interpersonal skills? She had actually face-slapped him! It was rather embarrassing for everyone concerned. Although the red mark on his cheek faded quickly afterwards, his understanding and interpretation of that word remained confined to that smutty realm. That slap had confirmed that was where it belonged. She had been an English student after all, which gave his own take on this word added meaning.

This meant he found it very difficult to answer any question related to this seriously. Smutty crudeness prevented his brain trying to think of employment terminology to use with it. When he tried to force himself to think like a pro, that made matters even worse. Street walkers selling their personal services flooding his thoughts. Although he laughed mostly about this immaturity, it did cause him some concern. Checking with his mates, male and female, he was relieved to discover they sometimes had similar thoughts when filling in this section of an application. When he reflected some more, he was not so reassured. This showing more the types of friends he had, rather than providing hard linguistic evidence of what a word meant.

He had written something at least. He skim-read it and it sounded all right (ish). He had mentioned communication a dozen times and still did not feel he had put the message across. It was the same for delegation, which he had dumped on the page without really explaining it. Listening he included as well, hoping they would hear his plea for the job. Even the new buzzword of 'Active Listening' he had mentioned, although not revealing his confusion with this. His rationale was that you either heard something or you did not. That was the activity. Acting on what you listened to was stressed in this supposedly new concept. Joe normally did, although it frustrated him that there seemed to be a total miss of an important fact. Surely, doing nothing about it was also an action? A few of his bosses qualified as active listeners on that score, but he did not say that.

Nor did he mention the socialising side of work which he had amazing and amazingly terrible experiences of. Alcohol and work colleagues, he had found, could create fun bonding or sad bombing, or even the odd fist fight. Generally, though, Joe was of the opinion that a few pints helped interpersonal relations at work. His mind thought of some of the true office romance rumours that had circulated about some serious interpersonal relations after work's dos. This brought him right back to agreeing with his conclusion that the smutty part of his brain was right about interpersonal relations.

A COMMITTED TEAMPLAYER

Joe threatened often that if he had heard the 'no 'I' in team' quote one more time, he was going to borrow the American phrase and say, "Eat me!" That may have used 'e' twice, but at least did use the letters that were in team! This proved that there may not have been an 'I' in it, but there certainly was 'me', which totally contradicted this patronising, in reality meaningless, quip. Having teams made up of mates, or at least people you got on with, was what Joe found worked best. People who just hit it off worked so much better together was his experience. Finding that combination was more luck than planning was his conclusion, and no jargon statement could replace that.

Joe had seen all these wonderfully designed boxes linked with 'communication', 'respect', 'skills utilisation', and other sickly-sweet-sounding word arrows pointing to 'teamwork' in the centre of flipcharts and PowerPoints. There were so many theories about making the best possible team to work together, Joe wondered if the business gurus had actually forgotten what the real world was like. Had they, like some university academics, become so cut off from the current world, they were drifting along on tides of pure theory? Joe just did his best to avoid drowning in all of this patronising piffle.

Teams, in Joe experience, even very successful ones, were always fragile. At the end of the day, whether it was a team of two or twenty, or a hundred, there were the same number of differing personalities. Personalities will always cause love or hate. The in-between bit will last only as long as those involved are willing to compromise and tolerate. In a work setting, both these are almost forced on all of the team members to comply and 'never lose sight of the end goal!' This was another classic jargon gibberish. When you are eight nil down with a minute to go, motivation for the end goal disappears completely. Likewise, when plans are changed and distorted so much that half a dozen sets of constantly moving goalposts are created, a team falls apart in arguments and sometimes tears.

He had written all the usual blurb about being a committed team player. Thinking of some of the teams he had been in, he was amazed at having survived those without either being red or yellow carded. He had, however, been sin binned once before, and that was a hell. Dealing effectively with the contrasting personalities in a team was, according to what he had written, one of Joe's many team working skills! What he did not mention was his endless patience testing and forced politeness to not give the lazy ones a good shake, tell the bolshie ones to just do as they have been asked, tell the arrogant ones to take it down about ten notches and the shy ones to grow a set! It frustrated him often at wasting so much time figuring out the right way to convey these specific messages to his team. It meant by the time he had found these right words he usually had missed the moment and needed to rethink how to politely tell them something else. Teamwork involved a lot of tiring timework.

Joe's attitude to teams was very simple and did not need fancy slogans and graphic designed boxes. Make sure everyone knows what they are meant to be doing and do it. Easier said than done many would say but they could not disagree with this simple, basic analysis. He had worded it a lot better, but Joe was quite pleased that he had actually included that in his spiel about fitting into this hoped-for 'new and exciting team'.

AN INSPIRING AND DRIVEN LEADER

This was the big one. This was top of Joe's 'What the hell do I put for this?' list. His brain had become lead trying to think how he had led in the past. He overcame the feeling of having no lead in his pencil for this section; he splurged out something onto the page. If he thought he could smell some of the other lingering nasty aromas he had written in other sections, this was an entire sewage treatment works. He joked that it was such a huge pile of crap it should have been written in brown ink!

He had been born without doubt, with a birth certificate and everything to prove this biological fact. Was he a born leader? Possibly or potentially he had been, but realistically and more than likely not. Well, not the type of leader that the training courses at work portrayed a leader to be. All this go-getting, sealing the deal, doing whatever it takes to ensure customer requirements are met, motivating your team (another word used by some for bullying and pushing in Joe's experience). Dedicated was used, when ruthless would have been more apt. Passionate was used, when obsessed would have been more accurate. Target-setter and achiever was used, when more, more, more was what was constantly demanded. There were other descriptions of so-called talents that equally did not apply to Joe's average range of talents. It did seriously concern him that, in this supposedly modern world, more and more people seemed to emulate and advocate such 'leadership' attributes, which Joe did not feel proficient in. Was this why the world was the way it was, he often asked himself, as we were and still are all led like this? Market share, increased sales, profit, profit and profit all leading us to what? Sharing rather than shareholders Joe felt was more important to make the world a better place.

Joe sighed as he thought of that. If this blurb was successful, he could end up being a small part of that corporate machine, leading other cogs to crank harder. Even though he had put all that stuff down on the page that was not Joseph (known as Joe as he explained in the very first application box) Oliver

232

Average. He had many leadership qualities but these took him and his followers in directions that were not always in line with corporate signage arrows. Previously, he had been authorised to try these alternative approaches and both he and his employer reaped rewards. Most times he failed to remove the blinkers and they did not heed his warnings that these would cause them not to see the edge of the cliff until it was too late. Other times he had not heeded warnings and regretted having led like a lemming.

Leadership for Joe was not purely about winning the battles, it was about simply doing the right thing for colleagues, customers, conservation and the cosmos. That was more than likely why he never had or probably would attain senior management roles. It was not a surprise to him, although it did shock others, that this did not bother him at all. As long as he made enough money to pay the bills and keep his family on the right track, that was the extent of his leadership ambitions. Do not lead by greed but by example, was Joe's motto.

ANY OTHER INFORMATION

As Joe placed the print-off in a large envelope, he was too tired to worry about his lack of yet another skill. His lack of origami ensured there were not ironed, neat folds. He reflected on what else he could have put in this last section he had just read before committing it to the envelope confines. He would have loved to have written down his true feelings about the huge amount of effort needed to apply for jobs nowadays in this final section. Looking for, along with the ominous and time-consuming task of applying for a new role, was a full-time job in itself. There was the emotional rollercoaster of the waiting for the response. There was the demoralising failure effect of the, no matter how softly worded, 'Unfortunately, on this occasion...' The brutal truth of the simpler message of 'No, it's not going to be you!' letter or email was still hard to take and accept. There were the even more anxious loop the loops of preparing for the next stage of an interview, after which the 'No it's not going to be you!' hit even harder.

As he block capital addressed the envelope, he could not explain why he felt his heart sink. Maybe exhaustion had sapped positivity from him. Doubts about why he had even tried for this job flowed through his head as he became nervous about the rapids ahead and if he had overcome the weirs and boulders these questions had placed before him. Why could he not just call in for a chat, have a week or month's trial and show how he could do the job advertised? That was the old way of doing things. However, he admitted this was open to all the isms of nepot, sectarian, race and sex which were considered so unfair and had created an ocean of additional bureaucracy. He had to accept that was the way things were and had to be. It was a historically justifiable fact that these additional frustrating forms were there to supposedly give everyone a fair crack of the whip.

Still, he felt embittered that this made the whole process even more of a flogging match. His bitterness intensified as he knew, as everyone did, that the system was still unfair. Who you knew was still as rife within the system as what! Jobs for the boys, and girls, remained underlying and often not so well hidden, to distort the job market. This caused Joe regret that he never seemed to know the right people, feeling he had to slog his way along the hard road rather than a relative or acquaintance opening a door for him to access easy street. That was the way things were and all he could do was keep working this confusing and time-consuming system.

Rising slowly from the seat, having placed the envelope on top of his car keys on the table so he would not forget it, he slumped up the stairs to bed. This was a job in itself as his weary legs felt like lead, his brain weighed down just as much with anxious thoughts. He had in reality no more information to give. What all those typed words had done was create an oblong with a square at one end to shape a footstep forward for the future he hoped. Joe tutted to himself as he focussed on trying to put his best foot forward for his family as much as for himself. This job application was part of that drive he had within him He tripped on a step and stumbled...

Layers

It was probably not the new 'Clear Desk' work policy itself that he hated. Although the bland, repetitive and far-too-numerous memos, emails and phone calls he had received about it in the past few weeks had certainly not helped. These had pushed this new policy so far down his 'Favourite Things' list that the devil himself was poking at it. It had come about 'primarily due to issues regarding the misallocation of sensitive material', as stated repeatedly in office correspondence. When translated into normal speak, this meant someone had ballsed up big time and lost stuff that could screw the company or the bosses over. The new policy brought horses and stable doors to Joe's mind, but he had to abide by this belated bolt that closed nothing.

It was probably more his application of it that was causing him his current muttered frustration. He was rummaging through his desk drawers simply looking for some spare staples which he thought he had. He probably did, but his own, possibly unique interpretation of 'clear desk' was causing some 'misfile location issues' of his own, as they would say in management speak. Recently, his last work act before leaving for home was the lifting of his computer keyboard, opening his desk drawers and sweeping anything on the desk with his forearm into his top two drawers. To Joe it was very efficient; his desk was perfectly clear and there was no company policy for 'tidy drawers'. Yet! He laughed a little thinking about this as he hoked about, wondering if there would be soon? Dear help him if there ever was!

"Jeremy and Lucinda want to see you!" Gary stated softly as he stood sipping coffee beside Joe's desk. Joe jumped a little as he always did when Gary arrived, feeling very unnerved. It was not just because he was distracted, looking in his desk in this instance, it was because Joe was actually becoming convinced that Gary could teleport himself! Either that or he was a magician. A colleague had suggested there were trap doors with secret tunnels under the floorboards that only Gary knew about and used, but everyone preferred the much more realistic time travelling, magician options. In the big, open-plan office, Gary managed everyone in it and had this abnormal ability to just suddenly appear at anyone's desk. Joe's workmates were regularly freaked-out victims of this too. It was very rare you actually saw him coming over from his desk or move about the office. He would just pop up as he had now.

Joe grunted an 'uh-huh!' in reply as he moved some papers about and smiled as he retrieved a crumpled box of small metal 'u's, pricking his finger as he did so. Gary quietly sipped his coffee again, simply quietly saying, "Now!" Joe looked up to reply but, like a puff of smoke, Gary was gone. Joe looked over the four desks to the all-seeing, all-knowing corner where Gary sat. He was able to see the top of his shiny, thinning-haired head back at his own desk. A shiver went down Joe's spine, a little supernaturally alarmed at how fast Gary had managed to return to his desk. Joe smiled a little saying to himself, that *If Gary the Time Lord has a Tardis, it is very small and well hidden. But I will find it someday, to prove I am right! Then I can become Office Time Lord!* His evil genius laugh actually leaked out loud. Admin Angela across the open-plan walkway in her extremely neat blue walled booth smiled over. She had become well used to Joe's strange rantings and ravings, being prone to a few herself. This meant they both had a strange sort of shared work bond, with an unwritten agreement. This 'I won't tell, if you don't' arrangement meant they were able to have a good, normal laugh about their strange shared utterances together at coffee breaks.

Before he became carried away with what he would do if he could change the past, present and future, he pulled himself together to answer his summons to enter the higher echelons world of Jeremy and Lucinda. Their offices were a short walk down the drearily decorated corridor, but Joe still felt he needed to step up a good bit when meeting them. This was a rare event. They did give their 'Monday Motivation' talk every week. This novel idea from top management had become an endurance hour for the whole team that would have sucked the life out of a stone. Rather than inspire great things that they would briefly excitedly talk about at these sessions, it had become more of a whinge fest – need more sales, need more efficiency, too much money spent on teabags, etc. It had become christened 'Monday Moaning' as a result. It was about as motivating as cutting an onion although there was less crying. Usually that was the case, although three staff had raced out of the room bawling their eyes out when it had been unexpectedly announced emotionlessly three Mondays ago that the Waterworks account had been lost, and they were redeploying staff as a result.

Joe had only been to see them twice on his own before in his time with the company. He straightened his tie and pulled it tight. Then he checked his armpits did not smell, with very fast but unsubtle nose sniffs of each. Suddenly he had a major moment of doubt. It was not about his sweaty armpits, as his deodorant was doing an impressive job of containing. He wondered if this sudden meeting had anything to do with the 'sensitive material'? He was sure he had not lost anything important like that. His filing system may have been a bit unorthodox, or maybe sporadic would be a better description, but it worked for him and everything was in there – somewhere! Or at least he was certain it was. "Wasn't it?" he asked himself out loud, receiving another angelic smile from Angela.

Joe dandered confidently through the mini maze of desks, computers and blue, panelled walkways. He saw Gary standing by his desk in the other corner, looked over to smile at Jimbo and Gemma in their shared corner cubicle, then spine shivered as he glanced around and saw Gary over beside Angela. That was back where Joe had set off from! "Freaky!" he muttered under his breath. Swinging the double glass doors open, he swaggered through like he had just entered a saloon. As the man walked towards him Joe pretended to fire off his six-shooters at Tex who returned the same thumb up finger pointed fire. Tex was originally from Birmingham, but was a huge Country and Western Music fan. He had more or less given himself his own nickname. He had even been putting on a southern USA twang of an accent for so long, it had almost become his normal way of speaking.

Joe always smirked at the thought of Tex being unsatisfied that his cowboy boots could not click across the boring grey carpet of the hallway, as they did on the canteen tiles. His belt buckle was brass cod piece sized, its intention of drawing eyes to marvel at what lay behind not working on Joe. Everything was meant to be bigger in the States, but according to the rumours Debbie in Marketing had supposedly put around a year or more ago, that was not always the case. However, as love comes in all sorts of sized packages, she was now Mrs Tex, with a growing-by-the-day stomach bump. Tex smiled back at Joe, firing off his pretend Winchester instead. Joe clutched at his chest and pretended to groan in death agony, before Tex opened his office door to return to riding his rodeo role in the Wild West of

IT Management Systems.

He tried Jeremy's office first, simply because that was the first one he came to. Lucinda's office was further down, in the corner with a coveted view of the staff car park and the concrete wall of the Tyre Depot across the road. It may not have been much but at least she could see outside, rather than staring at a blue panel or blank wall. Jeremy's office had a window view as well, of a red brick back wall with thin grass and moss mosaics adding their artistic touches to it. It was a modest office, but Jeremy was aiming even higher; much higher, and everyone in the office knew that.

Lucinda was in Jeremy's office; Joe could see through the vertical glass door panel. He knocked sharply four times on it, trying to make it sound cheery rather than thumpy. He saw Lucinda and Jeremy look up with a little surprise. They had been standing close beside each other, behind Jeremy's huge mahogany desk, but shuffled further apart a little before Jeremy authoritatively shouted, "Enter! Enter!" Joe walked in, smiling as best he could.

"Joe-Joe!" Jeremy called out as he strode over with outstretched hand. Joe hated being called that. He did mess about a bit, enjoying a laugh, but this made him sound like a clown. He, as he always did around Jeremy, buried his petty but growing resentment, smiled acceptingly and shook the offered hand vigorously. "Have a seat! Have a seat!" Jeremy continued, ushering Joe to a leather armchair in the corner with a wave of his hand. "Sit down! Sit Down! Great to see you! Yeah, great to see you!" Jeremy continued, reaffirming of both his, possibly unknown to him, nicknames of Echo and New York. Echo for obvious reasons, and New York in honour of Sinatra's famous song. Some called him Jeremy Jeremy. Joe refused to use that nickname, thinking Jeremy was not good enough to be named twice. Once was enough.

Joe sat down in a relaxed, causal manner. He coughed loudly in an attempt to conceal the squeaky fart noise that had just sounded as his trousers met the leather armchair. Jeremy sat down directly opposite Joe, paying absolutely no attention to the loud, farty noise his bum contact with the leather two-seater sofa made. Joe hid a smirk, nodded and admired the man's confidence. Lucinda finished looking at whatever it was on the desk, strolled over with a quick 'hi!' stirring a cup of coffee and sat down, squeak-free, beside Jeremy. She crossed her long, trousered legs and sat laid back, briefly adjusting her blouse and hair.

238

Joe went through his normal fidget when placed in such a chair as this, in front of people such as these. It always felt like the easiest option would be to detach his arms and place them on the floor beside him. He never knew what to do with his hands. The chair arms were straight out, and if he placed his hands at the ends off these it would make him look like he was itching to get away, which, although usually true, he could not show. If he let them flop by the side of the chair arms, it would make him look slovenly and having no interest at all. If he put his hands behind his head that would be way too relaxed and look almost cockily mocking. He could not cross his arms, as that was far too intimidating and shutting people out. Hands clasped in front of him would appear almost begging. So, although not perfect, he went for the tried and tested palms on kneecaps option. It may have looked a bit stiff and starchy but it was the best he could do. It also meant that in tense moments he could squeeze his kneecaps to ease the pressure and no one noticed.

"Why we have called you here, is that we both have been very impressed with your work in the year you have been with us. Very impressed with your work last year, and that is why we called you here," Jeremy said with his usual repeated nods. He was leaning forward, his elbows resting on his knees, his hands clasped in front of his chin. His forefingers were pointed upwards, their tips meeting just below the bit on his nose between his nasal holes. It was through this finger hole that Jeremy spoke, probably thinking it gave him a sort of authoritative, meditative look. Joe was not sure if it did, and looked more like Jeremy was talking through his arse, as usual. Joe was trying to think of the medical name for that below nose bit, besides his one of Nostril Splitter. Then he cancelled that thought and began to focus on what was being said. It sounded really good so far. Checking his sixth sense, he was confident this build up by Jeremy was not just the precursor to a 'but…'

"Let me just repeat what Jeremy has just said…" Lucinda put into the conversation. Joe hid a smile, thinking there was no need, Jeremy having done enough repetition already. "…We have been so pleased with your progress, how you work really well with everyone else in the team, your punctuality, your helpfulness with customers – Andy and Alison from ULC thinks the sun rises and sets in your arse, by the way… all of that great stuff!" She laughed loudly and waved her hand about flamboyantly. Joe was seriously wondering if she was talking about the same person, as that only partially sounded like him, but was pleased with the praise nonetheless. Andy and Alison were his favourite clients so he was glad to hear that. Then she leaned forward with a smiling sincerity. "Well, it all means that you are a perfect candidate to be one of the few selected to be positioned in the company's very impressive ASS."

Joe spluttered a little, then a lot, trying to contain a loud laugh and succeeding in doing so with a feeble little cough. His brain had just gone back to being eleven years old. Images of him going along lines of bare bums with a clipboard, assessing them and ticking off lists flashed into his mind. He gained control of himself and, truly admiring Jeremy and Lucinda's straight faces, tried to stall a little for time and replied, "Yeah, that sounds assome, I mean, awesome! Tell me a bit more about it please?" He coughed madly, wiping water from his eyes.

Lucinda coolly rolled off what was probably the word for word version on the company website. "It's the Advanced Supervisory Scheme where we take promising young professionals and provide them with expert in house training, mentoring and support; to fulfil both their own and the company's high expectations and ambitions. It has been running for five years now. It truly is an amazing scheme and you will learn so much from it. Both Jeremy and I completed it a while ago and look at both of us now. I received an award for being top of my ASS Class. My ASS really helped me, as, along with being Regional Manager, I am also Finance Director on the Board looking after all the company's assets." She let out a single guttural laugh as she slapped Jeremy's arm and repeated, "Assets!" before carrying on talking. "Jeremy only a few months ago became our Regional Sales Manager! And, as of yesterday, is our new Marketing Director on the Board as well."

Joe held back sniggers trying not to make an ass of himself. He attempted to remove the smutty child from his mind by distracting himself through focusing on and assessing their high-up company positions. However, he realised he had not known how much ASS had been involved in achieving these! This set off his internal sniggers again and inability to look at either of their straight faces. He had not known about Jeremy's very recent additional promotion, though. *What had he done to deserve that reward?* he wondered. Or perhaps who had he done would have been a better question, given his reputation.

They had told him their job titles every time he was in these sorts of,

240

thankfully not often, meetings with them, showing off in their own insecure way. It was impressive the first time he had heard it but now he was just bored with their patronising. He hoped his face did not show it. He was confident his smiling happiness at his selection hid any annoyance his face may have revealed. He was genuinely excited about their selection of him for the promotional management training, wondering why the company did not call it that instead. Then, he sniggered as he argued with himself that PMT was not any better! Lucinda carried on talking about how professional the ASS training was, industry recognised and all that. However, Joe's mind was elsewhere but not up his own one, as Lucinda showed she was as always up hers.

In Jeremy's case for sure, it was a very different ass that had helped him professionally climb. It was also where he put his own greasy pole that helped him slip up a few extra career rungs. As with all office gossip and rumours, there are always bits that you needed as much salt as an entire Lot's wife to believe. Although so very cool and with the ability to sell central heating to the Devil himself, in Jeremy's case there were just too many rumours, too many witnesses and too much circumstantial evidence for most of it not to be true. Just before Joe started working, Jeremy's old boss Rachel's unexplained pregnancy, marriage breakup and resignation was the start of it. Her replacement Malcolm, transferring suddenly to another Regional Office when he became closet-free, caused some seriously scandalous gossiping in the work's canteen. Jeremy was suspected of being, according to unknown sources, 'intimately helpful' in Malcolm's realisation as to who he really was.

Then Jimmy, Malcolm's replacement, went off on long-term sick after his marriage broke up. He was denied access to his kids, he was more off than in work, alcohol became his new partner and his life basically slid into a shithole. Jeremy and Jimmy's wife had been seen together a few times before all this kicked off and she had kicked Jimmy out. Supposedly, again sources unknown, Jimmy caught them nakedly joined at the hips. When the time came, a totally unfazed Jeremy moved smoothly into his old boss's role, stuck Jimmy's remaining stuff in a box and nonchalantly asked his secretary to find Jimmy's address (as if he did not know!) and post it to him. There were rumours now that Jeremy and Lucinda were playing away from their own matrimonial home grounds. Joe was finding that one very hard to swallow, although supposedly Anna the cleaner swore that Lucinda had no such problems at a late office meeting with Jeremy. It was a very murky world that Joe found hard to separate truth from rumour or from pure fantasy. He heard it all, not believing half of it and ignoring the other half as best he could. That was easier said than done as the whole company swam in these murky waters.

Joe, hard as he tried, could not avoid all these shenanigans, whether they were true or not. Whilst he heard what was going on he did not encourage it by passing it on. Some of it was just pure malicious lies, although he had to admit that, despite himself, some juicy bits did, regrettably, intrigue him. He was mystified as to how office gossip seemed to have as many different layers as the company's organisational charts. Somehow, the higher up the person the current scandal story was about, the quicker it seemed to disappear. That was unless the newspapers got hold of it, and then that was an entirely different league. The former Marketing Director of Joe's current company had had his face plastered all over the local papers and even a couple of national ones recently. So-called reliable but unnamed sources flailed about like a cat-o-nine-tails to whip up a financial storm and love triangle worthy of a Hollywood blockbuster. Joe had a fair suspicion about who that source probably was and was then sitting in the same room as him talking through and about ASS.

It was very different for other workers, with less impressive job titles and regardless of their ASS status. Joe saw those who were further down the company structural food chain as seeming to be easier pickings for the vitriolic office vultures. They faced smirking stares and previously unfriendly colleagues suddenly wanting to be best buddies, probing repeatedly with personal questions a Detective Inspector would be proud of. This could go on for weeks and months, continuing on even after other rumours and counter-rumours bounced around the office. There only needed the slightest whiff of smoke, real or imaginary, and an inferno could be started. Joe was always saddened by the burning potential of scalding-hot scandals. Even when they were proved to be completely non-combustible, there were still scars left. Joe wondered why it went on at all. No one ever won! Well, apart from those whose lives were so shallow that they took some sick titillation from the gossip. If even half of all the rife rumours about relationships, etc, were true, it would have amazed Joe how any work was done at all.

He had been a victim of this himself. Angela and him had, to summarise, supposedly broke company rules on foodstuffs only being allowed in the canteen and banned from the main office. According to the rumour they were both meant to have not been very stationary in their attempts at trying to hide a sausage in the large cupboard where the paper and pens were kept! Despite Joe being a little pleased that the rumour had been embellished a little to say it was a large sausage, it was an absolute and utter lie. Whilst Angela and him were friends as well as work colleagues, that was it! Both of them confronted the office chief shit stirrer. They ever-so-politely, aggressively, made sure that their threatened revelation of a few of this person's totally true personal details was broadcast hit home. Having taken away their spoon and made this nasty person frightened of other ones stirring a very different pot, the rumours stopped almost immediately.

To Joe, all of this felt like a strategic bullying, as if it was okay to carry on with the gossip for lower ranks, but stop asap when it came to those who had the power to sack you. There were always bits of banter going on, but he hated the sinister edge stuff like this had. Although Angela and him were able to stop their character assassinations going any further, others were not able to do so, lacking the power or self-esteem. He always assumed that when the management got wind of whatever rumour were circulating about them, they were able to blow it away with a few whispers in certain ears. Rarely did they tackle it head on at a team brief, but that was always an option.

Maybe Gary used his hidden Tardis for carrying out this boss counter-intelligence work, he wondered. As Joe snapped out of his daydream of whizzing about the office in an old phonebox zapping the gossipmongers, he realised Lucinda had finished with her grand hand gestures and over-the-top promotion of what a great company they worked for. He had heard the same spiel from her several times before at office briefings, which was why his mind had drifted off to how to have a 'clear desk' policy towards having to deal with fictitious, unwanted gossip crap.

"HR will e-mail you all the details. HR will be in touch to confirm dates and all that additional information," Lucinda continued, waving her arms around again and almost spilling her coffee. "So, congratulations and, if you need any help and advice at all, please do not hesitate and feel free to… get in touch with HR." She leaned forward and extended her hand. Joe slid forward on his seat, ignoring the squeaky fart noises and shook her slender hand delicately.

"Well done, Joe! Well done!" Jeremy added in and shook Joe's hand in turn vigorously. "Climbing the career ladder! Climbing up the ladder! You are on your way, Joe. You are on your way!" Jeremey said each very quickly the first time, then a lot slower and with emphasis the second. *Once, as always, would still have been enough*, Joe thought.

Joe smiled at them both and thanked them. Then he went into Jeremy mode and thanked them again. He rose slowly and fart noise-free, and started moving slowly over towards the door. Leaving them sitting on the sofa together talking intently, he walked briskly towards the door. He gave a small wave back towards them before he exited, which neither of them saw. Dandering back down the corridor, he knew he should have listened a lot more to what Lucinda had said but was excited about this big ASS of an opportunity. He had a few doubts about making an ass of himself on it, but he could not think of any big butts to stop him doing it. He decided he could but try. Besides, it meant he would have one day a week for the next six months off to train and study. That in itself was excellent.

He paused a moment at the big A3 sheet showing the company structure and who did what, blue tacked at a very slightly wonky angle to the white wall. There were layers upon layers of people, lines linking up all the regional offices and showing who was over who and in charge of what. There was large picture of the CEO at the very top, smiling like a fat cat would if it was covered in cream. Below him were decreasingly smaller portrait pictures of those in the top three rows. Joe noticed that the smiles on the pictures decreased as the list was gone down. The next two rows had just the person's names and the rows after that just names of positions, without any details at all, names or otherwise. He looked at where he was on it, just a little below the middle on an unnamed row. After this course, he could very possibly move up a notch and be right on that middle line with his name listed. He smiled contentedly at that, then wondered if he really wanted to go up another notch to have his photo up there? Before he could decide, he jumped a little as Gary appeared suddenly at his shoulder.

"So, ASS man, congratulations!" was all he said as he sipped his coffee. "Next thing you know you will be way up there." Gary laughed a little as he pointed at the Board of Directors on the wall chart. Joe followed his finger, read the directors' names again and, turning to reply, there was no one there to speak to. There was not even a puff of smoke to show that

Gary had even been. Joe swore out loud then shouted, to the empty corridor, "Would you ever lay off with all this sneaky stuff, Gary? It freaks everyone out."

Maybe he was too distracted with everything, but he could have sworn he heard Gary's voice reply, "I know! That's why I do it!" The noise of a printer in Tex's office rattling distorted what he had heard. If there had been anything there at all? It certainly added another layer of mystery to the supernatural Gary. Joe plodded on back to his desk shoulders slumping at the prospect of the layers of work that lay in wait for him there.

Liquored

It was difficult to decide if the reflection before him was pulsating in time to his booming head or the equally loud dance music that crept through all the gaps in the door of the gents. Nor could he decide if it was the wobbling image before him mirroring his unsteady stance or his eyes deceiving him. No matter how much he blinked, what he looked at still failed to stand still. He fumbled and turned on the tap, cupping his hands under the ice-cold water and began throwing as much water as he could in the general direction of his face. His vision confusingly became even more blurred. With a muttered curse, he removed his glasses, dried them roughly on the T-shirt tail that hung loosely from his jeans, and set them delicately beside the small sink. Repeating the cupping water collection, he swiftly raised his water-filled hands and rubbed them hard into his face. Deliberately, he had left his eyeballs open and relished the coldness that washed into them. After two repeat actions, he looked again, sighed and was relieved that he actually recognised the bedraggled face before him.

It was a stag do that had 'oh dear!' written all over it from the very first time it was mentioned. It had been a few years since his last one, and a lot had changed in his life. Returning from England, marrying Dee, having two young daughters – yes! A lot had gone on since he last wished a groom-to-be all the best by trying to drown him in alcohol. It was not just being out of practice, Joe just knew, from the Antler Bar starting point, to the planned Hind's Quarter pub finish, something was not right, and the buck would not end there.

The best man had decided on an animal theme and not just for the pub crawl that included the Bull and Calf, Red Lion, Fox and Hounds, and several others. There were a few puzzled questions as to how the Mermaid Inn fitted into that, being only half animal, but no real objections. There were, however, a lot more questioned protests at the T-shirts! 'The Wolf Pack on Tour' had sounded cool, they had all agreed. That changed when they were all roughly dished out the thin cotton shirts from a supermarket plastic carrier bag. The logo was okay, but the wolf's head on the front looked more like a sheep than a fearsome predator! Despite the objections they all donned their 'uniform' and, after a few pubs were ticked off the list, Joe and the others forgot about the possibility of them being a wolf in sheep's clothing.

There had been quite a few stags back home who Joe had fluidly helped to immortalise their supposed last night of freedom. There had also been, not once but twice, both very strange cases when the night had ended with more commiserating than celebrating. The partly known future grooms descending into a flood of drunken tears, half way through those evenings, had made those occasions like wet rags that any fun could not be wrung out of. Both times Joe and several others had made sure the supposed main man of the event had got home safe. Then they, to the shock of their own wives and girlfriends, arrived home before midnight, still semi-sober. Those two nights were memorably famous for their wished-for forgetfulness. Surprisingly enough, one of these marriages did not go ahead and the other did not last that much longer than the stag night had!

Thankfully those were exceptions. Very sad exceptions, but exceptions nonetheless. Other lads' nights out back home before the 'big day' had been very memorable, some of them scarily so when flashbacks of recollection came. As Joe's eyes and brain cleared slightly from the simple healing power of cold water, he was unsure if this one was going to be a class, medium or dud one. There had been elements of all three so far that afternoon and evening. There had been the usual mixture of great craic and jokes. There was the attempted banter and flirting with groups of girls to see if the future husband could receive one last kiss. The Stag had received quite a few lipstick smears on his cheeks and even one full on the lips, tongue down the throat snog which took him a while to get his breath back from. All the other lads were a bit breath taken by the forwardness of that particular girl's lack of backwardness. Then there was all the normal stuff from a group of drunken lads together – a few heated arguments, a couple of threatened fights and quite a lot of pissing and puking up in the alleys and hedges between pubs on the way. All in all, it had been okay fun-wise, verging on being a less enthusiastic all right, so far. All of them, with no drop outs, had achieved reaching the Bear Pit Club, their final animal Stag destination. They were all still surprisingly sober enough for the bouncers to let them in without any interrogations, although two large grizzled ones did growl menacingly at them with polar stares.

Joe stared at the black, strapped watch with the chipped glass on his wrist. After a few attempts he managed to figure out the hands told him it was almost two a.m. He groaned so loudly the fella at the sink beside him jumped a little. Joe just shook his head in a dismissive sort of way to make sure the big lad did not take it as some sort of threat, or think Joe was a bit mad. He probably did think the latter, but Joe was not bothered at all by that prospect of revealed truth. The big lad silently left with a blast of music coming through the temporarily open door. Joe was, however, more concerned with the regret at having decided to only take a half day off from work that Friday afternoon. He felt so, so tired now. It had been an even more frantic Friday than normal and, as usually happens, when you try to rush to complete all your tasks quicker, somehow the slow-motion button seems to be pressed instead. He had not slept well that night before either, partially excited about the prospect of a long-awaited night out, partially pissed off at the amount of work he had waiting for him that morning. Eventually he had left work an hour later than planned, with a couple of annoyed work colleagues and a long list on Monday's 'to do.' He had even asterisked a few, several with double asterisks, before he had escaped.

Apologising for being late, despite having come straight from work, he had arrived at the Antler Bar to a welcome pint already sitting at his place at the long, crowded, cluttered and very noisy table. Two waiters busily took the food orders over the hubbub of conversation and Joe piped up with his traditional steak and chips. That meal had seemed a lifetime and eleven pubs ago. The hot and cold buffet that the best man had very inaccurately pre-ordered timewise at the ninth pub had been sitting out for two hours before the gang of them eventually arrived. The now more-simplified cold buffet was an assortment of soggy sandwiches, cold cocktail sausages (that received some crude comments), greasy chicken legs and even greasier chips. Still, it was wolfed down by the pack and every single plate was cleared, even the pretend-posh parsley sprigs. The mere thought of that cold buffet now sent a chill through Joe's stomach that threatened to heat things up down there. Up was not a good word to be thinking about as he swallowed hard, ducked his head down and swigged several gulps of water from the tap.

A brief soundwave of house music vibrated off the tiled walls and floors as the gents' door flung open, then swung smoothly closed again. In walked, or rather forty-five degree swayed, the centre of attention, the soon-to-be-hitched man of the hour, or rather the past afternoon, evening and night. Joe smiled and loudly shouted his name. There was no response as he totally ignored Joe, fixated on something far more important. He flung open a cubicle door. Even in his overly drunken state that was one cubicle he did not want to go in, so he lunged into the next door one. Retching and that uniquely indescribable noise of vomit meeting porcelain and water was all Joe heard. Joe shook his head in a 'better out than in', caring way.

To the dulcet tones of unrecognisable murmuring music and the pity-inducing sound of dry retching, Joe thought about why he was here. This was not in an evolutionist-versus-creationist sort of way. He had already done that many times before in his daydreaming overthinking and had come to the conclusion that it was very possibly both. This time he was wondering why he had agreed to be part of this lads' night out? Why was he here at this particular club with this group of, even after a lot of beer, still mostly only partially known people. The now groaning and griping groom-to-be and one of the other 'wolves' were the only two people Joe knew really well. He had not seen or been in touch with either of them in months, or was it years? He had calculated, early on that evening, it was in fact nearly two years since he had seen either of them. They had chatted on the phone briefly, Joe excitedly agreeing to come along to his stag and saying all the right things about "It will be great to catch-up over a few beers…" Joe realised that when he had finished that phone call his heart was not really in wanting to come on a stag with a bunch of people he mostly did not know. He had rattled off a whole list of names to Joe over the phone, only a couple of whom Joe vaguely recognised after a bit of coaching with, 'you know Jake from your neck of the woods… got his legs waxed for a dare…"

Now Joe thought about it, Jake, who he found out had been two years below him at school, had been a bit of a turning point in the evening. There was not much to Jake, hence his school nickname of The Rake. He had obviously not beefed up much in the passing years. Jake had managed to pass out at pub number seven. Or was it eight? Anyway, Jake's head had been lying sideways on the sticky table, peanuts in his hair from the two lardy lads opposite trying to land a few unsuccessfully in his gaping mouth. The Best Man had jumped up and announced that everyone was to drink up, as he named the next pub on his list. He had then reached over and swilled the last of Jake's pint down his gullet with a smart-arse 'he obviously doesn't want this!' comment. After a few guttural laughs, they had all proceeded to leave. Joe had been busy talking away to one of the others he could not seem to remember the name of, despite repeating it to himself every time he heard it. Perhaps it was because he was not a memorable person and it was certainly not a memorable chat. It was more him talking at Joe than an actual two-way communication. He spouted off about how well he was doing as an investment banker. Then he spouted off some more about how well he was doing as an investment banker. Then a bit more, until Joe just went into nod mode, not investing anything into the conversation and spelling this particular banker with a 'w' instead.

They had been a few hundred yards up the street when Joe realised that Jake was not with them. He looked around the loud, laughing group. Joe whistled loudly to mostly successfully draw all of their attention and asked, "Where's Jake? Is he still back at the pub?"

There were a few replies of 'yeah, I think so!' and a few others saying 'he will be grand' and 'he'll catch up! Or go home! Whatever!' Then they all just carried on meandering up the street. The Best Man muttered jokingly about needing to keep to a tight schedule, as he strode off up the pavement with the others following. Joe felt a surge of alcohol-induced anger. He quelled it, partly, using his stomping off back to the pub to burn some of it off. Joe was not into all that US Marine movie hero drivel about 'no man left behind' testosterone crap. It was a lot simpler than that. It had been simply the right thing to do. He would not appreciate it at all if his so-called mates had abandoned him after a few too many beers.

When he had reached the pub, Jake still had been exactly where he had been. Joe had raised him up from his seat, slung Jake's arm around his shoulder and gave the barman a smile and a nod as they headed towards the door. "Thanks for helping me clear the table," the barman joked, wiping down the black wooden bar with a grimy cloth, as Joe levelled with him on the way out. The barflies on stools had buzzed with laughter together with the barman, Joe smirking as he passed. It was funny after all. Fresh air was like a bucket of cold water to Jake, who had come around blearily the instant they walked out the door. Dazed and confused he eventually realised what had happened, Joe filling in a few of the gaps. He thanked Joe a lot, promising to buy him a drink in the next pub. He never did, but Joe did not mind at all.

That was some time ago. Joe thought a bit more about it, as he heard the groom-to-be starting to swear loudly about being spaced out, having finished in his vomit comet cubicle. When almost leaving Jake behind was one of the 'highlights' of the evening so far, it did not say much. Even watching as that unknown girl had played tonsil tennis with the stag, had been funny at first with all the group cheering. Whilst the rest had carried on laughing and egging on, however, Joe had paused a moment and felt really uncomfortable watching. The stag was too drunk to realise what was happening but Joe found himself worrying about the girl that was doing the snogging. Was this just a bit of fun to her? A bit of a joke? Or was it more insecure than that?

As he still gazed into the mirror, hearing the toilet flush on the third attempt, he thought maybe that was it. Maybe the reason was not that he did not know most of the group, but simply that he had not really succeeded in getting to know them any better as the night went on. But there was more to it than that failure. Instead, was it because of where Joe was at in his life? Now he was a husband, a dad of two beautiful little daughters, half an orphan since his da passed away, as well as a brother, an uncle and still a mate to his own irregularly seen wolf pack. It was not just becoming older, certainly not wiser, but perhaps it was being responsible. Joe sniggered at the very thought of that, using him and the word responsible in the same sentence! Especially in his current drunken state! But that was probably what it was. He was a grown man who had jumped at the opportunity to behave like he was in his teens and twenties again. His jump had landed him somewhere he did not want to be. It had deposited him here with a bunch of very drunken mostly strangers from a banking world he knew little about. He had, he realised, wanted to jump back in time to those times when he had no responsibilities but that was impossible.

He sighed loudly and pulled out his wallet, realising he had probably spent a week's worth of groceries on this one night! Responsibilities sucked, he decided, or maybe not? Maybe it was the worry and guilt of these that sucked, as it was actually good to have things to be responsible for. It gave him a purpose, a reason to live and work hard, as well as have fun. This night should have been a lot of drunken fun. The drunken bit had happened for sure. The fun part had happened in dribs and drabs during the evening, and now it felt it was dribbling drab.

The cubicle door swung open and with several sharp coughs that threatened to have lumps, the stag sauntered over and threw his arm sloppily around Joe. "Great to have you here, Joe! Really great!" he slurred. "I am so sorry we lost touch there for a while. You are the best! We need to keep in touch more. Get out for a few beers now and again. Great night. Did I get a snog…?" He rambled on and Joe just nodded and smiled, nodded and smiled in response. There was a saying that a drunk person always tells the truth, based supposedly on the fact that the drink robs him or her of the wit to lie. In Joe's experience that possibly could be true. However, he thought there was usually too much pure crap to hoke through to try to find anything true amongst the usual slurred, emotional drivel. He knew too well that he too was so guilty of blabbing out incomprehensible rubbish with a few beers in him. That was certainly the truth of it.

The stag stopped talking, burped loudly and raced back to the cubicle, lips tightly sealed. He returned straightaway, nothing left to give, with a wide wobble to the left before he reached the still-standing, where-he-had-been Joe. He started gushing words again that made no sense but Joe could not really be arsed trying to figure them out. Joe had successfully refused and avoided spirits that he knew, from experience, would have come back to haunt him the following day. Strangely, for the amount of beer he had had, Joe felt weirdly clear-headed. His headache had dulled from hammering blows to a slight regular tap of annoyance. His stomach had settled for the time being, but he was nervous of for how long. He had also made a decision that made things clearer in his head. He was going home.

Grabbing the stag by the shoulders to steady him, to look him in the rolling eyes, Joe slightly wobbled himself as he told him that he was indeed going home. He thanked him for inviting him along but said he had to go. Job fobbed off the few half-hearted protests about staying, the night being young and all that. Suddenly the stag stopped talking, his face went into deer caught in headlights mode and he raced back into the cubicle with an urgent delivery to be made this time. Joe said, "Oh dear!" out loud, then took the opportunity to leave.

He went back to their table where Jake had passed out, again. Joe picked him up, slung his arm over his shoulder, again, and said his goodbyes to the few that sat and were not up trying to dance on the packed, sweaty-bodied floor. The music was too loud for them to really hear, so they just nodded as Joe moved up the drink sticky steps dragging Jake along too. Plonking Jake in an empty taxi, giving the grumpy driver the address from Jake's licence and a tenner from his own wallet, Joe looked around for a cab of his own. It started to rain as he waited for another taxi to show up, leaning against the wall of the club. It actually felt really good on his face. It felt like he was being washed. *Who needed sunshine when rain was equally as good?* he asked himself.

He had been well liquored up since lunchtime that day, but maybe his days of firing as much alcohol into him as possible were gone. Maybe he had outgrown that? It was the thought of it that appealed more than the reality, possibly. Perhaps that whole part of his life was winding down now, although there was still a big part of him wanted to keep it up. "Responsibilities?" he tutted to himself. "Responsibilities?" he tutted again as a taxi pulled up. He reached for his wallet and realised that he had given his last tenner to Jake's taximan. He swore loudly and waved the taxi on. He had left his bank cards at home, saying he did not want to lose them. In reality, it was more to do with the fact he did not want to spend any more money that what he had taken in cash. He had taken what he thought was loads more than enough and had hoped not to spend it all. This hope had sunk in the bottom of too many pint glasses. Swaying slightly, he tried to gather his bearings for the long, long walk home. "That was not very responsible, was it?" he swore as he trudged feeling as defeatedly licked as he was liquored but surprisingly happy at the same time.

Loophole

There was stuff to do. But then there was always stuff to do. Joe could not decide what should be first on his list. He muttered, "Stuff this," and decided to sit down with a cup of tea and have a think. Probably deliberately, the what he described as not really that urgent to do stuff did not come into his thoughts at all. Instead, obscurely, his mind turned to about what he wanted to do as a career. He had one, or possibly more than that, started or at least half started, but was unable to calculate where he was going with whatever number he had. This distracted him away from the other stuff and he drifted off, as he often did, into his ever-churning mind that never seemed to produce any cream or butter his life up in any way. Maybe he was milking too much sourness from that as he reassured himself about doing okay so far. Then he could be doing better. Then, like everyone else, he could always be doing better, so he left it at that and went back to his previous careering thoughts.

Joe truly admired those people from an early age, even almost as soon as they could walk and talk, who knew what they wanted to do 'when they grew up.' These included the whole selection – everything from firefighter, nurse, vet and all the other feasibly possible ones; to the astronaut and superhero ones that might take a bit more effort and a lot of luck, along with genetic modifications. Although many changed such wish lists, most still had a definite plan, a clear ambition and a fixed direction of travel. Joe's plan was more to go with the flow, his ambition remaining very muddied, and he was, in reality, continually standing at the side of the road thumbing a lift to see where he went. He was well grown up now, at least physically, and, although working, Joe still had not a baldy notion about where he wanted to head towards in the next five days let alone five years.

There seemed to be this obsession with job interviewers of five years, not one or ten but five. Joe could never figure this out, wondering if it was anything to do with Communist Russia and Chinas' obsession with five-year plans for absolutely everything? One interview he remembered vividly because that was what he imagined being interrogated by the communist secret police would be like? Then, as a shiver ran down his spine at the memory of it, he had wondered if there were batons and electric shock treatment pads hidden in the desk the dour faced panel sat intimidatingly behind. He remembered looking down at his hands afterwards, checking they had not removed any fingernails when he had eventually left that inner probing torture chamber. Surprisingly enough he did not get that job and was very relieved that it was some other poor sod working in that salt mine gulag now.

Despite his mocking, he did sometimes think, where did he see himself in five years? Five years older was all he could really come up with. However, he had always managed to come up with some reasonably truthful, but fundamentally vague, answer to such an obscure interview question when sweatily sitting in his only suit. The one he used purely for attending interviews, which sometimes felt like the joy of weddings and dread of funerals he also wore this jacket and trousers set for. He had been able, so far, to spew enough to fob off the stern faces of the panels before him up until now. Whilst he may not have achieved every job he was interviewed for, he had managed to pass enough interrogations to always have full time work.

No doubt it would become harder to answer this in reality meaningless question when he tried for better paid jobs. That was something he would need to prepare for if he wanted to fly high he knew, but he decided he would just wing it until that time came. It had worked out so far for him and would all turn out okay, he tried to convince himself without any fresh ideas taking off. He congratulated himself that his career might not be much at the moment, but at least being a career criminal had not been one of his achievements. He wondered if any kids had that as their future work wish. Maybe the ones currently organising the school dinner money extortion and cigarette smuggling rackets could well do. There were a couple of ones from his old school had used such 'work experience', rather than qualifications, to follow on in their profitable but definitely illegally dodgy family businesses.

He had loved the building sites, but the work dried up in the winter and he used the excuse he was too old at thirty-four to start leaning a trade. So far, his first proper jobs had been in offices, which he disliked, feeling almost claustrophobic in such hot, stale atmospheres with the constant slight smell of coffee, BO and cheap perfume. Whilst his potential future career list remained empty for the time being, he was increasingly thinking about it. However, there were several on that options sheet that he had most definitely blotted out with thick crosses. Being a doctor or nurse was on this x-ed list. Whilst truly admiring their professions, he had no inclination or desire to be sticking needles in people, or slicing them open, or just listening to whinging, healthy, hypochondriacs that he would want to write a prescription for a 'good kick up the arse and wise up' for. The whole medical sector was out as a job option as far as he was concerned, lacking the skills and patience for such complicated, dedicated work. However, above this, at the very top of his personal blacklist was a career Joe had absolutely no interest in and a dubious respect for at best, uninfluenced by Judge Dredd's insistence on upholding it – the law.

Joe knew some seriously dodgy characters, who treated the law like stretchy rubber, some amazingly managing to avoid long stretches inside. Other bent so-called businessmen, not being given any flexibility at their trials, were bounced off to prison. He also knew people who had shattered these rules entirely. Some of these individuals seemed to almost permanently remain free from any prospect of being caught, as if the system was goading them to try harder. Some had come so close that the legal razor shaved their jawline before becoming lost in the rest of the legislative foam, allowing them to escape the lawyer wolves by the hair of their chinny chin chins.

Then there were the others who feigned that they were pleased with the prospect of 'working abroad' or 'going away for a wee while.' In reality, the only joy they had was at Her Majesty's pleasure. Joe always thought that a very strange phrase. He thought it very unlikely that Elizabeth the Second actually even knew what it was like to turn the lock on a cellblock to confine a person there for twenty-three hours a day, let alone take pleasure in it. He would snigger when he thought of this elderly, regal lady doing a royal walkabout along an echoey prison corridor, jangling her keys and crown jewels, demanding lights out and maybe wistfully wishing you could still behead traitors. From the stories he had heard there was a lot more pain than pleasure in prison and they were not treated like the royalty some misguided commentators ranted about.

Joe did firmly believe in the old adage 'don't do the crime if you can't do the time'. Crime had to be punished. There had to be a deterrent to stop society falling apart any more than it already was. Joe was certain of that.

Then, he also thought it would be better to stop the causes of crime, such as poverty. Would this not be better than punishing some poor misguided teenager, consigning them to hokey cokey prison experiences that would shake them all about for the rest of their lives? Joe knew there were truly evil people, some he even agreed with about prison being too good for them. These, however, were the exception and he knew too many his age and a lot younger who did a stupid thing, became caught up in something they should not have, or were just simply in the wrong place at the wrong time. Drink and drugs usually seemed to always be involved. Either way, Joe genuinely felt that the criminals were victims of circumstance too. That was easy for him to say when he did not have to look at someone who had raped his daughter across a courtroom, or battled with insurance companies to try to receive compensation for the property or business damage done, or left in a wheelchair from thugs deciding to kick the crap out of some innocent passer-by. He deeply hoped he would never be in any of those scenarios, but the future could throw some very nasty surprises. And that was all the 'normal' crimes, without the bombings and shooting and extortions rackets and beatings and exiling and… and… and… the other lawlessness of the Troubles.

The criminals and victims were not the reasons why Joe certainly did not want to be a legal professional. Both certainly needed help, many a hell of a lot. It was the legal system itself that was the deterring factor. It was not that he had run-ins with the legal profession. A couple of verbal warnings from peelers and a parking and speeding ticket or two was as far as his criminal career had ever progressed to date. He would never be on some wanted poster and, if he was, his bounty would bound to never have been enough to take a hunter to paradise.

Basically, it all boiled down to guilt and money. These were the reasons why lawyers were not on his Christmas card list. They always talked about applying the letter of the law and that really irked him. No one every explained what that letter was but he had a fair idea it was 'f'. It was a farce. An 'f'ing arse, more like it, Joe thought. It was nothing to do with justice and certainly fairness seemed to have been taken to the fair. Trials were based on how wealthy the client was, not whether they were guilty or innocent. Justice was able to be bought just as easily as a car from a little bit fly second-hand dealer. No matter how much evidence the police had gathered; how duck's arse water tight witness statements were; even if there were videos of him or her doing it – they could still get off either scot-free, a fine or a token prison sentence that would be appealed and rescinded. There would always be some section of the law, regardless of how obscure or antiquated, that would be applied for exoneration. If you could pay enough, the lawyers would look hard enough. If not, the poor sod paid the price.

The legal system scared Joe, he truthfully had to admit, and never wanted to be embroiled in it. It took years for cases to come to trail. Joe was always amazed at the reporting of vividly clear witness statements about events surrounding the crime scene. The actual crime could have happened two, three, five, ten or even more years ago and yet they were still able to recall it exactly. He could hardly remember what he had for his tea the night before but he always wondered about the Chinese whispers effect in these hyped up, chop suey-ed, media sensationalised cases. How much was the witness's words and how much the lawyer's? How much did they really remember? Maybe he would be a good cross examiner after all. Or maybe he would just remain being cross when he examined the whole system.

He absolutely hated the slander allegation cases. The ones when some minor or even major celebrity took a newspaper to court for saying some facetious remark about their lifestyle. The weeks of time and oodles of money, and above all expensive legal expertise, wasted on such absolutely pointless attention seeking by both parties seriously annoyed Joe. All for a few grand to be passed over and an apology printed, with the newspaper concerned seeing its readership figures soar. As for the celebrity? They, whether losing or winning, had a huge ego boost as they were invited to appear on chat shows and celebrity talentless shows. Yet a young lad caught with a bag he was minding for a mate and not asked questions about is in and out of court in a couple of hours and behind bars that evening. He does not even have one line in a local or national newspaper, just a mention or two in the street gossip. As for his appeal and finding a way out for him, he cannot afford to even bother trying, so just has to suck it up.

Crime seemed to pay as well, and continue to do so. Pay very, very well, especially if you are a huge multi-national company who thinks tax laws are non-compulsory and apply to someone else. Joe may have had a few cash in hand jobs that the tax man did not know about, but these never exceeded Joe's tax threshold, or so he told himself. Small businesses received their letters from Her Majesty's Tax Department, promising that if they did not pay the stated amount, they would have a chance of possibly personally seeing the Queen swinging her keys and turning the key on their cell door. That was their only choice, pay or prison. The international big boys just dump their millions of profit in off-shore accounts, throw some lawyers a bit of money to keep the Tax Department off their back and that is it. Loopholes in the legal system means that is perfectly just. Legally it may apparently be, but fraud and stealing are what it is in reality, without even considering the moral side of it. "Sure, if you can pay to get away with it, why not?" Joe often berated sarcastically.

Joe did not like being pigeon holed. Maybe that was why he had no career path, yet. He would know when the time was right for him to start making those decisions but that time was not now. He would continue weaving his way through the employment fabric until he found the pattern he wanted. Until then, he would keep going searching out the loopholes, just like the lawyers do, to avoid making that commitment just yet. He would try out a few more things yet as he had not found a hot job, despite jumping through the fiery hoops his bosses demanded and hoping not to get burned. He would keep himself legal but would certainly not be soaring with those eagles only interested in the high fliers and pooping on the little guys below.

Laugh

Joe knew he had a good sense of humour a lot of the time, but not in a facetious, full-of-himself way. It was maybe more in a crude faeces sort of way? Maybe good was a bit of an exaggeration, an acquired taste being more apt. Whatever it was, he did have the ability to make people laugh, even if it was out of sympathy. It was definitely not in a stand-up comedian way either; more of a sit down, talking and sharing funny crap over a pint or a cuppa. It was mostly based on having a good memory for other people's funny stories and jokes. He was able to throw these, with good timing most of the time, without bothering to check copyrights or patents into conversations. He could tell a good story himself, seeing the funny side of the events of the life he had led so far. Even in his darkest times, black humour was able to shine a light when he looked back.

He knew there were many types of humour. He was not a big fan of high-level intellectual, sometimes called 'alternative' humour. A few times he had quietly sat and analysed what one of these reported to be 'alternative comedians' had said, only to find it about as funny as a magnolia painted wall. Others had almost laughed their heads off at the times, yet Joe could tell from their nervous eyes darting about they probably did not get the joke either. He thought it funny how people laughed along in such circumstances, thinking if they did not, others would somehow think they were stupid or uncultured. Joe had no such fears. If he did not find something worth laughing at, he simply did not. Some people thought that was a funny sort of attitude to have but 'so what!' was Joe's perspective. If people did not laugh at his jokes, he understood why. This was no different. Underneath he did not like it when someone did not laugh, saying they did not get it and needed him to explain what his joke was. Having to explain a joke took a huge percentage of the laugh ability out of it; even though he did the same thing when he was left confused and alone not laughing.

Joe had an affinity for the complete opposite end of the comic spectrum and revelled in toilet humour. Rarely was a comic autopsy needed to delve into the bowels of that type of joke to extract a laugh from it. Everyone he knew or had met, including himself, always laughed at that type of crude craic. Even high-brow intellectuals smirked at a really good joke about toilets and the activities that take place there. After all, eat, shit and die are core fundamentals of life, with a bit of procreating, thinking about procreating, work, sleep and other things making up the rest of a person's day. Regardless of what else goes on, piss and crap always make up some part of everyone's routine was Joe's view. Medicines or visits to the doctors are necessary if they do not, or when a person spends too much time squatting on porcelain without any results. Likewise, medical assistance is needed if there is too much of either. So why not take the piss out of this and see the funny side was Joe's constitutional position.

Everyone has toilet stories to tell, Joe maybe more than most. Elderly people especially in Joe's experience could provide too much extensive details about bowel movements, or lack of them. Sometimes these can be funny, but sometimes a bit too graphic, with even the threatened remote possibility of being shown the act either taking or not taking place! Joe may joke about what toilets receive, but one elderly lady actually scared him as he genuinely thought she was going to bring along a souvenir sample to show him on her way to the doctors. Joe nearly had a bowel movement of his own when she had suggested it. Thankfully she forgot. He knew some people thought it just crude, many having told him so, but then we are all as uniquely different as our own toilet habits. It would be a very boring world if we were all clones, only finding the same things funny. Joe often laughed at this thought.

Even worse was if a person had no sense of humour at all. Joe had met a few people that appeared to have had their ability to laugh surgically removed at birth. Those were conversations he remembered for all the wrong reasons. A couple of his teachers and one of his bosses fell into that category, along with a seriously dour couple he had met in the pub. They were only the same age as him, his girlfriend's cousins, but wow was that a night to forget! It was not just an evening as dull as dishwater, it was more akin to wanting to voluntarily drown yourself in it, just to add even a spark of excitement before you pruned up and dried. He prided himself on actually making both of them smile, just once the entire week and a half that those two hours felt like. And, surprisingly enough, it was a toilet joke that cracked their po faces.

Everyone may have a different sense of humour, but at least you hope they have one. When they do not? It not only sucks the enjoyment of life out of them but has the same effect on everyone they meet. It ends up such afflicted people are avoided by others, adding more finger hitting to their cliff hanging and fear of the downward journey towards the awaiting chasm. Even worse, they can ironically become the subject of jokes because of their often-self-inflicted misery. Joe fully appreciated everyone has off days, sometimes off weeks, months and even lives, full of worry and trauma that stain their entire personality. He certainly was guilty as charged, knowing he had at least courted with those things that hoover up happiness, leaving a vacuum that is filled with such woes. Life's downs are brought up by laughter was one of Joe's quirky mottos that worked for him.

Laughter is known to be a medicine. It is part of a person's happiness, self-confidence and well-being. Professional healthcare workers categorically state it reduces stress and all the ills that causes. It relaxes and distracts, taking both the teller and listener temporarily to a good place. More laughter and fun keep them there, but it has to be genuine. False laughter is not only annoying but as empty and unfulfilling as an empty joy cup that has no chance of overflowing.

Humour comes in many forms with the whiteness of the light laughter brings coming through in dark humour too. When the world generally or close to home is literally falling or being blown apart, humour is a way of coping. Northern Irish people often exhibit a humour of unlit coalmine proportions, joking about atrocities and brutality with no trouble at all. Violence, combined with a warped political, social and economic make-up of quantum physics confusing proportions, leaves humour as the only coping mechanism. If you cannot understand it, laughing at it seems to be the rationale. Macabre and potentially depressing as this sounds, it works.

The Northern Irish cities especially, where most of the physical and mental damage of The Troubles has been on stage, have created a people who have been able to stand up to the madness by laughing at it. Bravery is shown by phrases such as laughing in the face of adversity and even death. It shows defiance, strength of character and above all a will to survive. Irish and Scots Irish are renowned for their passion and fighting spirit. Laughter is a big part of these characteristics, being able to laugh at themselves as well as others, to overcome the bitterness and hatred that can chew a person up. With the amount of both of these still remaining in his still very troubled homeland, Joe and many others wanted much more laughter. Laughter may not cure every ill, but it makes us all feel so much better he believed. If there was more laughter then there would be less trouble was his simple wish.

Lucky

"OOOOHHHHH! FFFFUUU…!" Joe quietly yelled out loud but did not need to reach the last two letters. Both his feet were glued to the brake and clutch pedals as he had spent the past few seconds trying to shove them Fred Flintstone-like, right through the floor of their blue hatchback. Despite the doom that had overtaken his brain, this had worked, and he was now toddling along at ten miles per hour, behind a white van, panting extremely heavily. His million mile an hour heart seemed to have opened a door in his chest and stepped out, wanting to take its fight outside. It was almost as if it was looking upwards towards his brain, wagging its finger and shouting, "Look what you have done to me, you stupid bollocks! You nearly gave me an attack!" His brain did not step outside or respond. It remained hiding in its skull bone fortress, probably just too frazzled from ricocheting off its walls in those seconds of blind panic. His mind was numb, possibly from pure relief, or the remains of the pure fear that had overwhelmed him in those seconds, or a cocktail of both. Or maybe from pathetically trying to remember everything that had happened in that flash of the last minute or so.

Joe looked silently across at a speechless Dee. Her face was shit-scared white, a colour he never, ever saw listed on a paint chart! His face was probably the exact same colour. He hated seeing couples with colour coordination, but this time he would accept their matching as an exception. He could not change it anyway, even if he had wanted to. She was panting and breathing heavily, her chest ebbing and flowing like waves in a storm wind. Her right hand was clenching the base of her seven-month expanded stomach. Her left hand was at her shoulder, determinedly gripping her seatbelt as if she was trying to strangle it before it did her. He was gratefully relieved she was okay apart from scared witless, as he was. There were no physical injuries nor had the shock caused waters to be broken. He reached down between his own legs, to check that his own waters were still stored where they should be, and was relieved at the comforting dry feeling of the upholstery. Then Dee gently reached her right hand over and placed it on

Joe's thigh. With an enormous sigh, she simply said, "That was lucky!"

Joe's ego felt for a moment like it had been hit a slap. Surely it was not 'lucky', but his skill as a driver that had prevented them from brutally inserting their blue car into the rear of the white van like some automobile rapist. He had been well within the fifty-mph speed limit. Well, forty-nine or so is still below it, he argued with himself. Regardless of how close to it he was, not speeding was something he was even more strict about, protecting both a pregnant wife in the car beside him and his future da experience. It had not been his fault at all, either. The white van must have either not seen them or not bothered to look, as it shot out from the layby onto the, thankfully not very busy, carriageway. The few feet short of its bumper that he had managed to stop at, with hot brakes and banshee-like screaming tyres, felt like millimetres.

Immediately the front threat was controlled, he had in fearful dread looked into his rear-view mirror. He half expected the front of some HGV to be hurtling towards them to be seen, captured like a scene from an action movie. There were only two cars far back and Joe expressed his relief and gratitude with a semi-silent 'thank 'f' for that!' He had then allowed himself that moment to breathe and try to calm. Then he thought! What if there had been a lorry right behind them? What if he had been going a few miles faster? What if the van had pulled out a few seconds later? What if…? What if…? Maybe they were lucky after all and it was nothing at all to do with any of his skills, no matter how good or limited they were.

Joe believed in many things and saw absolutely no contradiction when some of these beliefs were totally contrasting entities. Whilst he fully justified that there was a divine power over everything, he also was sure that there was a separate spirit realm full of fairies and ghosts and their buddies, good and bad. He believed these fantastical beings and spirits were around and within us every day. They guided and shaped us as individuals, he felt, just as much as divine forces. Joe had always felt he could sense the presence of these. His sixth sense was erratic, to say the least, but when he did feel something through ESP, Boy, did he feel it!

Although these were poles apart, Joe did not see any conflict of interest in there being a supreme being and an Elysium fairyland or ghost kingdom co-existing together. Maybe the spirit world had been created, in the same way it used evolution to make the world, by the divine power? Perhaps the fairies and ghosts answered to it as well? No one knew, and probably never would, was Joe's conclusion, so carried on contentedly in his own views of the world, waiting for someone to prove him wrong.

Then, to add a third dimension to this already unproven and potentially conflicting partnership, Joe threw in his firm belief in luck. This made it an even more complicated ménage a trois of beliefs. One thing for sure, though, this complexity did mean that Joe, despite finding baseball even more boring than cricket, something he had thought impossible, certainly covered all his bases.

There were times Joe felt he was the luckiest man alive. Finding and marrying Dee, with their first baby now on the way, gave such feelings of being truly blessed. However, he knew this went far beyond luck. Luck might have kick-started such an amazing situation, but that was all it had contributed. Meeting Dee on the train had been luck. Some of Joe's cells swimming like crazy and joining some of Dee's was not only luck, it was a pure miracle. It was love and work and respect and all sorts of other things that kept what luck started going. In this way, Joe felt it was true that you could create your own luck. However, you still needed the real thing for genuine pure luck to start things off. Whether that was right or wrong did not matter. Likewise, what other people thought of his opinions or views was also irrelevant. It had worked for him so far, mostly, and he hoped he was lucky enough for it to continue that way.

He, with Dee, had, eventually, been lucky in love. Before Dee, he had to admit he had not been. That whole love minefield was something he wished to mostly forget, although he had some deeply cherished memories, especially those times when he had got lucky! He was lucky to have had near misses in love which had left him rattled, but often feeling fortunate. Even when there had been direct hits, he had been told he was lucky, especially in his life outside his love life. He vividly remembered the A&E doctor casually sticking a syringe repeatedly and agonisingly through a gaping gash in Joe's thigh, to freeze it before starting sewing. He had reassured Joe how lucky he had been! Whilst Joe winced and eye-watered through this endless procedure, the doctor had explained how major arteries and veins had been missed, nerve damage should be minimal and the scar would not be too noticeable. Joe had, rather angrily, thought about answering, but had not, letting the medic piece him back together. *Surely, lucky would have been that his leg would not have been sliced open and that he would have not needed the hospital at all!* he had thought.

That sort of statement by Joe opened up a whole other array of tangents for his mind to explore. He could start going completely off the rails into this convoluted philosophical world. That was where deep-thinking people like Niall, who he had met once at university, went into, voluntarily, no less. Joe was glad he had managed to avoid him afterwards, protecting and preserving his own brain from that combination of heavy, meaningful insights and possibly just pure shite that he saw philosophy composed of! Joe remembered thinking Niall was so far into this other world that he had lost contact with and could not handle the real one! Joe kept his luck simple, without any searching for hidden depths or meanings. Bad things happen, bad luck! Good things happen, good luck! However, there was something he did occasionally to challenge this simplicity. He rode his luck.

His and Dee's recent near intimate metallic experience with a white van was one of those out-of-the-blue scenarios that only luck knew the outcome of. However, when Joe consciously did decide to ride his luck, it was just like he was at a rodeo. He would attempt the impossible and try to control luck like it was a traumatised tonne of bucking beef between his legs. It was highly risky, with him always being thrown off eventually, but having had a hell of a ride until that happened. Sometime he was thrown off before he had really started, sometime landing unscathed on his feet, sometimes flat of his back with something broken, or even sometimes having the luck bull jump up and down on him a few times when he was grounded. This was why he did not take the chance very often. Now, as a new fatherhood loomed, he did not do or risk it at all! However, previously he had restricted the thrill of this in his single days to trying his luck with girls. He had survived all of those encounters, the majority of the time landing back on his feet. However, there were times his heart had been scarred and broken, and even that one terrifying time when, if she had caught him, he was convinced she would have stomped on his head! She had believed in a false rumour that had left her snorting and flaring her nostrils as she had embarrassingly chased him down the street. Even then he had felt lucky that she had not caught him.

Then there was the bad luck Joe had experienced in his life. He confessed that, although he had worked hard and gained rewards for some things, he had made an absolute hash of other things he could not control. These were the times when the good luck tap was suddenly turned off and all that spluttered out was brown and smelly. At times like these, no matter what Joe attempted, he could never reverse this, or change the way things were going. Luck had decided he was on a slippery slope and he had to just ride that out, hoping he would not hit the bottom too hard. These times always seemed to last so much longer compared to when he only briefly sailed along on lucky cloud number nine.

He turned to Dee to respond, and all he could say was, "Yeah!" He thought he should really blare his horn but the moment of rage and panic to do this had passed. Besides the horn on their car sounded like Noddy was coming along with a 'peep peep'. So, he let the van motor on ahead and left it at that, chalking up yet another one he owed good luck. They were still too shocked to talk, but after a time their breathing steadied, and they did. Joe reached over and placed his hand gently on her enlarged stomach, his attempt to apologise and reassure the growing baby contained within.

"Did you know that in Liberia, it is believed that if a stranger touches a pregnant woman's stomach it brings bad luck? Close family are allowed to, but if a stranger does it that could cause evil spirits to take the baby away. I hate it when people you don't know, or even ones you don't know that well, feel this urge to touch bump. They would never do that if I wasn't pregnant!" Dee said with a serious hint of pissed-off-ness.

"Oh! Right!" was all Joe replied. He had never found a four-leaf clover, thought horseshoes looked better on the hoof of a horse and, although he knew the rhyme, certainly did not believe the number of magpies he saw was significant. That was probably yet another of his contradictions; he believed in spirits, fairies, etc but did not class himself as superstitious. Some people looked for physical signs for good or bad luck. Joe just relied on his feeling, not knowing if this was a reliable gauge for deciding or not. "But then do some cultures not think that touching a pregnant woman's stomach brings the baby luck and also brings luck to them as well?"

"Nah! Had not heard of that one!" Dee replied as she held his hand in hers near her belly button. "But I am glad we do not have the nursery organised, or buggies bought, or anything like that. I do believe in that stuff about not tempting fate. Especially for our first little baby." She smiled sweetly.

"Does that mean you want more?" Joe smirked and she slapped the hand she held.

"Let's see how this goes, Mr Impatient." she smiled back.

"I am so lucky to have you." Joe said softly.

"What was that? Say that again!" Dee smiled as she spoke.

"I am so lucky to have you!" Joe replied a little louder.

"Sorry, still did not catch that. Say again!" she mocked him.

"I am so lucky to have you!" Joe half-shouted over to her, smiling in pretend frustration.

Dee smiled contentedly and said softly, "And me you!"

"What was that? Can you say that again?" Joe grinned as he asked. She did not repeat it as he had done, instead she just leaned over as best she could and, unable to reach his cheek, blew him a loud-sounding kiss from her pouted lips.

Red taillights appeared up the row of traffic ahead and a backward-staring, demon-eyed queue began as handbrakes were put on. A slow toddle forward began. Then a little bit further, things started moving a little bit quicker then slowed again. After their earlier near miss, Joe was content to just ease along not thinking he was unlucky to be stuck in this at all. They came to a long lay-by where a bright green bodied and gold roofed fifty-two-seater bus was parked. Exploring Eire was plastered across its side with a logo below it saying 'experience the landscape and luck of the Irish. A place you will always love.' Joe and Dee stopped right beside the driver who was certainly having no luck of the Irish, as he stood at the open bonnet, at stage four anger of a mechanical breakdown. He might have been on the verge of another sort as well as there was not much love being thrown his way, either.

There were three white haired men, in pastel shaded sweaters, yelling at him. An elderly lady was crying behind, another grey-haired woman with her arm around the sobbing shoulders. The bus driver danced between looking at the engine, then turning at right angles to hold his elbows at his ribs and move his hands up and down like he was patting the heads of two small children. His calming technique was not working as Dee snuck down her window to listen, as everyone does when there is an obvious argument going on. This naughty nosiness was not rewarded as not much could be heard apart from loud swearing and 'please calm down, sir!' from the driver. Joe and Dee moved on with Dee shouting, "Good luck!" out the window. She had been genuine and was a bit miffed the now red-faced driver gave her the finger thinking her sarcastic. Although she knew it would be unseen by him, she returned the middle digit salute to him.

They both went silent for a little while, caught in their own thoughts.

Joe remembered his Granda always wishing people 'luck and love and laughter' when said goodbye from them. A little sadness overcame him, having said a permanent goodbye to him a few years ago. Or possibly that goodbye was only temporary, until it was Joe's turn to see what lay on that mysterious other side and they met up again. He would find out when it happened, but until then he hoped his Granda was having luck and love and laughter wherever he was. Granny was with him now as well, so that should help a lot. Death had been lucky for her, taking away the ever-increasing suffering and pain that the tablets could no longer stop or contain. She was like Joe in many ways, believing you made your own luck. When Granda occasionally brought home a rabbit he had shot, Joe had always seen her kiss one of its feet before she prepared it for the pot. He knew she kept a real dried out rabbit's foot in her purse. He never asked and she never said, but he assumed maybe that one needed topped up now and again with additional luck from fresh ones. Joe always wondered if the shot rabbits thought their four feet had brought the luck of a quick death from a shotgun rather than a more painful one lying by a roadside, slowly dying after being the worse off from the front of a car?

"Do you know who must be the unluckiest person alive?" Dee said calmly, just as Joe saw a dead rabbit lying squished at the side of the road, wondering why, if it had four rabbit's feet, it had not been luckier?

"Who?" Joe replied.

"No, I did not mean it like that. I was asking if you could think of anyone really unlucky?"

Joe sighed a little and then snorted, "Me!" which was acknowledged by Dee punching him lightly on the arm.

"You have just said you were one of the luckiest people, so don't give me that! But it must be a terrible thing to believe that you are constantly unlucky. We all have good and bad luck, but imagine if it was always all bad?"

Joe could not really answer her. It was a good question, even if it was seriously macabre and sad. His da had always said that anyone could bring bad luck onto themselves, and some people were, simply by nature, unlucky. Joe had met some people with this reputation and, had to admit, he was genuinely scared to touch them in case it rubbed off on him. Having shook hands with one such person when he was ten or so, he remembered spending half an hour or scrubbing at that hand with soapy water.

269

Afterwards he had laughed at himself and had not been so judgemental or prone to overreaction since. However, there had been a few people, when he shook hands or hugged them, he had sensed something wrong within them, like they had been marked somehow.

Suddenly he felt very uptight as the memory of the gypsy curses came to him. This was something that marked a person for bad luck. Forever! Joe knew they were meant to be called travellers now, to be politically correct in the new wording of the times. However, the strength of a gypsy curse travelled far and wide through his land and beyond. He had heard many stories about rich people becoming poor overnight, healthy people reduced to walking death, some even becoming coffin confined corpses. Though he knew no one personally who had crossed a gypsy's path the wrong way and suffered the consequences, he knew enough to always be polite when he met those from the travelling community.

After all, everyone he knew, knew that a gypsy blessing would bring luck in the same abundance as a curse would bring the opposite. Joe had been blessed by a few gypsies he had met, once by a poor Romanian lady sitting on the street corner begging. He had just been paid and given her a fiver and her reaction was as if he had given her £100. She had grabbed his hand and spent five minutes, talking mostly Romanian which he had not a clue to interpret, but the English she spoke blessed him and his family with luck. He was very grateful and the next few days afterwards went smoothly enough, but he did not feel any more lucky than normal. To be fair he had not asked for times, or best before, or use by dates for the luck she had given him. Maybe he was only receiving that luck now? He did not want to mess about with or challenge it, in case there was still a big 'luck IOU' sitting with his name on it.

Joe was about to tell Dee some of the details of how unlucky those cursed had been when she suddenly came out with, "I have decided that bad luck does not exist! There is only good luck, bad things only happen because the good luck is not there, not because there is bad luck!"

Joe looked at her a little befuddled but, as he normally did, he agreed with her. "Yes, I can see how you could work that out. But I still think there is bad luck. However, I do my very best never to wish bad luck onto me. I always try to think positive so that, even when things do go a bit down the toilet, I console myself that things might have been a lot worse if I had not been thinking good thoughts. What do you think of that?"

"Yeah! I suppose that is fair enough. Definitely there are luck forces out there that we do not have a clue how to control or do anything with. We are just like boats sitting on a lough, waiting for the luck to blow our way. If it brings good luck, great, we can sail away happy. If it does not bring good luck, then all we can do is hold on tight to survive the storm and hope we do not sink!" Dee replied looking into the distant horizon through the car windscreen.

"Very profound," Joe slightly mocked but agreed. "So do you think we are lucky or not then?"

"Lucky. Definitely lucky. And this wee one will be lucky too!" she spoke quietly and confidently, placing her hand on her belly and moved it sideways, as if she was waving to its contents. Joe had no idea if either of them had been, were now, or would be in the future. He decided that whatever luck came their way, or went away, he would do what he sometimes did, but always wanted to do. Although he was sometimes too scared to try, he would ride that luck like a champion jockey whenever it was there. He would ride it until he fell off or he won the race. Either way, whether it is a lucky life or not, you only get one, so make the most of it he had decided long ago. The car in front braked suddenly. Joe slammed his foot brake to the floor as he yelled in a sort of profane implied prayer, "OH, LUCK…"

Latte

As he sat sipping and waiting, Joe thought it was always a strange sensation when you realise that you have been an eye-witness to history happening before your very gaze. It does not have to be, and usually is not, of epic proportions, such as taking part in battles – military, political or otherwise. Nor is it being alongside the political, economic or scientific leaders of the day, being part of the decisions they make, for the good or ill of humanity and planet Earth. They are the everyday things that change, affecting as many millions of lives as politics, economics and all that ever will. Being average by name and nature, Joe had never been in any of these situations to watch media hyped world changing events happen in person, only observing on TV or reading in the papers. He had never rubbed shoulders, or any other part of his body (despite how much he wished to meet certain actresses or help prop up a bar with a few beers with comedians), with any current history-making celebrity. However, he had seen history happen and change at his social level. This was the strata in society where most people lived, worked, played and died. It was where big changes always happened, even if they were not seen until they already existed. Of all the things he had seen in his life so far, one that really confused and worried him was coffee.

In the towns and villages he visited, in city streets and across his land, he saw it happen, sometimes slowly, sometimes almost instantly. This was as much a physical change to the look of streets and villages as it was a social one. It had been happening in his own wee village, others near him and in the towns nearby. In a corner of the world so obsessed with colours, the dark brown of coffee was staining everywhere, not caring if it was red, white and blue; or green, white and gold; or even if it was bright crimson. Previously coloured, fading sectarian mural gable ends, in newly developed areas, were transformed. They now paid tribute to coffee, instead of culture, as another mug shop sprung up on these corners. However, areas where the murals were still bright, the colours vibrant, tended to be ignored by these new frothy and frivolous coffee buildings on the block.

This left the existing mug of tea with milk and two sugars to survive and be served with pride to its area's misjudged and miscalled customers. It was like they were breeding unnoticed in the so-called 'better off' areas. Then suddenly a fully grown one would just appear from behind the boarded-up windows of a previously closed newsagents or corner shop. Coffee shops appeared to be taking over, undeterred in trying to create a new café culture amidst the common pissing rain and coldness of Ulster weather. Joe always laughed when he saw brave souls sitting outside on their metal seats, at their little round tables, with a bone-chilling wind, the beginnings of a rain shower, or simple damp coldness being sucked up through their soles into their coffee sipping souls. Nothing it appeared would deter such champions of the new culture from finishing their drink, even if it had become luke-warm as soon as it had met the air outside. He and Dee had done that once before, sitting outside with a coffee but being so frozen and soaked that they went down the road to the pub for a hot whiskey straight after.

There were still a few places that Joe knew of and went to that had the traditional choices. You would be asked by a smiling young waiter or waitress, or a homely Grandma type owner, if you wanted 'tea or coffee? Milk or sugar?' That was all! Those, to Joe, were simple and sensible choices. These traditional cafes were all about ordinary, decent, tasty food and drink. There were rarely any frills, unless you went to a posher one with paper doilies under your cup. Locals had supported them for years. Clockwork like regulars timed their weekly outing for fish and chips, with bread and butter and two teas, almost to the minute. Some of these still survived but some just locked up and went away, sometimes overnight. They could not compete with the true or imaginary perception that more choice was what customers wanted. It seemed strange to Joe that customers never seemed to have a choice in whether they wanted to limit the choices they had or not? It was just taken for granted that they always wanted more and more options. No one had ever asked him if he wanted his life to be made a lot simpler, choosing between two or three things, instead of wasting time and energy contemplating dozens or hundreds.

In these new coffee temples, it was like there were quite literally walls of choices, for customers to nod at in awestruck worshipful wonder. That day's specials would be chalked onto tablets of stone, spreading the word of those commandments. The list of options would be mantra-ed off by the

273

monk and nun-like black-uniformed staff who served in these places of worship to brown beans. These lists were long enough before the flavouring options were even added to the tempting allure. These would be mounted like spirit optics behind the coffee serving bar, even with the bottles upside down, almost like a two fingered salute to the pub trade such places were helping diminish. The smell drew the customers in, the hip and quirky décor enticed them through the door, being the 'place to be seen' encouraged them to come. In fact, the more Joe thought about it, the actual coffee only played a part role in the whole marketing scene of these establishments. Regardless, it amazed Joe how easily everyone seemed to be converted to this new way of life, wondering if the street preachers were taking notes.

Joe was concerned that coffee had become a new religion, or perhaps addiction would be a better description. He remembered Karl Marx's quote about 'religion being the opium of the masses'. This new coffee cult was just that, in Joe's view, and quite literally was wide scale legal drug selling and use. At home in his land, it was certainly not quite like the reputation of the coffee houses in Amsterdam. Not yet, anyway! Some of his mates and girlfriends would laugh at him when he presented his coffee addiction theory. When he explained it, a few would still laugh but most would, if not agree, at least rethink what was happening around them. After all, it had been scientifically proven that caffeine was a highly addictive substance, just like nicotine and alcohol. True, all three of these were and have been legal drugs for a very long time, but they are still drugs. In Joe's Coffee Shop he would have the drug menu clearly on display:

Mocha	Like the smell of tobacco in a cigarette to a smoker, the aroma and taste of chocolate and coffee are combined in this addictive drink.
Latte or Cappuccino	The cannabis equivalent of these smooth and too-easily-consumed beverages, providing a gentle hit and lift.
Regular or Americano	Moving up into the white powder, that is not powdered milk, but cocaine, giving a more powerful surge of caffeine.
Espresso	This is the coffee world's equivalent of the hard-hitting alphabetical drugs of LSD and 'E's.
Double Espresso	This may as well be labelled pure heroin with customers given a syringe instead of a cup.

Joe remembered the days of the mobile phone and the Filofax being the two, often flashed about, badges of being a true modern man or woman, out there fighting the battles always raging within capitalism. Such business people and wannabe business people now needed a third hand. More and more people Joe saw recently, as they walked about the streets, caught buses and trains, drove their cars and vans… all needed another hand as well. A handheld plastic or cardboard disposable coffee cup was almost a permanent feature on most people. He could rarely stop himself quietly laughing when he sat at a station amid the hurrying and scurrying people, amazed at how they managed to half run along and still never spill a drop. Well, most of the time, until there were coffee fireworks when cups and contents shot off into the air as commuters crashed. He noticed that it was rare to actually see people sitting and drinking these take away hot drinks. Mostly they just seemed to be used as something extra to carry and perhaps make the carrier feel a little more important? He wondered if it was freezing cold by the time they actually got them to their lips? If Joe wanted a tea or a coffee, he preferred to have a sit down somewhere for ten or fifteen minutes and actually enjoy the drink rather than use the cup like some sort of fashion accessory. Maybe that was just him? Maybe not?

It was as if the coffee was replacing alcohol as the drug of choice of so many. For every pub that closed down, three, or even more, of these new very different brewing establishments would replace it. It was this that concerned Joe the most. Joe certainly enjoyed a drink, sometimes enjoying it far too much and suffering the consequences. That was normal in many ways as alcohol had historically been a huge part of his Gaelic/Gallic culture. Both the Scottish and Irish were renowned for their hard-drinking, wild ways. Nevertheless, Joe always sniggered a little when he thought of Celtic medieval soldiers, instead of passing round a bottle of auburn liquid before going off to fight, each supping a bowl-shaped cup of frothy cappuccino! Even if there had been a little milky heart designed on it, he wondered if it would have given them much additional courage? Would coffee have won, or lost, the battle instead of whiskey or ale? Or those stories when the arrow or bullet was removed from a stick-chewing, not anaesthetised wounded warrior. Instead of douching the wound in whiskey to disinfect it, would an espresso do the same job?

Alcohol had always been there for generations, potatoes and barley put to a very different, perhaps much better use, than simply feeding people. The shebeens and coach house inns of old had transformed into the pubs and pub restaurants Joe frequented. Traditionally in any village, there was at least one, or many within a town, or in random locations seemingly in the middle of nowhere. In every community, in all these cases and places, the pub was, or had been, the hub. That was simply the way things were. The Scotch and Irish made sure the pubs thrived, no matter whether they stayed at home or staggered off to Piccadilly or Philadelphia or Papua New Guinea. This had always been how Joe's people socialised, how business deals were made, how life partners were met, how gossip was passed and scandals began. It was how most local stories he had ever heard began, be they romance or ghost – 'He was sitting in a pub with a pint...' Meeting up for a drink was the normal way things were done and adventures begun. In a way that was still the case, except the prospect of a coffee never sounded as enjoyable as a pint to Joe! He knew he was not alone in that.

Joe was very far from being some Luddite traditionalist, wanting to smash up espresso machines across the land to save the public houses. He was genuinely glad to see these new businesses set up and supported them. They provided local jobs and improved the look of the streets where once derelict properties had been. Sure, he baulked a bit sometimes when he saw the price of a slice of cake in these places, but he knew he was paying for an experience and not just the food and drink. Each of these coffee shops was trying to create its own identity, the same way pubs have been doing over the decades. Themed pubs often fascinated Joe, as all some of them seemed to do was nail furniture to the walls and ceilings! He would think about that for ages, trying to figure out what the reasoning was – an anti-theft theme? 'Stop your furniture being stolen – nail it to the ceiling?' Coffee shops he had been in or seen so far had not been so daft, so far. Maybe there are coffee shop owners out there now, with a claw hammer pulling nails from rocking chairs stuck to ceilings, after reading this?

All the coffee shops were trying to do was create that elusive thing called ambience. Like a pub, if a coffee shop did not have a welcoming feel people simply either never came or never stayed. The pubs that were closing were the ones that either could not or would not change to meet these new customer expectations. Joe resented the traditional pubs and wee old cafes dying off, but it was maybe just their time had come to an end. Maybe the coffee shops were just filling in the holes that were left, rather than helping it happen sooner rather than later. Joe, even if it was reluctantly, simply had to face the fact that it was happening.

Joe lamented especially the loss of what were just drinking pubs. The ones where the closest they had to a food menu was a choice between Cheese and Onion or Salt and Vinegar! Decent pints, fair measures of spirits and a bit of craic were what they focused on. There was sometimes a musician in a corner somewhere strumming or fiddling away, in these usually small places, his or her song words slurring unnoticed as the night progressed. Such places had an intimacy, a closeness with every single person in there knowing every single other person, if not at the start of an evening, definitely by the end.

Many fought hard to stay the same as they were, ignoring or belittling the strength of the winds of change blowing in their direction. After all, their clientele were loyal. But, as happens, these men and women, many with their own allocated or self-designated seats, became older and battered by the winds and storms of life. Younger ones would stop calling in as it became uncool. "Why you going there? That's an auld boys' pub!" Their regulars would literally start dying off. Also, the trend seemed to be that local people were not drinking as much alcohol, or at least not in the pubs, anyway. Cheap booze from the supermarkets meant more people were drinking at home, where no landlord or lady would stop them with a curt 'no more. You've had enough!'

Eventually, these stalwarts of the local community would lose their loyalty and custom to graveyards and competitors. After last orders, the landlord or lady would return the beer kegs and bottles. They would close its door for good, to possibly await its development into apartments in years to come, never to be a pub again. Rarely were these little pubs sold to a brewery or restaurant chain, determined to make a killing from it. The new owner, with sledge hammer wielding builders, would not totally resurrect it as a pub restaurant to rebrand, reprice and usually rename what had once been there. Instead, usually, and ironically as it was these that played a part in their death, most closed pubs were bought to be turned into coffee shops.

Dee was at the toilet as Joe sat and waited, slurping the dregs from his wide-mouthed mug. He stared around grateful they had at least kept the bar where it had been. The mirror was new and the optics were still in the same place, although all non-alcoholic flavourings now instead of vodka, gin, whiskey and the rest. The walls were all boarded up and painted black, which Joe thought a strange colour choice, darkening the entire place but making the little lights more obvious. It was more to create the quiet, darkened solitude that the black boards were used, he thought, rather than simply covering up where the dart board, and its surrounding five feet of holes from drunken misthrows used to be. The big fireplace was still where it was, and as he became transfixed by the flames, he remembered many times he had sat in front of that with friends and girls who were more than friends. Although a bit away from it, he could still feel its slight warmth on his cheeks. This made him laugh as it was always so hard to tell back then if someone's red rosy cheeks were from sitting too close to the fire or siting too close to the barrel or bottle. Both usually applied. Apart from that, everything else was gone. They had moved the entrance door to another wall and the toilets were in a totally different corner. He laughed again as the 'facilities' that were there before were limited to say the least. The gents had been little more than a trough with water flushed through it every hour or so, and the ladies was one cubicle.

Joe looked around and around the walls, from which hung framed sickly-sweet sayings or strange blobby artwork of nothing at all really. He saw the huge wall menu, the little tablets of today's specials, he saw the staff chanting the same messages to newly arrived customers but there was one thing he did not see at all. He saw nothing to tell of the history of what this building used to be. There was no mention of the family who had run it for three generations. There were no little plaques or leaflets to tell the part this place had played in local, national and even international history. He appreciated that there would never be enough space to tell the tales of all jokes and japes, arguments and agreements, romances and rows that would have bounced off these walls for decades and decades before the huge new espresso machine was installed. He had his own share of such personal tales of happenings within these walls. He reminisced of the smell of cigarette smoke and stale beer, so much sweeter in comparison instead of the overwhelming constant coffee stench that had filled his nostrils continually since they had arrived.

He saw Dee returning, gathered up the shopping bags and rose to his feet. He looked around again, smiled at another story from back then. It was not the coffee shop taking away his pub, or even its failure to keep a record of what this used to be that he realised annoyed him. It was the fact that this former pub had played a part in his life, shaping him to be the man he was

278

now. How good or bad he had turned out did not matter. All that mattered was that this old pub had been a part of his life, as it had been for many, many others. Now it was gone, leaving only memories, unless the walls and rafters could speak to tell their tales. It was a coffee house now and he had to move on and accept that. He realised that memories were important but the reason they were memories was because they were in the past. Things always change. For better for worse it does not matter, but it is his acceptance of that change that he needed to acknowledge. He needed to look at the now and the future, not just the past. He needed to stop looking for scapegoats and blaming coffee houses for changing society and places, as it was the other way around. Dee and their daughters were their future. They would make their own past, whether it involved coffee shops or pubs or not, in the future to come.

"That has been a long day but we are all sorted now We are getting the bus home, so how do you fancy stopping off for a pint on the way? I thought we would try that new pub that just opened where the Headless Horseman used to be?" She smiled at him cheekily as she spoke, before kissing him on the cheek, knowing his answer before he said it.

Lump

A single word has enormous power. Joe knew this. In many ways he always had. 'No' and 'quiet' and 'behave' were probably some of his earliest memories of the instant impact of this. When just such a single word was uttered by either, or both, of his parents he knew at once not to ask again, to stop talking or making noise, or to conform to the rules. Joe back then, and still now, did not necessarily like these words, resenting using them on his own future kids, even if it would be deemed them necessary. There were other words he loved as kid, and still did now, like 'cake', 'beach' and, despite conscious he had had an ever-growing number of them, 'birthday'.

'Lump' was just another word, with different meanings, that could mean good or bad. A 'lump' of cash was a great thing to have, even if Joe only sometimes did. A 'lump' of sugar sweetened Joe's tea. His cash lumps often dissolved like sugar lumps, but he accepted that was part of life's sweetness and bitter sweetness. The word 'lump' he listened to now did not enrich or sweeten his life, or that of his family. No matter how much in his mind he said 'no' in disbelief, or told his brother to be 'quiet' so he could listen more; or said 'behave' trying to convince himself that his da was overreacting or winding them up – it could not change anything. He could find no positivity to take away the powerful fear that single word had instilled in him. It had created a lump in his throat he could not get rid of. This tried futilely to block his ability to swallow the entirety of the reality of what his da had just said. It felt like this one word had also taken a lump out of his frantically beating heart. He regretfully realised he was going to have to lump it but did not like it in any way whatsoever.

His da's matter-of-fact way of telling it did not help. Joe and his younger brother Will knew it was serious before their da even spoke. They had arrived at their childhood home at the same time, Joe parking his old but functional, for the time being, car on the driveway. Will abandoned, rather than parked, his own newer and flashier one on the roadside, not concerned at all about parallel parking. They had both sensed it, whatever it was, meaning they just nodded and hugged a greeting to each other. They had walked silently up the driveway, arms of brotherly love around each other's shoulders. They arrived at the front door, freshly painted the same shade of red as it always had been.

Ma had opened the door, her eyes watery, but her smile sincere and loving as always. "My boys!" she simply said as she had reached up to hug them both tightly in turn, Will clinging on a little longer than Joe. "Yer da's at the kitchen table," was all she said quietly as she had walked down the hallway, turning slowly into the living room, leaving her sons standing and wondering if they had heard her sob or not.

Will had led the way down the neat narrow hall. They both entered the kitchen that had changed little since their childhood, apart from the colour of the paint on the walls. As he automatically did every time he went into the kitchen of his parent's home, Joe had looked to see if another layer of paint has managed to cover up the dark splodge he had created as a six-year-old beside the fridge. It usually made him smile when he noticed it had not. The stain had still shone though very faintly, only visible if you knew where to look. Any possibility of a smile being seen on Joe's face did not reveal itself; and he did not know where to start his search to find one amongst the tension.

Da had sat where he always sat, at the head of the white-with-roses-patterned, cloth-covered table. Will and Joe gave each other a questioning stare, wondering why the tablecloth was on? That only ever happened at family birthdays, Easter and Christmas! It was a strange, trivial thing that they both picked up on. It added another little level of concerned worry to their minds as they could tell, even from the way their da sat, this was no celebration. Even the bottle of beer sat a little precariously beside the big man's elbow somehow made it feel even less like a party atmosphere. That one bottle emitted sadness not joy, drinking to forget rather than live for the moment. The fact that it had remained almost full said a lot without a word.

"Grab yerselves a beer, sons, and sit down with me a minute! I've something to tell you," Da said quietly, only glancing up briefly, before returning his eyes to focus on his clasped hands in front of him. Joe had swung open the old but still working fridge door, with the row of tiny dents along the bottom from the playful toy car crashes Will and he had caused for fun years ago. Grabbing two chilled bottles, he had handed one to Will who had deftly produced his car keys from his pocket, flicking the top off in one smooth action with the attached bottle opener. He had jangled it into

Joe's hand, as he had necked the bottle to prevent any of the foaming liquid being wasted onto the floor. Joe had opened his, necked his bottle and jingled the keys back to Will. They had silently and instinctively sat in the same seats they always had, waiting tensely for their Da to speak.

"You know yer man in that old James Bond film?" Da rather confusingly had said as he quickly looked into their frowning with confusion faces. Da had smirked a little but Joe had seen the ever-present, unless angry, bright twinkle in his father's eyes was out like a candle. There was no normal fire in his eyes at all, not even a spark. It had not been there as they had entered the kitchen and there still was not. This unnerved Joe considerably. He could see it had, and was, weighing heavy on Will too as he slumped in his seat.

"What was his name? He had a special gun... It began with 's'... Scur... No...! Ska... Scaramanga! That was his name." Da had paused, then had congratulated himself for his memory by saying, "Scaramanga!" again softly. "Do ye remember he had a third nipple in the film? It was meant he had special powers because of it."

Will and Joe had just sat and swigged their beers and felt very wary. Normally they would have laughed, joked and slagged with their da, so it had felt unnatural that the brothers' will to do this was not there. They had had some very strange conversations with their da in the past, with him telling many strange, mostly unbelievable and equally as many too believable stories. Both of them could and had been able to talk to their da about anything! Anything at all! Anything, apart from being intimate with girls, of course! Once their da had reassured himself that both his sons knew what went where and the precautions they needed to take, then da had considered that was his job done and did not need to know any more details after that. Although their da had just spoken about nipples, it seemed a very long way from those feathered and buzzing conversations of long ago. In fact, to Joe, it felt a very long way from any of the conversations they had had before.

His da's weird reference to a 1970s movie to start a conversation was not that unusual. Da started many a chat and bit of craic with some obscure fact. When on good form, their da would always joke and tease and mess about. There had been none of that in his tone of voice or shown on his face. There still was not. Joe's ESP was still on overdrive as he sensed his da was nervous from the moment they had stepped into the kitchen. Scared, even?

In itself, Da being scared was hard to take in. Joe, and he was sure Will too, knew inwardly their da was in unchartered waters. It was unknown territory for Will and Joe too, their family now exposed to a stampeding herd charging towards them. Joe looked at Will and they both telepathically knew they were about to be trampled by whatever this news was.

"Well, I am a bit like Scarayerman, as you called him, Will, or Scarymango as you used to call him, Joe, when youse were wee and we watched the film together." Da had smiled a little at his wee joke and memory, but it was a forced smile. Da's eyes had shot up and intently stared into Joe's, then Will's, then back again and so on, back and forth. His eyes remained red and bloodshot, but not from alcohol. There was something else coursing through their da's veins, his eyes only the proof of that. "But I am not sure what special powers it will give me?" He had smiled again but his eyes, like his sons', were not laughing. "I have a third ball! A big lump of a one, too!"

There was the lump word that hammered home. Will spluttered his beer in both shock and an instant of amusement. His da's cold stare immediately stopped the inklings of a grin spread across Will's face. Joe's beer was left untouched on the table as he just stared at his da. Joe showed no emotion outwardly, as his body struggled to cope with it inwardly, at his da's short but devastating words. His da was trying, and failing, to laugh about it as Joe realised instantly the unfunny repercussions of this. He knew his da had been to hospital quite a bit recently. He knew he had been that day. Will knew too and so the very brief, summoning phone call home meant it was something that could not be said over the wires but had to be in person. If it had been a 'nothing to worry about', their ma would have told them, in amongst all the other extended news she would relay to them in her weekly update phone calls. Their da would have joked about it easily. He was trying to joke about it now but failed utterly. Joe was very like his da, and would try to laugh his way out of a problem. There was no laughing about this. His da's face spoke more than anything coming out of his mouth. This was a 'how much do we need to worry about this?' moment. From what Joe sensed, the answer was a lot. An awful lot.

"How can we find out?" Will had blurted out. "What? If it has given me super powers?" Da half-joked back. The smile on their da's face had seemed more genuine, perhaps in relief that he had now broken the news and it had shocked, but not broken, his grown-up sons. Will had replied a little angrily, "No, not that! I mean… you know… what's the medical words… benign! That's the good one, isn't it? If it's benign, it's okay?"

"Well, mine is not just a nine but a full blown ten out of ten! Performing live in your da's underpants we have third bollock performing his new single 'Three's Too Many'…" Da had replied with a sad smirk, before stopping suddenly and taking a small sip of his beer. "It's as malignant as malignant can get!" He then had taken a much longer swig of his beer and Joe had thought he saw a tear run down the side of his da's stubbly cheek. "So, your auld bull of a da could well soon find out what becoming a bullock is like!" He had been trying his damndest to be his easy going, larking about self but he could not. His sons could tell then that he was doing this out of habit, but his inner desire to do so was gone completely. Da had wiped his sleeve across his not so stiff top lip, sniffing hard, as he tried to control snot dripping from his nose. He had looked away from his two lads and muttered something about maybe he was getting a cold. It was certainly not an easily recovered from snotty nose medical issue both Will and Joe had realised then, so they had just sat and waited to be told more.

Da was a talker that was for sure. He could talk about anything. He had opinions about everything, usually taking an opposite opinion from someone else, even if he did not agree with it, just to get a bit of banter going. Then there were the things he could not or would not talk about. He was totally sincere and truly did love his wife, although times had been seriously tough in their early marriage years. Times were sometimes still hard but rarer. His love for his kids and his grandkids had no such constraints and was constantly freely given, even if he was occasionally shouting a reprimand to them. There was love, too, for Joe and Will's wives. Even their sister Joanne's husband had moved way up a good few notches on their Da's respect scale, but Joe knew love had not been achieved yet, for whatever reason.

However, that was as emotional as Da got, apart from anger. Love and hate had always been Da's driving forces. He was rarely in the middle, ignoring grey completely and preferring a straightforward black and white. Apart from love, emotional feelings were seen as too drab to his da. Maybe this was why his da never handled emotions well. Anger, anxiety, sadness and all the other plethora of feelings every human being had, would just explode from him or clam him up tight for days. His da had experienced all sorts of emotions, good and bad, but he was not at all good at swimming in these waters. Joe could see, sat at that kitchen table, the pool of feelings about this lump looked like it was about to drown his da before his very eyes.

"So, if they… you know… snip, snip… will that make everything okay apart from you not having any…?" Joe had mumbled as he unthinkingly made scissor motions with two of his fingers. He had quickly stopped doing this when he realised how inappropriate it was. His da had burst out a roar of laughter which made Joe and Will laugh too. It had actually felt good to laugh, Joe accepted, easing the tension.

"That's what I have to decide. But I do not know if I have the balls for it!" Da had burst out laughing again even louder, his sons joining in. Drawn by the noise, Ma had come in to join them then with a huge vacant looking grin on her face but her eyes still watery. She had quietly sat in her seat by the oven and looked longingly at the three men in front of her. Will had reached over and grabbed one of her hands gently. Joe had done the same to her other one. Joe remembered noticing the twinkle in Da's eye return as he stared expressively down the table at his life partner of over forty years. Ma had stared back, Joe able to see the smitten teenage girl shining out from behind the laughter line wrinkles and grey streaked long hair.

"But there is a bit more to it that just me applying for a job guarding a harem! Now that's a job I would not mind doing!" He had smiled cheekily at Ma as he joked, who returned a pretend scowl. "Naw, the doctors have done all sorts of tests in the past months. They have shoved things up where things have never gone in before, only out. They have probed about with fingers in there too." Da had winced and shuffled on his seat. Will and Joe had done the same. "They gave me stuff like vomit to drink and shoved a tube down my throat to take pictures that I do not think we will be putting in the family photo albums! Basically, they have looked and looked and looked… and they do not like what they see at all! If it was just my magical third ball that would be okay, but they are fairly sure there are more growths in my guts – on my stomach and probably my liver too…" Da had just suddenly stopped talking.

Ma had given a loud sniff and began to speak slowly and deliberately. "They can operate to remove the lump but are not sure if it will make any difference. They think the other ones are too advanced…" she had paused as tears flowed freely down both reddened cheeks. In one swift movement she had released her hand from Joe's and brought it up to her mouth as she made small squeaking noises. Joe and Wills' adam's apples had danced as they synchronised swallowing hard as they stared at their ma and da in turn.

"They are scared of opening me up and not buttering me up, but spreading it about even more!" Da had snorted a loud sarcastic laugh. "They want a decision as soon as possible. Ye know what the waiting lists are like. Even if we decide now to go for it, it could be months and months before they get around to putting me on the slice and dice list. The NHS used to be better at..." He had paused and looked at the table, stopping himself going off on a world-changing rant.

"Does Joanne know yet?" Joe had asked with a little cough, not having realised his throat was so dry. He had sipped the beer as his da and ma exchanged fretful looks. They were both about to reply but both had stopped. With a gentle nod of her head, Da then spoke to the totally attentive three faces in front of him. "Well, yer ma and me talked about how to tell ye all. We thought it would be easier to tell you both and then tell Joanne separately. You know how she is!" The brothers had nodded. "If she was any more highly strung, they would have her in the string section of the Ulster Orchestra! She is a worrier. She will take this seriously hard, especially now they have the twins. That is why we want to speak to her alone this evening when the wains are asleep."

Silence had descended and lasted. It had lasted some more. There was no uncomfortableness in the stillness, allowing time for that shocked acceptance of the shitty cards fate had just dealt to be absorbed. Joe's ESP had detected so much emotion quietly flying about in that room. It had not been a golden silence, more of a fearful golden gun that they all felt put to their heads. There were going to be multiple bullets fired in the next short while, hurting something precious and priceless. They were all bracing themselves for the hits and wounds these would leave. His da may not have had any super gadgets but he had always been a fighter, resisting everything life had thrown at him by wit, work and warrior will. This lump had simply just thrown him. As Joe had looked at him then across the table, he could see his da was never going to be able to say never again and knowing it was fantasy to think he would only live twice. Joe had hid it from his da as he wiped away a single tear that crawled down Joe's cheek. He had held his da's hand and looked deep into those old, tired eyes opposite him, looking desperately for the fight and fire that had always been there. Neither were, not even a flicker. Joe had squeezed his da's hand and let the next tear flow freely.

Lungs

She was two years, two months and two weeks old. Although they had tried putting her bottom on an ordinary kitchen chair, she would not sit still. She would sit nice and steady for a minute or so, raising her parents' hopes. However, this was only the start of the countdown. After that, she would either begin to slide to one side for whichever outside fielder parent was on duty to respond and grab her. Or else she would just become bored and try to scoot herself off the bottom of her seat to exploit her believed newly awarded freedom, again for the nearest fielding parent to imprison her back in their arms. Consequently, she was still strapped into her high chair for most meal times. This was a place she was starting to become increasingly frustrated with. She was voicing these issues to the overworked parental complaints department increasingly regularly. She vocalising this at the top of her lungs as often as she could when being placed in there, with little legs kicking and arms flailing all over the place. Mealtimes had become a sort of combination of a very loud, energetic dancing rave mixed with a WWF wrestling match. Whether either or both, neither the organisers nor star performer enjoyed participating, particularly when parents felt exhausted and pinned on the ropes.

However, this drama routine did cease. The majority of the time – well, over three quarters of the time – well, definitely over fifty per cent of the time… it stopped once she was strapped in. Experience had, eventually, taught her that by the strap click stage she had to accept defeat. Both wardens used the tried and tested, sharply spoken 'no!' assisted by the pointed finger, which let her know there was no point in arguing further. All she could do was wait it out, until her bail money or parole came through at the end of the meal, for her to be unstrapped. All this meant that during mealtimes, most times, Ava would eventually sit quietly and smile, waiting to see what was for breakfast, or lunch, or tea.

It was lunchtime on a Saturday. Things were a bit rushed and the choice of menu was limited. This happened quite often on a stressful Saturday. It was fish fingers and baked beans cooking away for all three of them. Not

287

just because it was Joe doing the cooking, more to do with the fact Dee was very late back with the groceries. Joe, Bella and two-year, two-month and two-week-old Ava were all hungry. Joe decided he would sort something out for Dee separately when she returned as hunger growled like a sore headed bear in the kitchen, Joe rapidly morphing into this in reality. Hungry Bella was quietly but constantly tugging Joe's trouser leg, in her attempt to hurry things up, as he bustled back and forth checking the fishy smelling grill, then stirred the warming beans in the grey steel pan.

Bella shuddered a little when the metal spoon met the steel base of the pot, making little bone tingling screeches. The toast sprung up in its usual dramatic way, already in its new golden to dark brown outfit to receive its buttery award for best supporting actor to baked beans. Joe slapped the hard-yellow butter on with a few scrapes and watched it sink in quickly to the pores of the hot hardened bread. He re-loaded another two slices, slotted them down in and braced himself for them firing off in a minute or two. Meantime, he cut one of the buttery slices into five and gave a piece to Bella. He passed a piece to the strapped in Ava and asked Bella to watch her. Bella nodded and agreed, ravenously ripping a piece of bread with her now complete set of baby teeth.

Burning himself a little on the volcano-hot grill through the hole in the oven glove almost made a curse erupt from him. Attempting, as he always did, to be a role model parent, this particular time he managed to contain it with a large suck in of breath. When he extracted the orangey, sizzling sticks, he placed them on the three plates, making sure he gave himself the three that had the blackened corners. Ma had always taught him that in cooking etiquette you always gave yourself the worst things, for example burnt, misshapen food and the best to the others eating with you. He dolloped out the beans, with no such concerns. Another two rounds of toast popped up and were rewarded by being slarried in butter as their last two breadbag mates had been, before being placed on the plates to soak up some bean juice.

Joe had seen all the James Bond and other secret-agent movies. He had seen how the spies in them had been trained to use all sorts of objects to end other people's lives. There was a bowler hat and deadly dental work, along with the much more subtle pens and paper, rings and belts. These ordinary items would be transformed to become mini assassin tools. Some of these, some totally impossible and unbelievable, still took his breath away, no matter how many times he saw them. One thing he never remembered being included but he was about to witness its capabilities for himself, Joe was totally unprepared for the deadly potential of a fish finger!

It was a blur of panic, his pure, white face contrasting with the blue of hers. He had not time to even feel an iota of guilt for him being the one that had put it in her hand a few seconds earlier to chomp on. The noise was deadly awful. Or rather the lack of noise, as Bella was stunned into stone silence. All Ava could do was cough and make wheezy noises. Within seconds of her first coughs, he had her emergency unstrapped and she was over his shoulder in a half fireman's lift for him to dance around with. Joe kept slapping her back every second or so. Nothing changed apart from her wheezes becoming worse. He slapped harder, then as hard as he dared, terrified he would break bones. He exceeded his set hard slap parameter and went the extra distance. His adrenaline-fuelled thinking was that broken bones could be repaired. Still, nothing but wheezes came out. These seemed to be less powerful as more blue moved across her face. The seriousness of the situation did not even trigger any Smurf jokes from him.

More radical action was called for. He could not slap her back harder and these had been rewarded with nothing. A second was spent wondering if he could do that Heinrich stomach thrust manoeuvre on a two-year, two-month and two-week-old child! Ringing Dee would have wasted too much time. Ringing for an ambulance would have been the same. Within a split second, whether consciously or from some sort of automatic first aid response, he grabbed her by both ankles. Swinging her upside down by these, he moved her up and down, up and down. He kept going, ignoring Bella's bewildered stares and silent, about to speak anxiousness. Twice more he did this. Improvised, imploring prayers poured out of him to whoever would listen. Panic poured into places he never knew existed as there was just so much of it in him. Desperation clouded his mind as he could not think of anything else to try if this spontaneous act did not work.

It did! With her hair hanging like she was being electrocuted, Ava sent a chunk of half chewed bright orange breadcrumbs and white fish skiting across the floor. This was followed by a splurge of puke that Joe was unable to describe in as much detail. She screamed loudly. Joe had never ever been so glad to hear Ava scream in all his life, having come so close to almost seeing the end of hers. He knew instantly that nothing would ever match that gladness.

As he held her so tightly to him, tears of joy ran freely down his face. As little Bella clung tightly to his left leg in relief and love, he yammered words of comfort to Ava, as much as to himself and Bella. They made no sense but he felt the need to talk, to reassure himself as much as his daughters. A million thoughts of what might have been flooded his mind, trying vainly to rationalise and explain the blind panic that had taken hold of him. How, he wondered, had a floppy piece of cooked fish and breadcrumbs almost so easily caused potential death and destruction to his family? He knew then that this would remain in the top ten of the scariest things that had or would ever happen to him in life. As he calmed and his thoughts became more focused, he moved it permanently into the top five.

Joe danced around with his daughters smiling, the mess of food, whether uneaten on plates, spilt or regurgitated, remained where it was. In his mind, those comparative trivialities could all wait. Now was a time for celebration. As laughter and joy came from all of them, Dee loudly opened the back door, shopping bags scrunching against the doorposts and surround.

"Sorry I am late. That town is getting more choked up every time I go there…" She stopped, dropped her bags and was almost bowled over by the charge of her arms outstretched family. "Easy! Easy!" she wheezed, "I can hardly breathe…"

Lickass

As an average fella, Joe felt he had, although unique to him, normal personality traits. Some of these he felt quite proud of, such as his ability to work hard and take a pride in his job the majority of the time. He was generally honest, with only the occasional white lie that may have had a greyish tinge sometimes. He was strong too, both physically and in his will. However, his strength of will could very quickly morph into the liability of stubbornness, then anger, then rage. Although he did not balloon up and turn green, it was incredible how quickly this could happen, particularly when Joe and information technology interacted. He knew he could write an entire chapter of a book about this love/hate relationship of IT, which Joe spelt with a silent 'sh'! Nevertheless, of all the strengths and weaknesses, attributes and short-comings, of his personality or character, there was one thing he never was or wanted to be – a brown nose.

Joe saw school as where it all started, especially big school, which he viewed as preparing you for the future work environment. It did this in so many other ways than simply giving you knowledge and a few letters after subjects on a bit of paper. It gave a routine and a structure to a day, by being at a certain place at a certain time in the morning, carrying out tasks that were instructed to be completed, having toilet and eating breaks, then allowed to leave at a certain time. School and work were so alike, being only able to go home if you did not voluntarily wish to carry out additional activities like training or skill building. There was also the option that if you had made a total Horlicks of something earlier in the day, you were told you had to stay on after hours, detention happening just as often in the work environment as school. Joe mostly successfully avoided this personal punishment both at school and work. However, he did get caught up in those times when everyone had to stay on working late, usually because another or a few of the others had either dropped or made a bollock.

He easily drew so many such similarities between school and work, but there was one exception. At school there was an overriding, unofficial rule that, when breached, was punishable by multiple verbal warnings. These, when the opportunity arose, would be followed by the skipping of any additional written warning and went straight to the trying to kick the living crap out of the offender. A tout was viewed as the lowest of the low in school, verbal and physical abuse the seen as justified penalty for such a major offence. Such reprimands and the threat of these kept a sort of status quo at school, entire classes musketeeringly all suffering a teacher's wrath or detention rather than squeal on the one. The one who caused such trouble was usual dealt with using the other unwritten pupils' school rules after the event. It was in many ways an honourable, if vigilante, approach to achieving acceptable school societal norms, outside of those stated in the official school rules handbook.

This changed totally at work, especially in an office environment, when these kid and adolescent rules were made obsolete by the protection adulthood, potential assault charges and company policies offered. In many ways, those working in construction, mining, transport and factories still held to these same school rules regarding sucking up and touting, but that was changing as lawyers and government policies became more and more involved. In offices especially, unlike at school, the whole system seemed to allow, sometimes even encourage, certain so-called work colleagues to tout and squeal and grass and basically screw over one of their colleagues at any opportunity. However, this was only one part of the whole skill set of sucking-up to the boss that Joe could never, and never wanted to be able to put on his CV.

He divided arse lickers into two types, not based on tongue size, length of time doing it, or such like criteria. Firstly, there were those who often drove themselves into ill health and broken relationships as they took on extra work and responsibilities to push themselves so far up their boss's backside that they could see his or her tonsils. These people tended to be very insular, extremely hard working and focused all their energies on making sure that they worked, even socialised, with those that could give them a shove up another step of their totally obsessed about personal career ladder. They lived to work rather than worked to live as Joe did. These people tended to ignore or merely tolerate those that did not have promotional powers or influence, a category Joe usually fell into.

Some of these types of people that Joe had met he genuinely admired, even if he had not particularly liked them as a person. Being so driven, so forward looking, so able to sacrifice anything to achieve their goals took a seriously strong character. Joe felt he had these attributes as well, only without any inclination to use these powers for self-gain, relying on the unreliable recognition of his work to do that instead. However, he also despised the fact that many of these people also tended to trample all over the top of their workmates, even best friends, to climb up another notch. Loyalty was one of Joe's personal strengths and anyone abusing such personal commitments to his friends, family, or even people he only vaguely knew, was something he detested. These stomping, career-obsessed sycophants would suffer in the future Joe believed, based on the very vague principles of 'what goes around, comes around' and 'what goes up must come down'. Such dizzying, disorientating core principles did not always bear fruit. Regardless he kept them to try to stop bitterness setting in when he was pipped.

Then there was the second type. He and everyone he knew, knew of these ones in their own workplaces. These were the jobsworths, usually immaculately dressed, who were sanctimoniously polite, slimy and generally as well liked as a curry fart in a slow moving, crowded lift. Joe wondered if there was a special hospital that produced these particular people as they appeared to be so different from everyone else. They would use the over the top 'Yes Sir/Miss! No Sir/Miss! Three bags full Sir/Miss!' insincere wooliness in the workplace, as they did in the classroom. They did not seem to care, some even revelling, in being the black sheep amongst those in their school class or workplace. These techniques would be experimented with their teachers initially, as a practice run to perfect such toadyism with future bosses to try to hop into favouritism. However, this did not necessarily mean these people worked harder or were very productive. It was often the complete opposite, as they skived and buck-passed with a greasy skill that infuriated everyone else in their vicinity. To Joe, these types of people were the ones who did not live life, they just weaselled their way through it.

Joe had very mixed views on the bosses' responses to this. Some he had had were good, fair and led by example. Some, quite simply, were not. There were some he had had that he observed paid too much attention to their creepy crawly staff, rewarding them for their sneakiness and trusting them more than what Joe classed as the 'real' workers. Those bosses tended to be cut from the same cloth, spooling tales in turn to their bosses, trying to thread their way into the fabric of the company's higher cut. Joe felt threadbare in comparison and it irked him when such deviousness paid off, occasionally leaving him feeling this was unsuitable clothing for his work to wear. Still, he was able to revel all the more in his own minor rewards for simple hard work and creativity, despite feeling three sheets to the wind a lot of the time. Dealing with this bootlicking at work was one thing; dealing with it within the family put this on another footing.

"Daddy?" Bella asked in an unmistakeable tone, as Joe cursed at the fingertip slipping loss of a tiny screw. He was trying to fix a bike in the living room while watching football on TV at the same time. This showed multitasking was something he only thought he could do. Joe mumbled a sarcastic 'uh huh?' as the side of his head rested on the carpet peering under to hopefully see a silver shiny thing in the sofa underworld.

"Daddy?" she repeated again with added sugariness, trying to gain his full attention, a challenge in itself sometimes.

"Uh Huh?" Joe repeated equally sarcastically, recognising that tone as he retrieved his valuable silver piece from amongst the fluff. He made a mental note to hoover under there when he was done with this 'simple,' one-hour-later bike repair. Maybe if he paid more attention to the bike than the football, he would have finished quicker?

"Daddy?" she asked again, the tone changing to show a little frustration, despite her efforts to hide it. Joe slotted the small screw into place as he knelt, twisted the screwdriver and flipped the bike over with a satisfied nod of his head. He set the screwdriver down beside him as he held the bike by the handlebars still kneeling.

"OK Bella!" he stated as he looked at her intently. "Go on, then. Hit me with it!" Her eyes gave a faked shock reaction, pretending she was not going to ask for something, even though she was. "Just stop with the suck-up voice and just ask!" Joe demanded a little too aggressively, he felt. Still, he had a lot to do, even without adding hoovering to the list. "What do you want?" he asked sort of kindly.

Joe could not figure out if the slight hurt showing in Bella's bright blue eyes was real or acted. Either way, he gave her an intense stare to tell her to 'get on with it!' which she did. "Daddy?" she began again with the same sickly-sweet tone, which received an even more intense stare from her da. "I have tidied my room and helped Mum in the kitchen. And I have all my homework done…"

Joe interrupted with, "Great! Well done!" As he lifted the bike up slightly and spun the wheel, focussing to check nothing more had or was going to fall off. Slightly miffed at having her rehearsed speech heckled like this she restrained herself and carried on. "I have done all my jobs..."

Joe butted in again with a frustrated "Yes! Yes! That's great but I know from the tone of your voice you are going to ask for something. So just ask. I've a lot to do!" He mumbled grumpily, "As usual," under his breath.

There was a flash of anger in her eyes that he did not see. She knew from past experience she had to approach this in a roundabout way. Previously, her simply demanding something never worked. It was almost guaranteed she would not get it if she behaved selfishly, which she was going almost overboard not to do. Her nerve went slightly, knocked off her course by her da's snappy intrusions to her word flow. "Would you like a cup of tea?" she asked instead.

Joe stopped what he was doing. As he rose to his feet ready to wheel the bike outside, he answered suspiciously, "Yeah! Sure!"

"Okay!" she replied, and scurried off to the kitchen.

As Joe manovered the bike through the doorway, not chipping paint more by luck than anything else, he sniggered sarcastically, "It must be a biggie she is going to ask for if she is making me a cup of tea!"

Joe was outside, moving all sorts of clutter to try to fit the bike back into the small shed which had well exceeded its storage capacity. He was confused as to how it had become even more disorganised since he had taken the bike out of it an hour or so ago. As he eventually slotted the bike back in, Bella arrived with a steaming cup of tea. The two half-melting digestive chocolate biccies and her face beaming a huge smile confirmed his suspicion that it must indeed be a big ask she was about to make. He thanked her genuinely gratefully, taking these from her as he sat down on the shed step. She jumped over and sat really close beside him.

"Daddy?" she began again, a little less sweetly than previously. Joe sipped his tea then sighed with a small laugh.

"Just ask, Bella!" he ordered her.

She composed herself before speaking. "Daddy, you know the way I am going out with my friends this afternoon shopping." She paused, inspecting his face closely. He skellied a look at her and nodded, thinking he knew what was coming but not sure. "Well, I want to buy some clothes and there is a jacket I would like to have. But I haven't enough money. My friends have the same one and I would really like to have the same as them.

A different colour, but…"

Her Da interrupted her again, causing Bella to sigh this time. "How much?" Joe exhaled out, slightly sickened at this phrase crossing his lips too often. Bella could sense his agitation and began to doubt if the timing was right. However, she realised she had no alternative and had to go for it.

"It's just another ten pounds… If that would be all right?" she spoke shyly and hopefully. Her da's mouth gaped a little and he uttered a questioning, "Huh?" As he looked at her, Bella sensed she was at that crucial point of yes or no, so she let rip with all that she had to push this the way she wanted.

"I will clean your car tomorrow, when I come home from school. And I will do all my chores. And I will help more around the house…"

Joe simply smiled silently at her, causing her to cease her list of the repayment options she thought appropriate and possible. It was a nice smile but she could not figure out if it was a 'yes' or a 'no' smile. Her da sipped his tea again, staring across the small garden and seemed to be thinking. This was not always a good thing in her experience. He could wander off into all sorts of weird worlds when he did that and then he would have to be brought back into the real one. This time, to her relief, he did not go off on a mental marathon. Almost immediately, he looked back at her as she snuggled closer into him, hoping that might help her cause. "You have been going on about that jacket for a while, haven't you?" he said with a knowing nod which she could not interpret. She nodded back enthusiastically, hoping this was looking positive. "Ten quid is a lot of extra money for you to ask for," he added, causing her to have unwanted negative doubts. Her Da's eyes twinkled causing hers to do the same. "All right!" was all he said and reached back to pull his wallet from his hip pocket. Setting his tea down, with the remaining half-eaten biscuit balanced precariously on top, he rummaged about in his wallet. Pulling out a crumpled ten-pound note, he handed this to her.

Gratefully clutching the banknote, she jumped up, kissed him on the cheek, said, "Thanks so much, Daddy," and was off running up the path.

Picking up his cooling tea, Joe threw the last of the biscuit into his mouth, chewed slowly and swallowed it. He felt poorer, but only by ten pounds. It was not a lot of money to give out really. Besides, his daughter's happiness was priceless. Besides, she rarely did ask for things and she deserved it, he rationalised. He also felt proud. Proud that his daughter knew how to go the right way, in his view, of getting what she wanted. Perhaps she had been a bit of a lickass around him, but he felt the warmth from her sincerity. She was also willing to work for it which was great, showing how much it meant to her.

It was so different at work compared to family, he snorted to himself. Bella had shown kindness, explained things fully and truthfully, was willing to repay the cost and more. All of these were admirable traits Joe proudly realised in his eldest daughter. She was only eleven, but was a lot more grown up than ones he had and was working with. There is no need to be a lickass, he concluded, just be a decent human being will achieve what you want in life. Sadness came over him that real life was not like that. Joe had learned that the hard way many times. Although he hoped not, he knew Bella and her sister would probably do so as well. With some regret at the way of the world, he steelily persevered with the fact that he wanted neither himself, nor his family, to have to be sycophantic simply to get on in life. Work hard, show love and caring and hope that will enable people to receive the rewards they deserve. It was a naïve hope, he knew absolutely, but still an aspiring goal to aim for. He swigged the last of his tea, rose to his feet and decided what was next on his to do list to make sure he kept in his wife's good books.

Lobotomy

"Nobody move! Nobody move!" Little snorts of laughter escaped from Robert as he quietly shouted, waving his hands in the air in mock panic. "Everybody stay perfectly still and start looking. It's just like that time June lost her contact lens! This will be very small and hard to find!" The other lads sniggered as they pretended to scan the floor, mimicking Robert's fake franticness.

"Very bloody funny! Ha ha!" Jonnie No H sarcastically replied with a strange little stammer in his voice. Joe saw a genuine look of what could only be described as real fear on his mate's face. This has been growing for days and had now reached a crescendo. Robert's light-hearted reply, to Jonnie's supposedly rhetorical question asking if his brain had fallen out, did very little, if anything at all, to reduce Jonnie's heavy mood.

Lenny passed the hipflask to Jonnie who took a short swig, a flash of wince passing his eyes as the hard liquor contents thumped the back of Jonnie's throat. With a brief nod of gratitude, Jonnie handed it back and Lenny took a short swig himself, before passing in on around the sofa and armchair-seated semi-circle of lads. Lenny had been a work and outside work mate with Jonnie a long time, so the rest of the gang of lads felt absolutely no inkling of being peeved at not having been chosen as best man. Joe, Brian and Robert, in truth, were very much relieved that they had not been asked. Extremely relieved, in fact, and much more than they would ever admit to Jonnie. There were far too many stories, real and rumour, that neither Jonnie nor his new bride-to-be's elderly and otherwise relatives would have wanted to hear. None of them being put in that position of possibly accidentally letting a few of these secrets escape from the confines of their brains, where they were filed under highly embarrassing or controversial, was something to be grateful for.

They had all discovered being a best man was a tough gig. It was agreed that it was the toughest part of any wedding in their combined experience. The bride and bridesmaids just had to look beautiful, although there were pressures associated with that, they all had been told. The mothers were able to splash out on posh outfits and worry only a little, although most fussed and fretted far more than was necessary. The FOB, as Jonnie kept referring to him, (father of the bride) was there for a bit of craic and a few beers after a short escort up the aisle and a proud dad speech. Ushers, like Brian and Joe, just needed to smile in uncomfortable hired suits, knowing their main role was asking 'bride or groom?' and directing people to their seats, with a bit of excessive smiling for photos later on in the day.

The best man, though, was so much more than just handing over the rings at the right time. That was the easy bit. Coordinating the others and delivering his own speech at the reception was the most daunting thing Joe, Brian and Robert had ever done. Jonnie had taken his turn, too, when his younger sister eventually married the father of her three born-out-of-wedlock children. Brendy was unexpectedly away with work, so could not make it today. He too had had some rough rides on the alcohol level exceeded rollercoasters of both his brothers' weddings. A best man needing a lot of Dutch, as well as additional European country's courage was a well-known fact. Whether this was true or not, did not really matter, as it was put into practice regardless. Then there was the additional liquid Dutch courage needed to make sure the worry about drinking too much Dutch courage and making a drunken arse of themselves of any European nationality proportions did not happen. This created a vicious little circle of angst that they had all experienced.

Lenny was normally so laid back about life it was amazing to see him vertical rather than horizontal! Now, though, he sat on the edge of the armchair, his eyes constantly drawn to the floor and his clasped fingers constantly moving. As the hip flask reached Joe, he took a grateful swig, silently wished Lenny all the very best and looking anxiously over at Jonnie. One of his oldest mates had changed so much in the past wee while, especially in the last few days. This morning it was as if someone had left the old Jonnie behind and brought out this completely new person that looked exactly like the Jonnie he should have known but did not. Lenny was a changed man too, and not for the best, as nerves altered him mentally and physically.

It was nine o'clock in the morning of Jonnie's wedding day. Jonnie's bride-to-be and her bridal party would be a lot more refined, sipping champagne at this hour of the morning but that was not what the lads wanted at all. It was one of the very few occasions when drinking whiskey from a hip flask this early was totally acceptable, without any scandal or the need for any addiction counselling. Mind you, when Joe looked over at the extra-long swig Jonnie took, maybe counselling was needed? He had seen Jonnie, like the rest of them drink a lot before, never quite succeeding in working towards, despite their sometimes-ludicrous liquid labours, drowning themselves from the inside out. This was different somehow, as there was an urgency to his draining of the hip flask, as if he was trying to wash something away but he did not know what it was. As he watched Jonnie take a large second swig, Joe wondered if it was not just one thing, but everything.

Jonnie was the last of them to get hitched. All of them had thought he never would, wanting to be the sportsman for ever, playing the field, home and away. That was until he met Shauna, who had taken his heart for sure. It was strange but actually very satisfying for the mates to observe Jonnie experiencing being actually and truly in love. They enjoyed even more Jonnie's concerned questioning of the physical effects this had on him. In his conversations with his mates, he often swayed from happily bathing in such feelings, to asking if a cold shower would wash away the palpitating worries as he asked them 'what is wrong with me?' They would mostly slag and tease to jokingly ease Jonnie's self-induced tensions. However, they would also have serious private chats about their own experiences. Then each of them would incoherently babble, attempting to explain the solid difference between true love, love and lust. All of them agreed that being solidly in love was in reality so different from the slushy, mushy fantasy portrayed in films and books.

Such chats as Joe had always ended with acknowledging that true love was started in and was centred on the heart. Being at the heart of everybody, once affected, possibly even infected, this spread like a virus to mess up the rest of body's functions. There was no antidote, apart from being with the person you were in love with. Only this cured the symptoms, making them ease or stop. That was of course until they were not beside you and it started all over again. This emotional up and down, round and around, Joe pondered if it was this motion that created the nausea of love sickness.

Jonnie had already genuinely experienced this 'in love' virus several times before he had met Shauna. These had been very real at the time, but in hindsight were only halfway up the bar that Shauna had set. Back then, he had had the cure taken away from him, being coronarily stabbed with 'there's someone else' or 'I don't love you any more' said by Jonnie or the object of these intense affections. His consoling mates all had their own tales to tell of broken relationships, even the long-term loyal Robert being together with Lisa since school, had a major pre-Lisa heart scar. Lenny and Brian had had their own major and minor surgery that had left their hearts open for a while, before Sue and June stitched them back together again and defibrillated them with new leases of life. Joe had several dead-end wrong roads of his own and a serious one of motorway bypass proportions. That was until he had met Dee and his life had taken a new fantastic road. Shauna had done the exact same thing to Jonnie, completely filling his heart with a balm as soothing as her liquid voice and her gentle personality of nurse like caring.

The heart was one thing, but Joe and the others were more than starting to be concerned about what Shauna was doing to Jonnie's head! Or maybe it was what Jonny was doing to his own head? There was a strange atmosphere in the crowded living room that somehow did not feel like a celebration. It was not only affecting Jonnie but Lenny seemed to have had a personality transplant. Lenny was not much of a talker anyway, and, normally, had a wickedly dry sense of humour. His words seemed to have dried up completely as his carpet staring and hand wringing were only broken up with the occasional 'oh! Wha?' and 'aw yeah!' when his name was called. After a brief response, he would constantly and silently return to his chosen spot on the carpet, in between sipping spirits to revive or help find his own. Brian and Robert were listening intently to Jonnie's now incessant nervous ramblings. Joe sat and watched as he ever-so-carefully filled the hip flask again from the ten-glass bottle sitting beside his feet. *Why they did not just pass the bottle around, instead of messing about with a hipflask?* was a question that popped into his head. He answered it, rather obscurely, that swigging from a whiskey bottle was not the done thing at nine o'clock in the morning? Drinking from a hipflask made it much more acceptable? A bit more refined possibly? He shrugged his shoulders as he screwed on the caps, taking a quick nip that pinched his tonsils on the way down his gullet.

"Of all the organs in the body, the brain is the one that makes human beings so unique," Joe's dreary Mr Mahoney, or as he pronounced it Mr M… aaaa …hooo… n… ey, his biology teacher had said those many years ago. Mr Agony had been his nickname, making learning about the miracles of how bodies worked a sickening and painful experience. His words sprung into Joe's head now as he wondered what Jonnie's cerebrum were cooking up in his obviously fried head. He knew what was going through Lenny's, having been there done that himself. He decided he would have a chat to Lenny in a bit, to try to calm his nerves, using his limited but valuable three stints as best man to hopefully comfort him a bit. Glancing over at the silent Lenny, lathering his hands with the sweat that almost dripped from them, Joe nodded and said to himself he would do that sooner rather than later.

As he contemplated what to say to Lenny, Joe rummaged about in his own disorganised brain to try to find the names of the bits that made brains tick. He was becoming ticked off with not quite being able to remember. Did that say something about the state of his brain that it did not even know what its parts were called? A moment of concern passed over him before he dismissed it based on the fact he was not medically minded. As if on cue, his brain pocketed that there were morons. He congratulated himself for a second but then snorted a scolding inner laugh at his stupidity. They were not morons! *It was neurons!* he lambasted himself. His own neurons seemed to be off kilter the past while. *They are the electric wires that connect it all together. Aren't they?* he argued within his own neurons wondering if these lacked a bit of charge. He stopped thinking about these very quickly when he started to question if you could become neurotic about your own neurons.

Changing tact, Joe became rather excited as he tried to recall the name of those things that whizzed around to make you feel good. Jonnie definitely needed a boost of those, with Lenny in dire need of any extras passed on to him. Although not feeling too bad, Joe reckoned he would help himself to a few as well if they were going spare. *But what were they called? What did they even start with? 'End' something wasn't it? Why did whales come into his mind? Or should that be dolphins?* He paused a moment, frustrated at his brain not functioning the way he wanted. *Did it ever?* he asked himself sarcastically as he started thinking about ins and outs. "Endorphins!" he spoke out loud, stopping the others chatting and all of them, even Lenny, turning to look at Joe strangely.

"What is going on in your head?" Brian asked Joe with a smirk, knowing how prone Joe was to strange outbursts. This certainly qualified on that score.

"Sorry, just got distracted thinking about how the brain works," Joe replied a little sheepishly.

"I didn't know yours did!" Jonnie retorted with a squealy laugh. The others nodded in agreement. *Possibly too much in agreement?* Joe detected. Joe raised his eyebrows back in reply but was relieved to see a twinkle in his eye that showed the Jonnie he knew was still in there somewhere.

"I was just thinking about how much we get ourselves into real stews about things that will always get served up okay in the end. We get all nervous and anxious and our brains start playing tricks on us. It keeps stirring up a whole pile of stuff we don't need to worry about. If our brains are working overtime on stupid worries, it stops the rest of the normal stuff happening. It affects how we act, our personalities, and we even end up mespro… mispronince… mispronouncing our words!" Joe rambled, stammering a bit at the end with nerves. That was not like him at all; he mildly panicked. In his mates' company he was probably even more relaxed than when with his family. *Was that something to worry about?* he asked himself. Before Joe could even decide if this was or not, Robert interrupted.

"Easy for you to say!" Robert teased. Joe just looked at the same spot on the floor Lenny had chosen before him. He felt totally ill-equipped mentally to be having a brain conversation.

"Sarah whatshername?" Brian threw into the conversation. "I read somewhere about Sarah something being important in the brain."

"Sarah Toner in our O level classes was really clever!" Joe chipped in. Brian gave him a slightly chastising look but then his eyes brightened. Joe smirked a little knowing Brian had a 'thing' for Sarah back then and wondering if he still did. "Was there a little Sarah scar still on Brian's heart or had that toned in?" Joe asked silently, knowing he would probably forget to ask Brian later.

"Cheers, Joe! That's it! Serotonin! That's the stuff that keeps everybody's brains, even yours, Jonnie, working well." Brian excitedly stated, slumping back on the sofa, squishing Robert a bit more.

Jonnie pressed the play button in his head to reply but it was as if the frontal lode of his overloaded brain had been lobbed sideways. His words were said clearly enough but there was no sense to his sentences. Like a butterfly in a flower meadow, he randomly flitted from one thing to the next. It was as if he had hit a release valve to try to empty out the contents of his head and ease the pressure, by verbally carrying out his own lobotomy. As with all medical treatments and surgery, there is always the chance of 'complications'. Complicated was the very word to describe Jonnie's erratic words, matched by the spinning compass direction of his floor pacing as he stood and stomped.

Lenny stood up abruptly a minute or two later. Jonnie's verbal diahorrea and here, there and everywhere short runs had eventually pissed him off more than his own nerves. Robert stood up too, although it took him longer to wriggle out of the sofa. He had to, whilst still seated, shoulder-charge Joe and Brian to squirm his way up onto his feet. Both Robert and Lenny took a shoulder each, placing their big hands there, which silenced Jonnie. There was a look of curious fear on Jonnie's face but he said nothing. With broad, smiling grins the two escorts almost frog-marched Jonnie back to his seat, Jonnie unable to utter a croak of protest. They lightly but determinedly pushed him down into his previous armchair. Lenny returned to his seat but Robert remained beside Jonnie.

Lenny, like Joe and Brian, sat forward to listen to their normally not as talkative as the rest, but definitely wiser mate. Robert knelt on one knee in front of a quizzical looking but much calmer Jonnie. Robert then spoke to put a proposition, that he had obviously put a lot of thought into. Once they heard it the others could tell it definitely would ring true with Jonnie. It was simple, heartfelt advice that did not require any of them, especially Jonnie, to be of brain-surgeon intelligence to understand. The lads watched a transformation occur in Jonnie before their eyes. Joe could only describe it as if Jonnie's heart and head had merged together in the contented acceptance that what he was doing later that day was the best decision of his future life.

What Robert told Jonnie, that had brought long-term inner peace to Jonnie's life, was…

Linen

It was as if the slow-motion button on the remote had been pressed. Yet, even with everything appearing to move at half speed or less, neither of them could do anything about it. In their head, they were moving at lightning speed. In reality, it was as if they were wading through a very much bigger bowl of the homemade apple jelly that was on the immaculate presented table. Joe corrected himself. Because neither of them could stop it, he realised his fear would become real in the next few seconds. It was going to be the table previously known as 'immaculate'!

The welcome was always so warm and friendly. The conversation was always interesting, entertaining and funny once the small talk eventually ended. They were lovely people. But, there was a but! Sitting on their two comfy but small sofas, Joe would not have been surprised if they had confessed to ironing the light, blue fabric they were covered in. They were so crease-free that was the only possible reason he could think of. It still amazed him how he managed to be the only one rising from those sofas that seemed to leave it as crumpled as a bed that was just got out of. It never seemed to happen to the others. And so it was that Joe had numerous nervousness reasons, including even the simplest of tasks such as sitting in this house, to have angst. That, in comparison to the main event, was a mere raindrop of sofa anxiety when the nerve-end jangling storm of a much more foreboding piece of furniture loomed – the lunch table!

Phil was restricted to a dog like role in its creation, simply acting immediately to 'fetch this…' or 'fetch that…', 'sit there a moment' or 'stay…!' Joe liked Phil a lot. Amazingly, there was a sparkle of life and rebellion in this elderly man that still burned brightly, surviving intact the thirty-three years of marriage to Edith and her 'little ways' as she herself described them. Edith was truly lovely too, being consistently kind and caring to all those she knew or met. She never missed sending any of them birthday cards with her own handwritten, from-the-heart messages inside. As the years went on, these smile, even joyful tear, inducing bespoke, poetic words meant more than the crisp five-pound note always included, no matter what the age of the birthday wishes recipient.

Both Phil and Edith were huggers. They would both bear hug and squeeze all of their visitors, or those they were visiting. They both acted like those before them were previously 'missing, presumed dead' but had returned alive and well years after the war had ended. This would happen whether they had seen them last year, or the day before last. It was when it came to the table that General Edith's military precision went into overload and Private Phil was harried and harangued with orders. Between them they would create a masterpiece battleplan, including seating arrangements, that Eisenhower or Montgomery would have envied. Today was Joe Average and his family's D Day, a very different day from the name they had given to Dee's birthday. Dee was as nervous as Joe was, squeezing his hand a little tighter as the precise time of lunch arrived.

Joe saw Edith glance at the mantelpiece clock. Her eyes went vacant for a split second, Joe surmising that she was calculating in her head how long it would take them all to move from the sofas to the table to be seated. The answer must have been five minutes, which meant it was now that this had to happen. As Edith instructed them all to come on over to the table, she, as usual, made light conversation of her blown-out-of-proportion minor problems organising today. These were never in any way seeking additional praise for her efforts, or most certainly did not make her guests feel guilty at the effort she put in. These were just her ways of making small talk, Joe thinking it was a way to ventilate and distract from her own self-imposed and unnecessary nerves. She would talk about the problems of finding what she would describe as 'proper tomatoes,' lettuces having become so small that two are needed instead of one, hams being not what they used to be and those sorts of multitude of trivial, but important to her and her generation, modern changes. Edith talked away, smiling radiantly as the family moved over. Touching Bella and Ava's cheeks delicately as they passed her, she gave them both a special scrunched up nose face which made them laugh as usual.

Joe felt it well up inside him. Likewise, he could see it spread across his wife's face, his tightly squeezing her hand doing nothing to ease or stop the mild fear. The cutely summer-dressed Bella and Ava had previously sat obediently on their parents' knees, there being only two two-seater sofas in Phil and Edith's terraced house. Whether their daughters picked up on their parents' tension or not, both of them tensed as they moved to stand, each clutching hard on a grown-up hand. With a pretend cheeriness, they moved slowly into the excessively neat kitchen and dining area. In comparison to the small hallway and living room, this massive eating and cooking area was impressive, if rather incongruous. It had been the result of a redundancy funded house extension out the back twelve years previous. Central to this large room was the table! Joe knew that shark would definitely not be on the menu, but he could have sworn he heard that spine chilling music. Scanning his family, he was sure they could hear it too, all of their jaws firmly clenched.

All four sitting successfully brought, unknown to them all at the time, a soon-to-be-extinguished spark of relief. When Bella and Ava carefully placed their napkins on their laps, as they had been asked to do, Joe gave them both a little 'well-done!' wink. On a previous visit, Joe and Dee felt like their kin had been caught napping without any bed linen of an excuse prepared. One of their daughters, a younger Bella possibly, had asked why there was a hanky on the table? There had been laughter then at that, but it hid a tiny accusation of unsophistication, even ill-manners. The embarrassment of accepting the truth of this was hid in the thinly-stretched laughter cover too. Napkins were never used in the Average household. Even when guests came, they remained dust gathering in the bottom drawer, with the exception of when Phil and Edith came for a meal. After that very minor misunderstanding, preparations were made for the next time, as they had been for this visit, and there was no more cloth uncouth.

The small talk flowed endlessly for a few minutes but never grew any bigger as everyone settled into their chairs. Then the serving up and slow stretching began. All the salad items had been split into individual bowls and plates, now spread, Joe wondered possibly in alphabetical order, in two central circles. Such food organisation had confused Joe since boyhood. So much more effort, so much more washing up, so much more hassle than dishing up directly onto the plate from pan, pot or packet that was his family's normal method. With a slight shake of his head at such a mystery, he watched plates and bowls being asked for politely. 'Thank you's were exchanged on receipt and returned after one or two items were removed. Maybe that was why this elaborate method was used, Joe concluded, simply to enable people to interact with each other without pressure. A sort of 'pass the chutney' icebreaker. That may have worked in some circumstances, but for Joe it just caused the pressure to build and his blood turn to ice. He knew it would stay like that until this meal was over, so steeled himself for the next while. Joe put a couple of tomato slices on top of the ham on the delicately decorated china plates before them. Like everyone else, he, conveyor belt-like, passed the bowls or plates to Dee beside him. He was about to go anti-clockwise, but a kind but assertive look from Edith redirected him in the right direction. He grimaced a little by way of apology and conformed to the food flow.

So, the plate-filling continued until everyone had a piece of everything they wanted. Or, in the case of lettuce, Bella and Ava had been ordered to take and eat. Dee managed to increase Ava's green quotient on her plate by over two hundred per cent, through subtly adding more lettuce than the fifty pence piece token gesture Ava had selected. An ensuing huff face was puffed out by a single look and one shake of the head by Dee. The clatter and chatter died away as all at the table now had plates full of food. With an 'everyone loaded up? Let's get stuck in!' comment from a smirking Phil, they all did. That was apart from Edith, who delayed lifting her super shiny cutlery for a moment, about to chastise Phil with her eyes for his somewhat vulgar statement. Smiling at him instead, he winked at her, saying sweetly in that closed for a second eye that he was proud of her and loved her.

As Edith surveyed her table scene, matching it almost exactly to the one she had planned, it happened. The Ava-versus-lettuce situation had, in Ava's view, not been resolved to her satisfaction. Ava reached to provide her own solution to the enforced extra lettuce delegation. In one quick-as-a-flash-motion, she rose up in her chair, stood on it and stretched over for the custard-coloured salad cream she had just spotted in a glass bowl near Edith. Edith was busy sorting beside her, filling Bella's glass with blackcurrant juice she had bought specially for her great nieces, so had not noticed. That was probably another reason why Ava went for it herself, rather than ask as she had done for the other things. Dee and Joe were distracted, laughing at another one of Phil's anecdotes they had not heard before, so they did not notice Ava's tableware clambering until it was too late.

It was a long reach for her but, with her parents' hearts skipping a beat or two, she had made the outward journey without incident. Ava had lifted the glass bowl, smiling over at Joe and Dee who still telepathically forced out the 'be careful!' message. Then the slow-motion horror show began, with the large bowl of beetroot playing the lead role. It sat untouched out of pure fear from Joe and Dee of repercussions, with only Phil taking a few slices from it. Bella and Ava did not like beetroot and that was one vegetable their parents let them off with. Greens were a different story, but now was not the time to tell that, as another gory tale was unfolding at that time.

The matching cloth belt in Ava's dress defied the laws of physics and mathematics and manged to entrap the handle of the large spoon protruding from the bowl of purple liquids and solids. As she moved back, the spoon acted like one of those things they used for throwing rocks at castles. Trebuchet did not come into Joe's mind as he had no time to rummage in his mind dictionary at that moment. He had time to do nothing else but freeze and have only one-word echo in his head – "Nooooooo…!"

The spoon acted like a spring as it tinged out of the bowl firing beetroot and its juice in an arc across the table. Two small globes of beetroot landed, defying the laws of chance on the extensively cluttered and covered table, between the lettuce plate and the ham. The sprayed juice landed on plates, bowls and spaces with the randomness of a machine gun.

Ava sat back down in her seat, her salad cream bowl with its spoon still in her hand. Joe saw the laws of chance had yet again been defied, as her dress was totally untouched. Her little face was pale with worry, as were the rest of her family's. As the slow-motion stopped Joe stared over at Edith at normal speed. Her face was like nothing he had seen before. It was vivid purple with rage. He very quickly concluded that this was not her attempt to match her recently recoloured tablecloth! Phil's red face appearing suddenly from bursting out laughing was certainly not going to help tone down any colours.

Edith silently and suddenly stood up, reached over and moved the lettuce and ham plates to sit on top of other bowls. Joe remained seating but stretched himself up, as did Dee and everyone else at the table, to see better. Edith swiftly spooned the beetroot balls back into their bowl and pressed her large white linen napkin into the small pond of purple on the tablecloth. Dee silently mimicked her shoving her napkin in too, to watch it rapidly dye. Dye was what was happening before their eyes, with Joe and Dee feeling they wanted to do a different spelling and dictionary definition of this word. Although a very common phrase Joe had never hear of anyone actually having embarrassment as the cause on a death certificate. There was, however, always a first time for everything. He wondered if Dee and him would be recorded as the first.

Phil began to rummage about, moving other plates, jars and cutlery as he tried to tackle the arc of juice that had made a uniquely original tie-dye pattern. Joe felt compelled to help, as they both dabbed and dobbed at this freshly painted artwork, their napkin purpling as a result. *How had so much managed to be spilt?* was an enduring question in Joe's head that he had no answer for. Ava and Bella just sat totally silent. Ava was in a state of shock almost. Her da's sympathetic, unable-to-hide-embarrassment smiles were doing nothing to ease that. Joe's raised eyebrow stare at Bella did convey the intended message that she most certainly should not be gloating and the beginnings of her smug smile were removed. With a stare at Ava and a flick of his head towards Edith, this unspoken message was delivered too. Ava spoke out, loudly and clearly. "I am so, so sorry Auntie Edith. Really sorry! I did not mean to do that. I don't know how it happened…" Her words petered out into sobs as she sat back down in her seat and the tears began to flow. Edith just looked back at her but said nothing.

Edith had tried to use her frantic cleaning up as a way of venting her anger to no avail. No one spoke to her, nor she to them, terrified of making things worse with a flippant remark or overstressing the seriousness of what was in reality a very small accident. All four damp napkins were varying shades of purple, with Dee and Joe arming themselves with Bella and Ava's as well. This extra ammunition did not change the course of the battle. The small pools of purple liquid had been defeated and swabbed up, but there was remaining fluid trapped within the linen fibres of the tablecloth like some untouchable underground resistance. This steadily oozed out wider and wider, the continuing frantic dabbing attacks making little or no difference in impeding its spread. The table was cleared more and more of crockery, cups and cutlery to prevent any collateral damage. All these were hurriedly set on counter tops or even on chairs. The bowl of beetroot had been taken to the cluttering up sink by Phil like it was Semtex with a ten second fuse. All this clearing of the table revealed the extent of the purple invasion. Joe truly thought Edith was about to cry. Phil looked at his wife the same way, unsure what to say or do next. They all were just standing now, waiting to see what Edith would instruct next. No directions came to make things right, everyone emotional about this simple lunch having gone up the left.

There was hope, however, as linen was an extremely durable material. It had sewn a big patch in the arse of Ulster's huge industrial trousers for centuries, right up until the 1960s. Scattered pockets of it remained in towns and villages, still supplying the world's demand for the quality Irish Linen was always credited with. That brand name was still used, even if no flax for cloth was grown on the island of Ireland, and most of the thirteen processes needed from harvesting to finished product were carried out elsewhere. Because even one of these, or even if it was only packaging it up, occurred on the island of Ireland, then this allowed Irish Linen stamped on the product. It shocked Joe when he found this out. It shocked him even more when that seemed to be the one thing with every branded product nowadays, with no one claiming they were being conned.

Regardless of the authenticity, Joe was glad linen items were still being made. Edith had told the story, as she did every time, of the history of this table cloth. It had been handed down from her mother, with every female member of her family embroidering something on it. At that point in her repeated story, she would always look hopefully at Dee and her daughters, a sadness at her not having kids of own always prevalent on Edith's face at such a moment. However, Dee had mastered the art of how to not answer that question, even if she had not mastered sewing. The tablecloth was easily replaceable, the history of it not so. This made Joe reluctant but felt compelled to do so. As he was about to apologise and offer to buy a new one, Ava sprang from her seat.

Ava raced over to Edith and, tears flowing freely, hugged her Great Aunt as tight as her arms would let her. Ava pressed repeat play and a muffled "Sorry. I am so sorry…" went on and with Ava's face buried in Edith's flowery dress. There was a slight hesitation from Edith but then she placed her hand on Ava's head and tears flowed freely from her older eyes too. Her hands clasped around Ava's shoulders and she pulled her in tighter. Touched by the scene, Dee whispered in Joe's ear, a little tearful herself, "Forgiveness does not have to always be spoken, just shown."

While Joe had been thinking about shops that sold similar table cloths and was about to offer to buy one, Dee had been flicking about on her phone. Joe could not see what she was doing, questioning if this was really the right time to check emails and messages. She had not been and instead, with a deserved but ungiven trumpet fanfare, now shoved her phone in front of Edith. Edith was unable to see for tears and waved her away. Dee showed Phil, whose face visibly lit up. Phil said, "That is fantastic. We will give them a call to sort that." As Dee flashed the phone in front of Joe, he saw the specialist cleaners' website displayed.

"No! No! No! We will pay for the clean-up. No buts about that at all. We will have this looking good as new for you both," Joe stated with a flourish as Dee poked and prodded at her phone some more. She held the phone in front of Joe's face again with a shocked and questioning look on her face. Joe could feel the blood drain from his face, just about stopping intense swearing escaping into reality at the estimated on-line quote. Backtracking a little, he said a little sheepishly, "We will sort something out! It is only cleaning up. That's all! Don't worry Edith, we will sort it for you. And besides, no one is hurt and that is the main thing!"

Joe felt the burn of Edith's eyes on him at his last statement that her tears were not quenching. He swallowed hard thinking for a moment that there was still the possibility of someone being hurt. Probably him if he came out with any more statements like that. Her eyes changed just as quickly, back to the caring ones she seemed to have almost constantly. "I am sorry too. I should not be so fussy. It is just the way I am with my little ways. This tablecloth is just so special and youse all coming today is a special occasion. If we can have if cleaned up then great. Let's finish our lunch and forget all about it…" Edith spoke with sadness but acceptance.

All of the adults removed the last of the bits from the table. Ava returned to her seat, Bella not having moved from hers during the entire thing, quietly staying out of the way sipping away at her juice. The stained table cloth was removed and a fresh, lot less fancy one threw over instead. Within a few minutes the adults had scurried back and forth to fill the table up with all the previous items. Except for the beetroot, which was left at the sink, no one even asking if anyone would want any. There was some jiggling about, to make sure everyone had the food filled plates they had before. Ava was less than delighted that the lettuce was still on hers, wondering if there was actually more on her plate. Edith footered about a bit with where the plates and pots were placed but soon gave up. Sad tears dried up, replaced by fun ones, smiles returned to faces and chat began.

"Okay! Everyone loaded up. Let's get stuck in!" Phil called out again. There was no silent reprimand from Edith this time. Bella moved forward to grab her knife and, slow motion happened again. Joe and Dee watched the horror sequel as Bella's elbow bowled over her juice. It flowed like a fluid torrent, swirling under the plates and bowls, purpling everything! Joe just gawped in disbelief. Currently, this was turning out to be a black day,

Joe doomstered, with yet more dirty linen to sort out. The way his life went sometimes he thought about extending the wash-line he already had. It was full of already hung-out soaking wet things that he never felt he was able to dry. Removing the stains, whether beetroot or currant or whatever, was an even bigger challenge he had so far failed to meet.

"Leave it!" Edith barked sharply as everyone was about to stand again. Bella was about to apologise but was restrained silently by Edith's held up palm. "Let's just eat and we will sort it all out afterwards," was all she said with a deflated smile.

Lithuanian

The sun was a ball of fire, the few fluffy clouds like wisps of white smoke dotted across the otherwise totally clear blue sky. Joe gazed up with half closed eyes, shielding his pupils from the hot radiance pouring down from above. He gave a satisfied smile. As in life, he always felt you needed the rain to appreciate the sunshine and today shone brilliantly, a very appreciated change from the heavy downpours and annoying drizzle of previous days. He and his little Average family were here to make the most of it, as were others. A hot sunny day in Ulster was a weather lottery when everyone won and felt, maybe not like millionaires, but certainly an awful lot richer for it.

He felt the warm sand trickle between his toes as he strode along, his trainers bunged in another bag. Or had he left them in the car? He knew he had regretted not wearing them. The car park's stabbing tarmac stones penetrated through the hard skin on his feet soles, causing him to walk the few metres embarrassingly, like he was busting for the toilet, before he was on the silky-smooth sand. The grains of silica provided a soothing, comforting sensation on his feet, almost succeeding in taking his mind off the strap digging into his left shoulder through his thin T-shirt. His wrist was starting to ache a bit too. The almost-as-bright-blue-as-the-sky cool box in his right hand he had thought not that heavy when they had left the car park. He was increasingly rethinking that assessment, sure that he could feel his arm lengthen with the imagined increasing weight. He thought it must have been eating the contents and gaining a few pounds, as it definitely felt slightly heavier with every stride. He shifted the strap of the hold-all containing more food and assorted bits with his left hand. The adjustment brought a moment of relief, before it starting burning and rubbing into the fresh skin it now occupied. Still, he smiled with satisfaction, determined these minor irritants would not spoil the fun family day ahead.

Dee was beside him, as he hoped she always would be. She too smiled as she lugged her overstuffed handbag and another open bag, obviously with heavier things in it besides the stuffed-in tartan rugs sticking out of it. An unwritten law of physics was shown by their kids when walking with their parents, Bella was ten feet ahead and Ava was ten feet behind. That was normal, Joe concluded, and nothing to do with them not wanting to be beside their inaccurately labelled uncool ma and da. Or at least that was what he hoped. Bella bounced along eagerly with the rucksack on her back containing twice as much as it really should, plastic spade shafts sticking out to make her look like a balding toy hedgehog. Ava dawdled behind, only carrying the plastic buckets in one hand, with a rainbow-coloured beach ball tucked precariously under her other arm, gazing all around. Her regular five-minute 'come on, Ava!' encouraged gently by her ma, increasingly not so from her da, made her speed up for five seconds. After this, she would return to her dawdling daydreaming, smiling as always with that innocence of a seven-year-old.

As the sun beamed down, Joe felt like he was being singled out for intense cooking. Sweat beaded on his brow and he felt little salty rivulets run down his cheek. Still, he smiled contentedly as he scanned around. There were other families already set up or doing the same as them, trudging along happily and slowly to find their own sand spot by the sea. He smirked as he thought of those holiday adverts for Costa Del Wherever. He pictured those seal colony packed beaches of bronzing bodies and congested parasols, all crammed together like some enormous tourist traffic jam. He shook his head and snorted. That was not for him and his family agreed. He believed family days out were to escape the crowds, not be a part of an even worse one than normal.

They were on the North Coast, with its miles and miles of golden beaches, each council area in a cleanliness competition to ensure Blue Flags kept flying and the tourists, and their money, kept coming. He silently praised them for their successes, then heard a plastic bottle crackle under his foot. The beach was so open, the green fields behind and the expanse of sea beyond. Further along the coast they would have seen the small and not really frightening uninhabited Skerries islands. In the opposite direction, the lovely L-shaped lived on Rathlin Island. Here there was nothing but ocean and sea between where they were and the well named Iceland and the hypothermic Arctic. This not surprisingly, did affect the sea temperatures. So, although the beaches here looked as good, or better in Joe's totally unbiased opinion, than the Med, the seawater did tend to be a little cooler.

Well – quite a bit cooler sometimes but then it was all a matter of… what was the word he was looking for? Acclimatisation was what he decided on as the best fit.

Since he was a kid, he had waded in slowly to these waters in his swimmers, feeling the numbness crawl up from his feet to his shins, then his thighs. Then the chilly water would reach that very delicate bit as the sharp coldness touched his trunks covered groin. No matter how much he inhaled, it was not going to go away. His boy, and now man, bits, would try to curl back up into his body in fear of the wet coldness. He would ignore this, persevering and wading out further. He would summon his courage to take those next two steps. After the compulsory making of multiple monkey noises, once the water was lapping against his belly button, he knew he had made it. The boundary had been crossed. Although the cold would continue to crawl up the rest of his torso, encouraged by the splashings of his parents or siblings, mates or girlfriends, or wife and kids, or whoever he was with, that never mattered. A numbness would come over all of him and he would dive and splash and flap about as if he was as free and immune to the cold as a dolphin.

Then the whole process would happen in reverse when he left the water. Rushing up the beach, shivering and shaking, lips and teeth butting against each other almost electrically, he would race for the rug claimed family spot. A towel would be grabbed and flung desperately around his shoulders. Within seconds there would be a steamy warmth created within, when the shivering and chattering would ease. A refreshing contented happiness would overcome him. As a kid at that point, he would usually be handed a semi-warm tuna or egg sandwich. Back then he remembered the bread tasting a little of the tupperware box it had been sweating in, having sat in the sun for too long. He moved his grip on the coolbox handle and congratulated himself that the food today would at least be cool and, all being well, plastic-tasting free.

As Joe reflected, he wondered what was in today's sandwiches. Dee had made them while he had equally calmed, excited and chastised the kids whilst loading the car with what was needed and rejecting the strange and endless unnecessary items, they presented to him. Bella wanting to bring her nightie to sleep on the beach fell into this last category. Ava's teddy had likewise been tearfully returned to her bed. Just as he was hoping it was neither egg nor tuna, although knowing he would eat it if they were, he heard his name shouted, from a voice he knew he should know, from a few feet away.

"Joe 'Ain't So' Average! How the hell are you?" became louder as the speaker came nearer to him.

Joe looked to the side and grinned. "Stevie 'Slick' Ross! Not so bad! What about you?" His bag burdens softly thudded as he let them drop to the sand. He threw his arms around Stevie as he strode the last few steps to receive the embrace, as Stevie did him. They slapped backs and then broke off shaking hands vigorously, pausing to look at each other. There were a few face lines and tiny flecks of grey in Stevie's jet-black, heavily-gelled hair. Apart from that, his face was still the same. He wore only shorts and his toned, muscled body had no trace of the beginnings of a beer belly he had from student days. He was seriously tanned too, a tan never achieved in the erratic sunshine of Northern Ireland/North of Ireland alone. It made his white teeth shine out from his broad smile even more. Joe wondered what Stevie made of him with his slightly pinkish, light brown, purely locally gained tan; his, not so bad for someone who never went to a gym, body; his fairly grey free hair and slightly crooked teeth of a lesser whiteness. Before his paranoia went any further, Dee was at his side, looking radiant and friendly as always.

Joe introduced her to him and his former course mate from uni to her, only giving her these basic facts. He was hoping Stevie would let his stories and adventures of student life with Joe wait until later, or never for some of them. Stevie shook her hand delicately but firmly, kissing her on both cheeks. "Lovely to meet you. Did you get a special grant from the government to marry this one?" Stevie joked to her.

"I cannot tell you the amount, but it was a six-figure sum!" Dee laughed back at him and Joe laughed along sarcastically.

"Come on up and join us! Meet my better half and the wains," Stevie said as he started walking back up the beach, obviously not taking no for an answer. Joe and Dee shared an apprehensive look. Both had probably just had the same very recent memory of their kids meeting other ones. Bella had aimed and fired a knee into the bully boy bollocks of one of the sons of Dee's former work colleagues they had met in the forest playpark. They believed Bella and little Ava's version of events, that he had pushed Ava off the rope swing, then pulled Bella's hair when she tried to pick up her cut knee sister. Joe had seen it happen and all four parents had rushed over as the crumpled-in-a-pile Bullyboy's brother started wailing for their ma. Joe had watched, but could not hear what she had said, as Bella had verbally laid into the bigger lad. He had pushed her away and that was when she had swiftly let her knee meet where his testes should have been. Picking on smaller girls had made Joe wonder if he had any balls at all? The force she hit him with made Joe think he certainly would not have after that!

He had struggled to stop the overwhelming pride in her, overcoming the concerned parent part, as the four adults had run over. When they arrived at the scene there was a long, embarrassed silence between the parents, no-one knowing what to say, not wanting to make it appear their precious little angels were at fault. So, they had all gathered up their kids, checked the ground for any round shaped items and then had quietly moved away. Both Joe and Dee silently agreed that had been a one-off and glad their girls defended themselves. With a look between them acknowledging that was an exceptional event for their normally well-behaved daughters, Joe picked up his bags and Dee shouted to Bella and Ava, who appeared instantly at their sides and raced ahead of them after Stevie.

Stevie introduced his wife. 'This is Sophia,' not stressing the 'i', her bright blue eyes silently scolding her smirking husband. 'Hi, I am Sophia,' emphasising the 'i' as she spoke greeting them. She shook Joe's hand and then kissed him on both cheeks.

"Hello, Mrs Ross. I'm Joe. Are you a Rossian, then?" he asked, noticing her ice blue eyes were covered a moment or two longer than necessary by an extended blink of long eyelashes responding to Joe's question.

She responded abruptly but politely, "No I not, but speak Russian! I Lithuanian!" Joe nodded and smiled, repeating very slowly.

"Rossian! Mrs Ross!"

Her eyes lightened and she laughed out loud, getting the joke. She continued to laugh as she snorted a little as she said, "I not Lithuanian any more I suppose, now that I am a Rossian! Now I am Irish, Northern Irish, British, Ulsterwoman, Ulster Scots... All of them! I have many identities now I live here in this very confusing land!" Sophia moved over to kiss and hug Dee as Stevie introduced her. The two mothers seemed to hit it off instantly, chatting away like friends of old as they moved over to check on their offspring.

As kids do, while the parents had spent those few minutes talking, they had all jumped in a wide hole together. Joe looked and ducked to avoid a faceful of sand which was spewing out like a tornado as swiftly grabbed plastic spades were put into overdrive. Joe and Dee had been talking about Australia recently, talking a lot about it in fact, and much more besides. The sand was flying everywhere and Joe wondered if his girls, with the help of Stevie's kids, were planning to scoot down under to have a sneaky peak at Australia for themselves. At the rate they were going they should be there by lunchtime, he estimated.

As he peered in the hole, he tried to count the number of bodies. Besides his own two there were five other kids in there. "Wow, youse have your hands full!" Joe said, nudging Stevie. "Five!"

"Yeah! I am from a big family and so is Sophia," making a point of loudly saying the 'i' part of her name, "so we just kind of kept going once we started. Jakob is the oldest at twelve, and little Sasha is our wee baby at three. Jakob! Easy now! Watch out for your little sister!" Stevie replied as a tight-muscled, lean lad looked up and nodded, Joe seeing kindness in his sand-blasted face.

"Fancy a cold one?" Stevie asked as he flicked open a bright blue cool box, identical to Joe's. "As if you would say no?"

Joe gazed over to Dee, made a mime of moving a pint glass to his mouth, mentally asking her if she would be okay driving home? She delayed a second but then nodded, laughing away with Sophia as they neatly laid out the rugs on the sand and sat down on them relaxed.

Joe and Stevie slumped down on the sand beside the rugs, both synchronising the cracking open of their cans and savouring the satisfaction of that sound. Joe took a refreshing swig, sighed contentedly and looked over to Stevie. "It's amazing what you can get on the internet nowadays!" Joe said with a wicked grin, nudging Stevie with his elbow to make sure he knew he was joking.

"Oh, do not even start with all that crap!" Stevie said laughing but with a hint of sickened frustration. "We met at my work. My first job when I finished studying, would you believe? I am still there. Manager of Business Development now. Great job. Money's really good, bonuses and company car and get to travel a fair bit. Miss the family when I am away, though." Stevie paused as he looked over proudly at his considerably larger brood than Joe's.

"Five kids, means you are not away that much!" Joe joked unable to hide an admiring but jealous undertone. Stevie laughed very loudly and a little proudly.

As the Average family laid out their bags and beach gear beside Stevie and Sophias' family's spread of beach essentials, there was an instant friendliness, and talk came easily. Although he had not seen Stevie since they finished studying, the occasional phone call the only catch-up, Joe still never felt intimidated by Stevie. Stevie was one of those people who never boasted, or at least it never seemed he did. He would just state facts and was as genuinely likeable now as he was back then. Joe was about to say something about his less impressive past and present job titles, his probably a lot less money and his limited travel, but Stevie was back responding to Joe's internet jibe.

"Sophia is Lithuanian. She is certainly not one of those Russian internet brides. It was because of the Russians she moved over here, so they are certainly not her favourite race of people. God! We think we have it tough over here?" Stevie shook his head and Joe became much more alert.

Joe swigged his can as his eyes encouraged Stevie to tell him more. "It's supposedly an independent country, but the Russians have control. More and more Russians living there, whether by choice or not, to give Russia even more and more influence..." Stevie carried on telling more stories about the impact on the still existing Cold War going on in that small country with icy relations between locals and its vast neighbour. Joe listened intently, lying on the rug soaking up the hot sun rays. "Just a minute..." Stevie interrupted his own story, rose quickly and grabbed a piece of broken plastic bucket the kids' excavation had uncovered, placing it in a plastic bag containing crisp packets and other rubbish. "Bloody litter!" Stevie muttered as he lay back down.

"Just proves Russia is still the same as it always was, maybe even worse," Joe quipped, and Stevie nodded.

"Then you have to appreciate it is a very proud country that has had the USA on its case for decades. That makes it even more paranoid in the modern world I suppose," Stevie replied in agreement begrudgingly, still showing contempt for the country that had impacted his now-wife's life.

"Besides, it means if it was not for the Russians, Sophia would never have come here, and you would never have met! Fate, destiny, divine will, whatever you call it works in strange ways!" Joe added. Stevie looked towards Joe, his eyes diverted to the sand as he let that fact sink in. Stevie nodded increasingly contentedly, obviously not having thought about or really appreciated that fact before.

The kids all decided in an instant that they were going into the sea, springing out of their ever-deepening hole surrounded by sandcastles, to all tell their close-by parents in unison. Bella and Ava stripped off their outer T-shirts and shorts to reveal their swimsuits underneath, flinging these over to Dee before running full pelt down the beach with the other kids. Jakob was holding little Sasha's hand as she tried to make her legs go faster to catch up. All four parents were able to clearly see where they were at the edge of the gently lapping waves, meaning the adults could relax in each other's company.

"Enough international politics! So, what did you parents say about you bringing home a foreign wife then?" Stevie asked jokingly. Joe was stunned a little at the incongruousness of the question. However, he could not reply as he did not want a 'your wife is more foreign than my wife' competition starting. After a second or two, Joe answered with a 'because she's English?' and Stevie mumbled an 'u-huh!' as he sipped from his can.

"They were fine about it and never really make an issue of it, apart from talking slower when she was with them. Thankfully they all get on really well. Had not really thought that much about it to be honest. Why do you ask? Do your folks and Sophia not get on?" Joe spoke reflectively and curiously.

"You remember my folks, don't you?" Stevie asked tentatively with his face showing a little apprehension. Joe could not really but nodded anyway. "They are like far too many others over here and a bit hung up on the religion thing that our part of the world takes to a whole new level!" Stevie tutted sadly and Joe mimicked him equally sadly. "My da especially could not hide his shock when I told him that Sophia was devout in her religion, that is opposite to my folks. It created a cold war between us for a while, that thankfully had no nuclear warheads involved!" Stevie laughed but not in a happy way. "There was tension when we were married, but, since the kids arrived, things have thawed an awful lot and they have almost totally accepted Sophia." Stevie rolled his eyes a little then went quiet a moment.

The time passed as easily as the conversation came. After a while, the kids came charging up the beach, all of them not showing any signs of cold as the sun's warmth increased. They all splattered down on the rugs and let parents know that hunger had drove them from the sea. The adults starting opening the boxes and placed sandwiches and bags of crisps in the conveyor belt of grasping little hands. Joe was the last to reach into the bottom of the sandwich box to make sure he had his own hunger sated. It was an egg sandwich which drooped his enthusiasm, but he bit in and chomped away.

Amongst the hubbub of excited conversations, Joe thought a moment that he had brought Dee to this probably not-so-foreign a land to her as Sophia would have experienced. He thought of all of those from Eastern Europe who had come to his homeland for work and to start new lives. He admired their bravery in coming into this still messed-up land that no one seemed to be tidying up. He thought about their family plans to go in the opposite direction and emigrate out. As he overheard Dee telling about their Australian plans, he felt a true warmth from Stevie and Sophia's encouragement. They used words like 'awesome' and 'exciting' to describe what Joe and Dee were talking about doing, totally agreeing with and justifying all their reasons for moving away.

Joe and Dee had had so many doubts, thinking it was such a big, big challenge, but these were dispersed by Stevie and Sophia's positivity. For some reason, it was so much easier to hear this message from people they hardly knew rather than family and close friends. Joe and Dee had not even told those close to them yet as they were just dreaming about a new life stage and had not really put any wheels in motion to move it along. Dee gave Joe a contented, reassuring smile and he returned one. The kids jumped back into their ever-deepening crater in the sand and again created a sandstorm of sand removal.

"If we leave these ones to it, we will not have to pay any air fares and just travel down their tunnel," Joe joked but with a new seriousness in his commitment to an international change for his family. Dee nodded silently and happily, as Stevie and Sophia laughed encouragingly. Joe knew then that the time had come to start making the dream a reality. He sensed Dee had too.

"Fancy a swim?" Stevie asked, looking at Joe. "No one should be calling out 'Shark in the water' on the North Coast!" he joked in a mock-Australian accent. Joe nodded but as he stood to remove his T-shirt, he silently added sharks to the possible deterrents for not going to Australia. He removed this downer almost instantaneously, now firmly resolved in this Great White Hope for his family. There were too many very real sharks with multiple sharp teeth in this place which he had always referred to as his homeland. These were scaring Joe and his family far away, to want to be in a country where those huge masters of the deep seemed like minnows in compassion.

Light

'Dimmer switch' were the two words that rather madly, but at the same time extremely logically, came into Joe's mind to describe it. Many, many times he had experienced it before. As he listened to him nervously babbling away before him, he nodded as much in agreement with his electrical fitting description of it as he did out of politeness. The words continued to be uttered, with a very slight stammer occurring to allow a second to decide on yet another random topic to ensure an awkward silence did not exist. Joe wondered if awkward over-talking was truly preferable? As he tried to decide, his mind flicked through his mental dictionary to find the poncy sounding word for talking too much. A moment later garrulous popped in there, causing him to smile. Then verbosity came out of nowhere and he smiled wider. This was an even better adjective for the person, still rabbiting on in front of him on the slightly busy and drizzly town centre street with its warrens of shops.

He was telling Joe all about what he had done since they had last seen each other. They had been standing in the street for nearly ten minutes, meaning he obviously thought there was quite a lot to tell. That last time had been in the huge, bland, concrete block building of a school, with its equally bland rectangular classrooms that no amount of colourful, informative posters could brighten up. It was a place where they had been both truly inspired, and where they had equally felt their brain cells dying of boredom. Since then, it certainly appeared that he had decided what had happened to him was much more important that Joe's life story. Joe felt relegated to a listener role, not a conversation participant beyond a random 'yeah' or 'really?' What surprised Joe was the fact that he did not resent this. He actually felt quite content to nod with pretend interest and not have to think of or make profound or funny responses. In a way, the flow of words he did not truly need to listen to was therapeutic, allowing him time to do what he knew he did too much of – think.

As a result of this, the moveable light switch analogy had emerged from his normal, enduring flurry of mind activity. Friendships, or the rather grand-sounding and pretentious-sounding interpersonal relationships he often heard from so-called relationship gurus on the telly were just like that, he felt. For sure, bright light had shone during that time at school with the now chubbier and more facially haired man talking to him. They had been school mates. Good school mates in fourth and fifth year, both inside that big building and outside in the testing of restricted freedom allowed teenage lads of urban streets and rural fields. Different A-Level subjects drove a wedge between them as they drifted off to form other class friendships. Very soon after school, through less and less contact by phone and even less sharing of physical presence, that light had reduced and reduced. That was until, although never having been switched off from an argument or disagreement, it had been slowly turned down until no light was left. The inclination to turn it back up flickered occasionally in those early post-school years, but soon dimmed down completely as well.

Joe was trying hard to twiddle this dial up as he listened. Now he felt like he was back in one of several of those less than interesting crowded classrooms. As back then, he was now maintaining a facial expression that showed he was still hearing what was said, even if it was not being noted down in his grey matter. He tried hard to brighten the one-way conversation up by trying to twirl the dial, several times. All he succeeded in doing was achieving a couple of brief sparkles of illumination as he remembered funny incidents, adventures, sporting successes but mostly failures, and the broken spirits left from giggling girls dismissing proposed dates when the courage had been eventually gathered. Eventually he gave up and, as he often did, fixed his face to show some sort of attentiveness and allowed his thoughts to wander down his ever-multiplying multitude of neuron pathways, to torture himself even more to figure out life.

Joe knew a lot of people. Not just relatives and the endless discovering of second, third, fourth, etc cousins scattered across his homeland and foreign lands beyond. Nor the sliding scale of those he had been at school with, knowing some really well, others much less so. This graph of knowing slid downwards until he reached those schoolkids that he only knew the name of and did not want to, for reasons of bullying or nerdiness, never want to go beyond that imposed restriction. There were the girls he knew too and ones he still to this day wished he had known better, or at least tried to. There were those girls at school whose very name still made him cringe at the embarrassment of a disastrous attempted asking out, and very real spine shudders at even more disastrous dates and attempted first kisses. After school this trend continued, as he still searched for 'the one.' He restrained a little laugh, causing a curious look from the still talking fella in front, as he still found it shocking that he had managed to find her. It was even more shocking that she had not only agreed to be Mrs Average, but a very clever Dee Average as well.

There were work colleagues and neighbours too and, of course, housemates, as well. Some of which truly were, others the best he could say of was that it was an experience never to be repeated. There were the shopkeepers he only knew by name and making small talk with. There were those random conversations at bus stops and in other queues that meant they could be placed in that very vague and open to interpretation category of 'knew to see.' All of these people and more, Joe contemplated, had impacted his life at all sorts of levels. Some had shone bright lights, some provided mere glimmers of hope and others were a constant beacon. There were also those, thankfully few, who had brought only pure darkness. He buried these deep in the dark recesses of his memory, never willingly resurrecting them. A psychologist would say this was the wrong thing to do with the dark stuff, but Joe knew he was no Luke Skywalker. All he could do was use the force he had to put such dark to the side and be an evader of as much of this darth as possible. Dwelling as much in the light, on all sides, as much possible was what he tried to do. He mostly succeeded.

All of these people that brought light into his life, when he thought about it, were part of who he was. In the same way he was part of who they were. How much or little, he decided, depended on personalities. As Joe listened to a long list of room descriptions and the electronic gadgets each contained in the large new property the constant speaker had moved to recently, gardens popped into Joe's mind. A little confused initially, he followed this through and nodded in agreement with himself that personalities were just like gardens. Sizes of both were very different for a start, from a couple of pots by the front door to acres of assorted plants. The flora varied enormously too; enormous trees, dominating everything, to tiny, almost inconspicuous but very special flower heads that brought both beauty and joy. Then there were the weeds and overgrown areas too. He sniggered a little, causing another curious look from the talker, knowing it would take more than a strimmer and chemical sprays to sort out his own wilderness bits and long rooted perennial weeds out. That applied as much to him as it did the outside space back and front of his owned home, in another hundred and fifty or so mortgage payments.

As words still wafted over his head, the biblical parable of the sower was thrown into his pondering, as he rediscovered a distant relic from Sunday School days. This grew into remembering the seed not able to grow well on thin soil, not growing at all on a pathway, choked by the weeds he had just thought about and, of course, the good seed that grew well. Gratefully, he remembered the people who had planted seeds in him, kind faces flashing across his mind vision as he pictured them. A little anxiously, he thought about the seeds he had planted in others. Smirking again to remove the teenage, hormone-driven association with seed planting that still remained with him as a grown man, he paused a moment to feel the pride of being a da of two beautiful daughters. Both Dee and him were doing all they could to provide good soil parenting for them. Then light came to him again, philosophising about the need for light for any of these seeds to even have a chance to grow.

'And what about you?' was the question that bulldozed into Joe's ears. He had listened to thousands of words and yet these four had managed to barge all the trees, flowers and faces over the edge of a cliff. They cleared his brain and brought him abruptly back to where he was in the real world. A mixture of anger and confusion left Joe only able to say 'mmmmm?' He felt frustration too that this was probably one of the reasons he thought too much – because his thinking kept being interrupted before he had finished. Then he caught himself on and accepted he would never, ever finish thinking.

'And what about you?' was repeated a little impatiently, almost demanding an answer immediately. Joe found the tone, as he had with most of what had been said before, irksome after his enforced marathon listening session. In that second, he regretted not having just walked away but politeness had overruled, and he had stayed and endured.

"Well! Went to uni. Was over working in England for a couple of years. Came back to a job here and working away. Married the girl of my dreams. We've two beautiful daughters and a decent enough house. Life is full of ups and downs but then – you know – that's life!" As he finished speaking, it was as if Joe had set himself the challenge of successfully summarised and condensing the last fifteen years of his life into as few words as possible. He certainly succeeded in that.

"Aw, come on! You can shed a bit more light on all that. Especially the girl of your dreams bit!" he asked Joe with an annoying nosiness. It was as if he had divulged, then divulged some more, about his life to Joe. So now he felt justified in demanding payback with all Joe's details. Joe tried to recall what he could of the excessive information of the past ten minutes. It was undoubtedly a very good, well-paid job with an electricity company his old schoolmate had, but his life seemed bland. Everything was about the stuff he owned, the value of it, rather than the stories behind it. He had described his house like an estate agent would, making it about property market investment rather than creating a home. He even had talked about his wife and kids like they were possessions, listing their career and school achievements like the performance review of a car or television.

This analysis, blended with Joe's gut reaction and tingling sixth sense, gave Joe three reasons for him to be very reluctant to tell any more about his own life. He paused, looking at the intensely curious face of the designer stubbled face that seemed to have moved closer to his clean shaven one, eager for more information that Joe was becoming even more reticent to divulge. "Well, it's funny you should say light," Joe replied cryptically. "My wife and kids are the lights of my life. They always have been, even when I have not realised it. My family are all that matter to me and always will be."

"Yeah! It is great to have them to be able to tell people how well they are doing." Joe found that reply not only disturbing but seriously obnoxious. It implied as if family, especially kids, were something to add to a CV! Joe genuinely believed and felt his family were in an entirely separate category to possessions, forming, as they did, the core reason for his very existence. He could feel the frown form on his brow and see the confused reaction on the face opposite him.

As he refused the offered cigarette from the box shoved before him, he watched silently as one was shoved into the lips amongst the stubble and lit up. Joe could not really think of a reply. He rapidly came to the conclusion that he had endured this long enough and, quite simply, did not want to be here any more.

"Well, here I've got to go! Lunch hour is nearly over. I am sure you need to get back to work to keep those pylons piling on the power and lighting up the world! My job lights things up in a very different way. I hope it does, anyway. I try, at least. Anyway! Good to see you and all the very best." Joe quickly reached and almost had to grab the hand to shake it as it lingered by the side of the other man who was clearly reluctant to leave.

Joe turned on his heel and was striding up the street, flicking up his frayed coat collar as the rain became more persistent. He could hear more words being thrown at him with numbers and a half-heard address, but these bounced off his back, as he determinedly moved on. Despite himself, he could not help feeling some guilt at his rather abrupt departure. Nevertheless, he had endured enough and knew that there was no chance of any rekindling of that too long-dormant friendship. Who he had met had become just another name on the list of Joe's known people. He was another someone who Joe might bump into again sometime but would probably try hard not to. It was simply too awkward. It was a former friendship that they both had grown too far apart from. Time and energy were too precious to waste on trying to thump life into a torch that the batteries had died in.

Just as he was about to turn into his dreary concrete work entrance, the clouds parted and the sun shoved its way through, bringing a beam of light that shone directly onto Joe's path. Joe did believe in signs, knowing that despite his sporadic attempts at looking hard, he missed many. This beam of sunlight, in a dismal grey sky, certainly had all the hallmarks of a sign of some sort. Joe stopped and glanced upwards to see if any celestial being or words appeared. Neither did, so he just sighed and welcomed the sun. However, as he walked the last few hundred metres in the sunlit guided path, feeling the warmth on his back, he wondered if he was walking lighter on his feet. Had some sort of burden been lifted from him he wondered? Shrugging his shoulders dismissively, he entered the main door to gloomy darkness and even gloomier faced work colleagues. The power was off. Joe could not help but smile realising the light he had in his family was more enduring than anything pylons and wires could provide. There was the added bonus that, with no power for his computer, his work would have to wait. That lightened his mood even more so, even when he realised that the kettle would not work for a cup of tea did not darken that thought.

Labels

"Daddy, it's sticking out!" Ava shouted up at him as they walked hand in hand down the street.

"Well, that's a good thing," Joe replied with a smirk, prompting the usual happy grimaces of confusion from his daughters.

It was Bella who sighed then grumpily asked the obvious question. "Okay? Why is sticking out a good thing?"

"It's a Belfast saying, but if something is really good, they'll say it is 'sticking out'!" Joe replied. The girls probably did not understand it totally, but brightened up a lot at such a quick and short answer. They had prepared themselves for some long historical explanation so this was a nice surprise. They both drearily admitted that they did need to be told about history, or politics, or economics, or whatever, to understand what was going on to have their life questions answered sometimes. Their Daddy did try to keep it as straightforward as he could, but even then, he wandered off topic sometimes. Both girls had given up entirely on ever having a simple answer to any of the Northern Ireland/North of Ireland questions they had. Even simply finding out what label where they lived had, or should have, on a map seemed far more complicated than it should have been. Asking if their homeland was even a country would send their Daddy off on politics, religions, money, and more spiel.

"But it is still sticking out, Daddy," Bella reminded him.

"And is that not still a good thing?" Joe instantly replied, causing Bella to roll her eyes and jokingly tut a little. She reached up to the back of his neck and shoved his shirt label back down in between collar and skin.

"What did you do that for?" Joe pretend-scolded.

"Because it looks untidy," Bella scolded back.

"When we are out with our Daddy, we want him to be presentable," Ava added, Joe impressed she knew the word presentable. Then he had a minor panic about his compliance with this brand-new rule he had just been told about. "In case we meet any of our friends, or people from school, and have to introduce you to them or their parents." Joe just nodded a little nervously, whilst looking down at his scuffed shoes, jaded blue jeans and unironed shirt, apprehensively repeating the word 'presentable' under his breath.

None of his clothes, either currently on his body or stuffed in his wardrobe or drawers back home, could be called designer. His image was scruffier than he probably imagined. There were a couple of things he had that were knock-offs of designer stuff, and a few charity-shop bought bits, but that was about the extent of his current fashion designer label compliance. Even if he had spring cleaned his entire wardrobe it would still remain 'so last season' fashion. Probably even the season before that in reality! Joe never had or would covet a fashion award. Jeans and shirts were his clothing mainstay style. By not wearing anything too flamboyant or trendy, he thought this might ensure he would not be fashionably hung out to dry. It had worked so far, he hoped.

"But I should have the label on display. Everyone should!" Joe jokingly continued. "Sure, look at those rappers that have their baggy trousers half way down their arses and their boxers on display. What do you call them? I mean their band name, not what a lot of people would call them! Everyone thinks that's cool and even copy them. Maybe I should try that?" He let go of Ava's hand and reached for his belt buckle. Both his daughters straight away grabbed his hands. Laughing as he was, they gripped on tight, just on the off chance he might be serious. Bella was at the age where holding hands with Daddy was not a cool look any more. Her independence was growing as fast as she was, worryingly faster sometimes, Joe thought. She hung on all the same, desperate to avoid any potential parental induced mortification. The older she became, the more this threat loomed and was something she was telling him more and more. Joe carried on speaking, smiling wickedly. "So I could start a new trend of having clothes labels sticking out everywhere." This proved her point that she was right to worry.

"Why would you want to do that, Daddy?" Ava asked, her face obviously trying to figure out a good reason and failing to do so.

"Because that is what you pay for, so you may as well display it?" Joe simply replied. His daughters were lost at this too confusingly simple explanation and their faces showed it. They were well used to their Daddy's often mad and erratic thoughts. He often made them laugh and it was usually fun trying to figure out what was going on in his weirdly-wired head. But this latest one made no sense.

Joe carried on. "Because at least half the price, probably lots more, of clothes is purely for the label!" His girls actually nodded, remembering having these conversations before. "The label is all about advertising. It is not about better quality, or comfier, or better fitting. Definitely neither longer lasting, nor even necessarily better designed. It is purely about the name on the label, for those wearing it to show off how cool, or how rich, or how stylish (or not!) they are!"

"So, you mean designer labels? Not the cheaper, ordinary stuff?" Bella asked.

"The thing is. Most of the time those big, expensive label's clothes that the stinking rich buy, are made in the same sweatshop in the Far East as the chain store ones. There is no difference in the amount of material used or how it is sewn together. Certainly, the workers out there are still paid the same dollar a day, or whatever other pittance they are given, whether their shirts, jeans or whatever go to some poncy brand shop, or a big, cheap clothes retailer. The extra you pay for that label is just pure profit, not making things any better for the workers making them, and only putting a bigger hole in the finances of the mug that buys these supposedly exclusive items." Joe paused realising he was going off on one, as he was prone to do. His daughters' increasingly drooping faces confirming he was.

Ava seized her moment and butted in. "I get it, Daddy. I really do. We have talked about this before. Everything seems to have got worse as well. Not better. I saw pictures on TV about those poor ladies over in Bangles Dash…"

"Bangladesh," her Daddy corrected her.

"Bangladesh." She continued, eager to get all she had to say out. "They start really early and finish when it is dark. They hardly see their families. I felt so sorry for them. Why do those big companies not make things better for those poor people? Surely they can afford to help?"

"But that is just it Ava. And Bella. It is, as with most things in the world, all about money!" He saw their faces visibly groan as, yet again, money was the reason for everything good and bad in the world it seemed.

He scanned around to check where they were going before he continued. He directed them to cut across the very small park, or rather three trees, two flowerbeds, some grass and two seats. They were cutting through to the shops, this having been the day labelled on the calendar for their own list of back-to-school clothing to be completed. Joe had offered to do it this year. With a bemused but exceedingly grateful look from Dee, she had handed the list to him. Dee had already done the school shoe shopping, so Joe felt guilted into contributing. She had given him a final chance of escape with her 'if you are sure?' that morning. He did not take her up on the offer, so she had smiled, kissed him on the cheek and wished him, rather menacingly. "All the very best of luck!" It was going fine so far, them having been lucky with parking up easily and they were having a bit of daddy-daughter time as they walked. Joe's ESP was annoyingly telling him that this happy time was all about to change. Despite the bright blue sky overhead, calm and storm came to his mind warily.

To distract him from unproved gloomy thoughts, Joe said to them both, "Look at them two on the bench! Don't think they got value for money for buying those identical tops? Why are they both wearing the exact same thing, anyway? They are definitely not twins? Do they not have styles of their own? They certainly went for style over comfort. Not for warmth, either!" he said, using a slight nod of his head instead of a pointed finger to direct his daughters' gazes. He did take a moment to glance over himself at the possibly eighteen- or nineteen-year-old girls, wondering what it was they were half wearing. Was it a half shirt, or half T-shirt? Whatever it was, half the top half of both their bodies was bare skin, somehow managing to defy gravity and cover essential bits, just about. A younger Joe would have had much different thoughts about those partially exposed young women. Father Joe worried more about modesty, and catching a chill still sat strangely with him in his thoughts.

Bella and Ava almost instantaneously named the make and where the shop was where the two bench sitters would have bought their tops. That freaked him more than he wanted it to. Girls and people in general being fashion clothing aware was a very normal thing, even if he did not have much more than a thread of interest in it. Bella started telling Ava about the price Nicola in her class paid for a top like that. Joe could not resist a 'you what!' to interrupt. Bella just looked up and shook her shoulders, betraying the view that this was not that expensive in comparison to other things.

"Seriously – for that?" he added. Although considering himself not being a tight arse by any means, Joe knew he needed to clench a bit more to stop it flowing out of him. The cost of that single half top thing was genuinely gobsmacking. It was not just at the price either, but the acceptance of that price, even by his young daughters, that people were willing to pay it.

"Nicola, a twelve-year-old in your class, paid that amount for that half-top thing! You would think she would get it at least half price?" he mocked as Bella and Ava groaned their usual Dad joke response. "Where do they get the money from?" He decided not to go down the appropriate dress code for different ages road. A few of those recent conversations had ended in dead-end crashes, even with the younger Ava. Either parent had huffily admitted defeat, or daughters huffily left a silence hanging while they thought of different tactics. Neither side came away clothed in glory or agreeing what the daughters should be clothed in. Agreement did happen easily when clothes shopping. This only applied to deciding on where to go, types, number of items to be bought, along with the amount of money that could be spent. The contrasting views on appropriateness of some selected items for possible purchase, made Joe feel like he was some sort of starched Victorian in his children's eyes. 'But that is the fashion nowadays! That is what everybody is wearing!' were arguments they soon gave up using on him as they made absolutely no difference. Clothes shopping was never his favourite, but he thought uniform shopping should be really easy in comparison, as the only choices that had to be made were the sizes and that they fitted. That was what he was thinking anyway when Bella disturbed his random thoughts.

"Most of the ones in my class have clothing money given to them! As well as pocket money!" Bella said with a hint of indignation in her voice tone and a sharp glint in her eyes below her flicked eyebrows.

"In my class, too," Ava added with an accusing nod and staring with hard eyes. Joe just about held in a swear and whirred that information around in his brain before he spoke. He was becoming better at doing that, instead of his unfiltered thoughts coming out verbally and causing embarrassment, offence, or, potentially, in this case, money.

"Look, we have been through this all before. You get money when you need it. You buy clothes when you need them. Just because so-and-so has this or that, does not mean that you must have this or that," he replied sternly. Both daughters smirked, having succeeding in hitting one of his raw nerves, yet again. They were becoming too good at that, he admitted, worrying a little if he had too many raw nerves. He worried some more if these, like the half-top girls in the park, were too exposed and easy targets for his daughters. They were now able to play entire tunes tugging on his heart strings too. He knew they were only winding this time but kept his stern tone, just in case, when he added, "Okay!" They nodded and rolled their eyes which told him they were tuning up for another go soon.

They were on the shopping street now, threading their way through several buggies and the bawling babies they contained. He could not help but notice even the babies were wearing branded clothes that were as juice-stained as ordinary clothes. He did not pass any comments and ushered his two along. For many, back-to-school shopping was put off as long as possible, trying to extend that holiday feeling a bit further. Brave parents kitted their kids out at the start of the summer when everything was a bit cheaper. However, that was a big gamble that in the space of two months legs and arms were not several inches longer and sleeves and trouser legs several inches shorter! Maybe it was the sunshine of a great summer, or the rain of a wet one, or both. Whatever it was, growth was certain during the summer months and kids were not exempt. In the end, before it was really too late and there was nothing left to shop for in the right sizes, the kids had to be torn away from their play to reluctantly play dress up in school uniform shops.

Maybe intentionally, maybe not, both girls wandered past the school uniform shop. Joe called them and they turned on their heels to trudge beside him. As they stared it the window, they could see it was packed out with people mingling about between the clothing and shoe racks. Joe managed to hold in another swear. He was not a big shopping fan to start with and crowds made it even less enjoyable for him. His ESP went into 'told you so' mode.

"Let's go!" Joe said snappily, rummaging the list from his jean pocket as they stepped in the entrance, Joe was keen to have this over and done with. Bella and Ava straightaway split in separate directions. Joe paused a moment, wondering which to follow. Seeing where Bella stopped, at a rack with absolutely no uniform clothes on it at all, he thought she would be a while looking at tops and jeans labelled up as in the sale. He strode over to the younger Ava, excusing himself past a Mum about to tantrum at two small boys starting to stamp their feet on a countdown to their own. As he reached Ava picking out a pair of pink sandals that were not recommended footwear on the school's list, the Mum and two boys' tempers broke. They siren screeched at each other, before the bright-red faced Mum dragged both of them out of the shop. Joe manoeuvred Ava off to the side, not only to escape any tirade fallout, but to actually put her in front of what they had come for – a skirt and a jumper.

Joe became more defensive by the minute. Other parents insistently reached into the rack he was looking at and grabbed out jumpers that he was just about to. This tried his patience a lot. His deliberate elbow to a very persistent probing arm resulted in a guiltily satisfying small yell of pain from a particularly pushing in parent, which he insincerely apologised for. Joe grabbed four jumpers, with Ava's school's crest on them, shoving them in front of her with his arched eyebrows telling her to try them on. She took off her light jacket, passed it to Joe and pulled one woolly jumper over her head. It was too tight to even get over. He passed her the next one which was far too baggy and would have held two Avas. The next was so long in the sleeves they almost touched the floor. The last one was short on her back. Frustrated by four failures following each other, Joe reached and grabbed a random jumper from the rack. The sleeves were slightly too long when Ava pulled in on. Joe flicked up the cuffs and nodded. Ava nodded with a reluctant acceptance too. This was the one. It even had growing room which Dee had stressed to him before they left that morning.

Joe neatly hung those jumpers he had lifted back on their hangers, placing them into the rack. Looking around, he saw many had not bothered to do this. A jumper earthquake littered the floor as a sales assistant tried to not become buried amongst it. Leaving her to it, Joe had to progressively shoulder-charge his way through to the skirts section, manners not being observed more and more. The exact same hell of uniform-finding was taking its toll on everyone, even before they had to face the devil to pay. This he had expected would have been easier, yet his ESP rang even louder. He listened to that warning bell this time. Even still, what could go wrong? He knew her waist size and they were all the same length. About to grab one, he realised there were actually four different designs – plain with no pleat, one pleat, two pleat and one with a belt.

"Which one do you like best?" Joe asked attempting to be cheery. Ava just shrugged her shoulders. In her mind they were all school skirts, so absolutely nothing to be excited about. "Come on, pick one, please?" Joe uttered pleadingly as he was simultaneously whacked on the ankle by a buggy being pushed by a fleeing five-year-old and felt elbowed in the back. As he rubbed his ankle with one hand he looked around and saw the very pushy Mum from the jumper rack close enough to touch elbows with him.

She had a satisfied smirk on her face but he let it go. "Pick one that you like!" he demanded from Ava. She again shrugged and made a token gesture of flicking a few of the hung-up skirts with her hands. "PICK ONE!" Joe said a lot more aggressively than he intended.

He managed to hold back yet another swear as he realised he had crossed the line. Water was welling up in Ava's eyes. He went down on a knee in front of her, held her upper arm with his jumper free hand and quietly spoke to her. "I'm sorry. I did not mean to shout. We just need to get you a skirt and then you are all sorted." Ava nodded as she held back the tears. Normally she was not this sensitive, he justified to himself, blaming it on the bustling and boisterousness of the heaving with people shop. She did not look at all at the skirts and her hand shot forward to do as instructed.

"That's not your size!" Joe stated with a poor attempt at calming when he checked the label. She thranly grabbed another, her own temper flaring and dispelling the threat of tears. "That one's too big! Concentrate, please!" Joe rebuked. He reached and quickly grabbed three in her size. "Right – this – this – or this? Which one is it to be?" he pointed in turn as his eyes glared at her to decide.

"But I want a belt one," she said tightly. Joe scanned his selection and saw none of them had a belt. He turned around, hoked through the belted skirt rack. Not able to find her size, he quickly checked the few that had fell on the floor. With a small triumphant 'yes!' he rose up and placed it in Bella's arms. "But it's been on the floor," she half-whinged.

Joe said nothing in response apart from, "That's you sorted, now Bella! Okay!" As they walked across, Ava began asking why she had to wear a skirt anyway? She would prefer to wear trousers like the boys, so she could play football with them easier.

Rather than start a whole debate, Joe simply said "Sorry, those are the school rules." That did not, unsurprisingly, bring a smile to her face.

When they eventually had made their way over to where he had last seen Bella, she was thankfully not far away. Handing Ava her still-to-be-bought jumper and skirt, he asked her to hold onto them tightly. He held Ava's hand tight and pulled her with him to where he saw Bella's head sticking up. With a few 'excuse me, please!' requests, some ignored, some not, he reached her, only to find her arms full of jeans, tops and a jacket.

Excitedly she turned around, dropped the hangers and clothes on the floor and began to put on the jacket saying, "I love this, Daddy. Wait 'til you see it on. And the top and jeans go really well with it…" She started mentioning who the clothes had been made by, which meant they were really popular and arguing they were good value for money. Joe was not listening to the last of what she said, busy picking up her other items. As he stood, he saw her face sink with the knowledge that, although he had not spoken, she knew what was coming. All he did was look, shake his head and put them into her arms. She did not budge, so he clearly and definitively said the words, "Back! Uniform only today!"

She scuttled off as he crouched down beside Ava, giving her a hug to calm her and apologise. They were both almost bowled over by charging teenage lads. Joe stood up and pulled Ava close to him. He scanned around looking for Bella, thinking her away too long to return a couple of items, even in the crowded shop. Then he saw her return, a huge smile on her face. As she neared them, she held up a very pretty top with flowers on it. Before she launched into her purchase pitch, she received the look and repeated, "Back! Uniform only today!"

Bella's blouses were easy enough to find, as were her tights. Although not on the list, they gathered up two pairs for Ava as well. They were plain grey but had mermaids and flat fishes on the soles, allowing Ava to feel a little rebellious. These were thrown into their basket. It was Bella's first year at Big School, so she needed the whole list. As the first child, she needed the entire lot of hundreds of pounds worth of bespoke clothing. She did not want a school jumper as that was so uncool, even in first year. Bella eventually stopped skirting around the choices and picked one, Joe's begging angry face speeding up the decision. Blazers were next, Joe glad the girls' section was not as much of a rugby scrum as it was over at the boys'. Bella wriggled in to grab a couple her size she thought. She tried on the first one that fitted absolutely perfectly. Her smile was soon removed when her da said that one would not do at all. Growing room was needed for such an expensive item he explained to her, as she gave an unseen 'whatever!' look back. The next one had sleeves that covered her hands. When she gave a 'seriously!' look, her da agreed and she returned it. The goldilocks one was found on the third attempt. The sleeves were still a bit long, coming to her first thumb joint and it was baggy around her shoulders. She nodded her head side to side transmitting a 'will this do?' compromise message to her Daddy.

Joe nodded his head, saying with relief, "Yeah! That one will do fine!"

"Let's go get these paid for then!" Joe announced very happily. It took a while at the tills, as two barcode readers failed. Long sixteen- or twenty-digit numbers had to be manually typed into the till. Joe had to laugh thinking putting in £20.50 or £9.99 would be so much simpler, but that was too 'old school' people would say. For Joe, old did not mean obsolete and everyday was a school day we all had to realise, as we should always be learning. Today was teaching him, yet again, that shopping trips of any sort aged him considerably.

Joe intently watched a flustered young male sales assistant offer technical support by banging a reader off the counter. After probably failing to press any life into it via the buttons, Joe saw the shocked smile on his face that this innovative technique had worked. Still high on one success, he tried the other barcode reader and managed to split it in half, exposing its guts wiring, after an over enthusiastic counter clout. Another sales assistant took it off him and sent him off to do something else potentially less destructive. The waiting customers laughed, glad of the entertainment relieving their queuing boredom.

As they waited, Bella spoke up, having decided to delay her wardrobe adding until another day. "School uniforms are just clothing labels, aren't they?" she stated clearly and concisely. Joe looked into her sincere eyes thinking there was a 'but' coming. He waited a moment, but none came.

"Yes, that is true," he answered, not sure where she was going with this.

"But you were saying that clothing labels were bad. That we were just paying for the labels and not the quality of the clothes," Bella continued. Ava showed no interest whatsoever, staring at unicorn patterned socks in the row where they stood, possibly plucking up the courage to ask for them to be bought.

"The same applies to school uniforms too. They are so expensive, especially the blazers. All for the sake of that school label of a coat of arms and a bit of Latin underneath. But are school uniforms a great thing? Yes, I would say to that. They keep everyone the same, making everyone appear equal and not showing off wealth. Imagine school without it and all the rich kids coming in with their designer gear and the poorer kids not!" Joe replied, quite pleased with how he had explained that. He had felt a tug at his jeans from Ava halfway through what he was saying but ignored it apart from a passing nod. When he finished talking, he looked over caringly and she stood content with a smile on her face.

Bella nodded and hummed, showing she was clearly thinking. They moved forward to the free payment point with the working bar code. The first thing that was scanned was a pair of unicorn socks. Joe glared down at Ava who innocently looked up with a 'you said yes!' He did not argue and let it go. Everything was bundled into a big plastic bag, and Joe was sure his credit card squealed in pain at paying so much for not much. He was just glad that was done. Walking out of the shop past the jacket she had tried on earlier, Bella made a few half-hearted attempts at being given a second chance of plea and appeal. "Christmas!" was all Joe said, hoping that would be a long enough stall and other things would be found in between times. Bella grunted, begrudgingly accepting the verdict.

As they left the shop, Joe scanned the list again, he pleasingly ticked off each of the items. He dropped it when Ava bumped his hand with her head accidentally. As he picked it up with the blazer and what he thought was everything list face downwards, he saw the sports kit listed on the back! This time he could not hold the swear back. Labelling himself an eejit, he turned his daughters around and back into the still-seething shop, seething himself. Bella made another appeal for her jacket and Ava reached for another pair of unicorn socks as they entered...

Longshot

After an initial, stunned, 'Oh!' followed by a muttered, 'No shit!' Brian paused long enough for Joe to feel even more uncomfortable than he already did. Brian's intent, guilt-inducing stare may have prevented Joe from being able to speak, but it in no way made him have second thoughts about the whole thing. This was despite him feeling the burning ball in his stomach bounce around even more. Brian broke the strange silence with an even stranger comment. "It's like receiving a note saying, 'Sorry I missed you' and it being signed by an assassin!" Joe processed Brian's statement with a confused cocktail of emotions, half controlled remotely as they channel hopped across his face. He half-laughed, as Brian added, "And I will of course miss you. But not in that way! This had just blown me away. Not that I want to do that to you, of course." Brian was fumbling his words, clearly stunned at the reality of the news Joe had just broken to him, possibly feeling a bit broken himself because of it. It was a killer blow Joe knew, which probably explained Brian's assassin quip. Joe repressed a flashing surge of anger, disliking it being implied that he was a killer of sorts, but quenched this with the knowledge that Brian would not have meant it this way. 'Would he?' nevertheless lingered. The comment brought up black happiness and red sadness from the ocean depths of Joe's memory banks, too. Joe sensed this in Brian, not because he worked in banking, who he thought was totalling up his own profit and loss mental sheet using Joe's statement as the pencil to draw with.

Joe could still not reply. Before Brian spoke again, Joe had realised the assassin reference was in fact very apt. What Joe had emotionally just told Brian was indeed like an on-target bullet, ending one life. That was where the comparison stopped. Unlike the stealthy or hidden sniper assassin, this was not some bolt from the blue or a sudden deadly ambush. Brian knew what Joe was doing, and had been given a running commentary at almost every stage of Joe and his family's emigration marathon. Brian probably knew better than Joe did sometimes, in truth. Joe's mind was so styachied with organising this, along with the mayhem of 'ordinary' work and family life he had, a few times, had to ring Brian for him to remind him of where he was at with everything.

Brian had, like the majority of others, been sceptical when Joe first started mentioning this. He confessed, several times, that he had initially thought, like many other friends and family, that it was just a phase or a dose of the head staggers after a bad day at work. 'It'll pass' was what Brian had honestly told Joe was what he believed would happen at the start. He saw it akin to that time both of them, along with Robert and Jonnie, started planning to jointly buy a holiday home in France, for them all to share throughout the year. It was a bit mad, none truly with enough spare finances to invest in such a crazy notion, but it had huge potential. Perhaps a small part, even Average part, was Joe wanting to return to his dubious French family roots with potential royal connections.

The twenty-seven French words they counted they had between the four of them, excluding Brian and Joes' ability of still, over two decades later, being able to count to a hundred in the language, had not deterred them at all. Jonnie No H had even signed up for French classes but, like the French property searching, gave up after four sessions. They, nor their wives and kids, could agree on the location, let alone the cost. Money for this increasingly mad project caused numerous rows across their homes, even more than it did in normal arguments. And so, without any more time investment, and certainly no real Euros changing bank accounts, after eight weeks the bright star of the French house idea faded from all of their thoughts until it became as invisible in the darkness of space as a black hole. There was a constant moan from Lisa, Robert's wife, right from the start, that this would be what the foreign holiday home idea would have been for their finances. There was no more whining at the now cheesy idea and, before it was baguette to be consigned to being just another crumby idea.

Joe and his family emigrating had persisted a lot, lot longer than a French-tainted eight weeks. Yet Brian had confessed to Joe that as every step progressed, even up to them on the verge of receiving their visas, Brian still thought it would not happen. Joe knew this was not in any way Brian being malicious or doubting their abilities to do it. Brian had stressed this many times that he in no way wished to jinx the Average family or undermine them. Brian had just thought that it simply would not happen for whatever reason and certainly not because he was a nasty sandman to Joe, Dee and their girls' down under dreams. What Joe had just told him had truly burst him out of that denial bubble and splatted him onto the hard reality of solid fact.

In the quiet neither of them wanted between them, as they both stared up at the cliff face, there were patches of rock still visible through the straggly brave willow and ash trees clinging tentatively to the vertical drop. Joe, and he thought Brian was likewise doing, was looking for the narrow, treacherous path to the top they had taken way back when they were in their mad mid-teens. It seemed appropriate that Joe had driven them both here. He had collected Brian and driven a tour of the roads, rivers, woods and fields of their growing up. They had nostalgically reminisced, laughing and joking as they always did. They always remembered the good stuff. They converted the bad into something to laugh about too, cherry-picking what they wanted and discarding the nastier parts. The cliff before them in the old quarry had been their greatest conquest and the scariest thing either of them had ever done. Joe and his family had just completed a long quest to reach the first step of an even more challenging journey to adventure. It had all hung on a cliff edge for a long time but that was over.

Robert 'Builder', with Jonnie 'No H' riding shotgun, skidded to a halt on the loose gravel in the black shiny four by four jeep. Robert smirked and waved out the windscreen. Joe only caught this out of the corner of his eye, giving a quick and modest upward hand flick in response. Jonnie was too busy glaring at Robert and rubbing at his seatbelt snapped neck to greet in any way. Builder prised himself out of the driver's seat, placed his booted feet on the ground and slammed the driver's door so hard the jeep rocked slightly just as Jonnie was about to get out himself. Builder long-strided over to Joe and Brian, bear-hugging each in turn. Jonnie closed his door lightly and sauntered over to them, rolling his neck side to side as if trying to crack it. When he reached them, he friendly-punched Robert, perhaps a little too hard, on the unflinching left shoulder of Robert. "Ya big…"

He could not finish the insult so instead said, "Your driving is still like you have lead in your boots when you brake and clutch, ya hallion! I think you've bust my neck!" Robert just smirked Jonnie away with a 'quit yer yapping!' look. Jonnie tutted back as he tightly hugged Joe, then a less responsive Brian.

"Seriously, Joe! Why did we have to meet here of all places? You know the reputation this place still has for toad in the hole! I do not want people thinking I am up here with youse three playing leapfrog!" Jonnie barked at them, thrusting his hips back and forth, uttering short laughs in between his sentences that hinted of genuine concern. "If I had not such a good reputation…" he began to continue, before Brian and Robert's loud snorted laughter and 'bollocks!' comments stopped him talking.

Joe grinned and shook his head as he interrupted them all by asking, "You remember we climbed that cliff?" All three heads nodded. "You remember it scared the crap clean out of all of us! Even you Jonnie?" Three heads nodded vigorously, especially Jonnie's. "Well, I have been on a cliff like that, climbing it and getting more scared as we got nearer the finish. Now…" Joe paused, looking deep into all three expectant faces "Now me, Dee and our girls are at the top of that, and we are about to jump to the next level. We were terrified of going down when we climbed that cliff as teenagers, and now I and my wee family are going down even further. It is just like that cliff, seriously scary but exciting! I got the job in Canberra and that means we – me, Dee, Bella, Ava and bump – are all going there." Joe paused nervously.

"Oh!" Robert and Jonnie said together. Then after a brief pause, they muttered 'no shit!' almost in unison as well. Brian looked at both of them, shrugging his shoulders once. The other two could see that Brian had already been told but made no issue of it. Brian and Joe had been mates years before Robert and Jonnie made up the rest of the gang. There was no resentment at that. There was not time for them to think like that anyway as they came to terms with Joe's news that they were going to a very far away land. Jonnie mumbled out loud, "The other side of the world! That's a long, long way from here to shoot over to!"

"Yeah! I know!" was all Joe replied, unable to say anything else.

"I know you have told us what's going on, but…" Robert started. He was still not much of a talker, compared to the rest of them, finding it especially hard when it was about emotional stuff. "But… you know… we all thought it was what ye call it… a… I don't know! There have been a few like it, but it's the same as that time with the house in France? By the way, I know that was years ago, but I still swear Lisa gives me this weird stare when we pass the French wines in the supermarket! Anyway, nothing happened with that in the end and we thought the same would happen with this!" Jonnie remained silent, a rare thing in itself, and just nodded in agreement.

"So! None of the three of you thought I would actually go ahead with this and pull it off!" Joe's voice was raised more than he had wanted it to be, caused by an injection of angry disappointment that he knew was not an antidote to calm the emotions going on. He gave each of them a schoolteacher glare, asking the same question with a steely stare. None of them answered beyond a shrug. Joe spun around with a spoilt brat sounding 'humf!' to stare again at the now well-overgrown cliff compared to when they were teenagers. He stepped forward until he reached the mound where they had all stood as lads, gazing up at the rockface with a face like stone. Joe did not look round, but heard the rustle of clothing and scrunch of boots knowing the others were joining him. He felt a hand on his tense shoulder that made it jerk, then tighten some more. Still, he did not look round as Jonnie spoke gently beside him to his left, Robert and Brian he was able to see, corner eye clearly, standing to his right,

"Mate! Mate! Mate!" Jonnie began slowly and deliberately. "You know where we are coming from? Don't ye?" He paused a moment because, even though it would have been positive, his silence made it a negative response and he somehow wanted them to suffer a little for his inexplicably hurt feelings. Jonnie shot his head round, directly in front of Joe's, so that Jonnie's beaming face was all Joe could see. Joe looked down but could not resist a snigger. "I know! I know!" blurted out of Joe before he could stop it. "Yes, I have had my fair share of false starts, firing off on mad schemes and directions that came to nothing. So yes, I know, why you would have thought this was probably going to be another one. But it is not! It is real, very real. Scarily real, and about to happen very soon." Jonnie squeezed Joe's shoulder, tilted his head but said nothing.

"When do you start?" Brian asked to break the strange quiet surrounding them all. Joe told Brian the date. "Oh shit! Four weeks' time!" Brian's mouth gaped. "In four weeks, you, Dee and all will be in Australia? Twenty whatever days and you are gone...!" Brian was wanting to say more but all that denial about it happening had come back to haunt him like some poltergeist ransacking his brain. It had built up in Brian's head that, although Joe was telling him they were another step closer, he still pictured them moving up a down escalator. Although they told him they were another step closer, he believed them just to be still standing exactly where they were. Every step up by them, to Brian, was a step to stand still. This four-week realisation was the gunpowder that fired him like a cannon ball straight up to the escalator top step.

Jonnie's hand was still on Joe's shoulder and he silently squeezed it tighter now. Builder, or Robert as he was meant to be called, started babbling. As uncharacteristic as Jonnie No H's silence was, so was Robert's surge of words compared to his usual concise conversations. Robert was asking all about length of the flight, where it stopped off, packing, food and a whole random assortment of questions. Joe had lost track after the fifth one, so answered none of them, which did not really bother Robert at all. He seemed happy enough just filling the air with noise, possibly to stop himself thinking about the after from that now close departure date of his mate with his family.

This was hard for Joe. He had worried less about telling his brother and sister than telling these three mates that he had been through so much together with. His widowed ma had been the hardest conversation, tears flowing freely from both of them at the kitchen table when all the Average family events and news had been discussed over the decades. Telling his employer had actually been joyful, with Joe easily able to ignore all the false best wishes. Dee was the same telling her bosses but her telling her widowed mother by phone had given Joe several concerns. Firstly, there was the length of the call but that was understandable, and, as it was cordless, Dee had taken it to bed to continue the conversation. Secondly, there was the worry about electricity and water mixing as Dee's tears dripped for intermittent long periods all over the phone. All Joe had done was supply cups of tea and hugs to see her through it until he fell asleep, and they were still talking.

Where they were now, Joe had elected to try to make it easier in the final hard telling he had to do. This was a place that had changed all four of the mates. After they had climbed this, it gave them the confidence to take on the challenges of life. It also taught them to not be so bloody stupid in deciding what to do. It made them realise that life is short, so do not do anything to shorten it even quicker. The long and the short of it was that Joe had dithered a lot about where to tell his mates. It was not about selecting what words to use for the direct how. That was the easy part, as he could tell his mates anything despite their in recent years erratic meeting up due to work and family commitments. The when was already decided as it had to be very soon after Joe's accepting the far-off job offer. Where was what perplexed him, as it was the most important. He wanted it to be meaningful and memorable for them all. His selection of this special memory place of a long-disused quarry had had that desired effect. He could not congratulate himself, as he had been totally unprepared for how deep their lack of belief in it happening was.

Robert picked up a stone and fired it off towards the dark lake below the quarried cliff face they had climbed those many years ago. It was a long shot but resulted in a, pleasing to Robert, loud single slosh as it made water contact. Brian picked up two stones and fired them off in quick succession, one falling short and the other bouncing off a shoreline boulder and landing with a quiet plop in the shallow water lapping the lake's shoreline. "Still counts!" Brian laughed. Jonnie took his hands-off Joe's shoulder and fired a flatish stone off at a low angle, managing to make it skip once when contact with the water was made, then twice more before sinking. Jonnie rubbed his knuckles against where his lapel would have been, if he was wearing a jacket, in smug self-congratulation as the others tutted. They were burning off their awkwardness and waring emotions by shooting these off from the hip with every stone thrown. Joe smiled sadly realising he was certainly going to physically be more than a stone throw's away from these rock-solid friends very soon.

All three of them knew, as Joe did, that the next four weeks would be intense. They had drifted away a lot since they were cycle-riding teenagers and pub-crawling older lads. Work and their own families left little playtime but they still kept in touch, meeting up now and again. Joe going to the other side of the world would make meeting up in person out there a once-in-a-lifetime event. Phone calls, emails and even the still-used air mail they all knew would keep a contact still alive. It would not be the same, though.

However, one thing they all had learned over the years was that they had to accept that life was full of change as everyone charged through it. Each person's life was led very differently and not always from the front. Some of us have bayonets fixed ready for anything. Some of us seem to always have lots of ammunition to keep reloading and firing off again. Others would constantly grab for the new and shiny that sometimes backfired, others preferring the reliability of tried and tested. As they messed about like the big kids they always were, they relaxed a little, then a lot. They laughed, cheered and slagged off poor shots, such a simple game entertaining them. As they picked and chucked, it allowed time for Joe's news to sink in. As they relaxed, they were becoming more happy for him and his family's adventure, rather than sad for their loss of them all from their lives.

Joe picked up a stone but plonked his backside down onto the gravelly grass, sharp stone edges only slightly annoying him. He twirled it delicately in his right-hand fingers and thumb, closely inspecting it like he was expecting it to hatch. It was flat and squarish, with chipped off top corners left and right, and a big chunk out of the bottom centre. He could not decide if it was quartz or not, but there was a big, blue-ish blob of it right in the central heart of the stone. There were half a dozen small, erratic lines running across the surface spirally from the central quartz. He ignored the stone splashes and 'oh that was close!' and 'oh that was lucky!' calls of the others. As he followed the lines, he imagined the six county borders, noticing another smaller blob of quartz on the right-hand side, at the end of a triangular gouge. With a loud sigh he rose. He gripped his stone map firmly, swung his arm back and launched it into flight. It flew and flew for ages, landing far into the lake. It did not, however, hit water but connected instead with a boulder poking out above the surface like a whale breaking the surface to breathe. Joe's map stone shattered into pieces, strafing the surrounding area around the elongated, rounded boulder. It both shocked and surprised Joe how he felt about that. There was that feeling when you work and wait for ages to reach a point and when you do, it feels more alien than you expect it to be.

As Brian shouted, "Impressive!" over at him, Joe bent down to pick up another stone to throw. Joe still was going for the single shot, rather than Jonnie, after Joe's display, grabbing multiple small stones and machine gunning the shoreline and water at random with fine gravel. Joe loudly snorted with a chortle. The stone he had picked up was boomerang shaped. He wondered briefly if this would come back if he threw it. He laughed at the silliness of this thought but it still lingered. He hesitated longer than he thought he would, before thinking about firing it off up into the sun. He stopped, with his stone loaded arm outstretched. Bringing it close to his face, he displayed it in the flat of his palm. Nodding contentedly, he placed it in his jacket pocket. That was a keeper, just like the three fully grown men beside him behaving like the happy youngsters they always would be in Joe's eyes and memories.

Lundy

Joe always thought that surely it was always better to go up. Up was seen as a good thing. People saying, usually with jealousy or genuine respect, that so and so was 'getting up in the world' was recognition of that person doing well for themselves. Rising up through the ranks was likewise seen as a good thing, both inside and outside defence forces. Such promotions were due to either recognition of the individual's abilities, hard work and courage. Alternatively, there were the person's family connections and, of course, wealth, which may or may not have needed any of these additional admirable factors? The only time when up was not good, that he could think of, was when it involved travelling a brown, smelly river and the lack of an essential piece of boating equipment. So, when he thought about it, going down in history seemed in a way contradictory. Yet, many people aspired to do this too. There were also many who unintentionally ended up going down like this, not always for the right reasons.

It was a uniquely stunning city. It was neither big in area, nor, with only just over one hundred thousand residents, population. It sat atop a hill, up above the expanding sprawl of housing and streets that webbed out from this dense centre. Geographically it was above its immediate surroundings, but socially and economically there were depths of poverty that Joe had seen in this city like nowhere else. It was the legacy of a city even harder hit than Belfast with bombs, bullets and bitterness. He had seen the derelict houses, those living on the streets, the lack of investment in lots of other cities, big and small. Here, however, his sixth sense tingled with sadness and sympathy, in response to what his other senses soaked up, when he had moved through the dejected back streets and rundown council estates.

Things were changing, though, and quickly. Joe had seen the transformation in his infrequent visits. This remained such an awesome place and the locals were working hard to bring in business and tourism. Although living only an hour down the road from it, Joe and his family were here today as local tourists for the first time. They were with a group of English, French, a couple from the United States and a few other locals from both sides of the border. It lifted Joe's spirits as he knew this group would visit the quirky local shops, have a meal and enjoy a drink, or maybe three, bringing in a bit of much needed revenue to the city.

This was a city that had sprawled beyond its ancient physical wall. What had happened at these walls centuries ago had, Joe realised and regretted, created a siege mentality causing other bitter barriers to be emulated and erected in minds, bodies and spirits. Some of these were built in as hard as the black stone and brick. As they walked his family were starting to appreciate that too. Joe loved history. His family would have usually used a different verb, with 'like' being the best Joe usually achieved. There were exceptions and this was one of them. Of thirty other walled cities on the island of Ireland, this is the only one to have complete walls. More evidence, if any was needed, of a warring past. The chatty, funny tour guide had said they were a mile long, striding along the top of them, stopping often to allow time for admiring the stunning views across the Foyle. Joe and Dee followed his lead and looked in awe, in between making sure neither of their kids got their heads stuck in the mouth of a cannon. They were old enough to know not to but, as every parent knows, you never know.

As the guide continued with his easy-to-listen-to history telling, it was the Siege that the city was most famous for, long, long before the so-called Troubles. The Siege had some big personalities involved and it was part of a wider European conflict that changed the course of history. As always happens in history, individuals stand out. One man did make the hard decision to make a stand back then, to do what he could and thought was the right thing. Then decided it was not going to work, making reverse decisions and taking actions that he believed were the best for the future. From wanting to fight, he changed to surrender mode. There was resistance to this, resulting in ousting him from his leadership position. This provoked the much overused 'no surrender' which lived on and on in Ulster's history since for good and ill.

Joe reflected that happens all the time and we all change our minds based on changing circumstances. The thing was, this man was not just making personal decisions, the fate of a city and its people hung on the outcome of this one man's mental debates. He was not hung in real life for his alleged crimes, although in the three hundred years plus since it happened, he has been hung in effigy countless times. Dressed-up likenesses in straw and paper are burned, one of a selection of traditional punishment for traitors, real or only accused.

"Was Lundy really a traitor or just trying to do the right thing and what was best for the people of Derry/Londonderry?" the guide asked rather rhetorically. Joe thought maybe near the, unknown to those behind the walls, end of the siege they might have been having a bit of a rethink about Lundy, their former leader. As they were chewing on a rat's leg as their only meal of the day; as they listened to the screams and groans of those slowly dying of starvation and blood poisoning from battle wounds; they would, no doubt, have been having second and third and more thoughts, on a daily basis. Surrender might have not been so bad? Relief eventually came and the siege was lifted before those thoughts were put into action.

Joe's mood dropped as he made this historical situation more personal and current. Was Joe that leader who was a traitor? The fact was that he had felt he had done what he could to make a life here, only to discover that things had not worked out the way he had hoped. Joe had made decisions and taken actions to change things and make things better in the future. Not just for him, but for his family too. The difference between Joe and Robert Lundy was that Joe's followers, his ever-loyal wife Dee and their two understanding daughters also believed they were doing the right thing. Joe often felt like he was a traitor to his homeland as they made their preparations to emigrate. But maybe it was his homeland that had betrayed him?

Loyalty was and remained a family and personal trait Joe continued to be loyal to. Betrayal of such loyalty was more than just treacherous, it was unacceptable. Inside the family circle anything and everything could and would be discussed, emotions allowed to run free. Sometimes too free at times! Outside the family, loyalty to what had been said within the confines of the family had to be kept there. As Joe pondered on this, he saw clearly the analogy of Derry's city walls being just like that, keeping what was inside, and what was beyond the walls out there. Family loyalty was not just something requiring protection but was and is in itself protective of the family Joe decided. He realised Dee was smiling at him. She cheekily shook her head, knowing he was deep in his thoughts. She ran over to Ava as she stood closely peering into one of the mouths of the cannons. She was protecting her own family in her own way, constantly working on the basis that prevention is better than cure. This meant she had a lot of work to do. As he watched, he smartly paced over to distract their daughters; it gave him yet another boost to the love he continued to have for them. It was this that ensured his loyalty to doing the very best he could for them all, and not just himself.

That was where he was continuing to have his Lundy dilemma. Although never out of work, he had tried and failed to succeed at several jobs, moving on to the next one in hopeful expectation. More money seemed to make no difference, any extra disappearing into the extra bills. Other job titles made absolutely no difference; Joe's still undecided career path not driven by these badges. However, there was no feeling of treachery at Joe having left workplaces for others. That was just the way things went. A few previous jobs he had resentment towards for various reasons, but the fact they had let him down, as well as vice versa possibly, still did not make Joe feel treachery in any shape of form had been involved.

He, Dee and even his young daughters to an extent, felt absolutely no sense of betrayal to the government institutions of Northern Ireland at planning to leave. If anything, it was in completely the opposite direction. Joe's family were not alone with many, many local people feeling they had been and continued to be the sufferers of duplicity in such a still split society. Joe nodded to himself firmly as he walked, certain that he felt no need for further justification that the warped politics, economics and society that the governments seemed unable to resolve were justification enough for him to take his family away.

He would miss the land and its history too; this factored into his thoughts. However, these were part of his past, not his future. Today's visit to scale these city walls, the fields he had ran through, the highest mountains he had not mourned climbing – all of these discoveries of everything the land of his birth had to offer left him still not having found what he was looking for. Some of these experiences had profoundly influenced him, some changing him in opinions and viewpoints, but none of these places of his past were enough to be part of his future. So, Joe had no perfidy about leaving behind the amazing histories and cultural expressions of his wished to be former homeland.

It was, as with everything, family that was where he felt his implied, at times feeling very real, treachery rested. It was not Dee or his daughters or their new baby on the way. They were agreed and certain they were doing the right thing for them by heading to what was originally known as Van Diemen's Land. Both Joe and Dee wanted to hold their family now and, in the future, together until the hour had come around and they were gone. No, they were determined that, no matter what the rattle and hum, they were going for a better life. It was his widowed mother, his brother, his sister, the nieces and nephews he had just started to get to know that tugged at Joe's heart. These feelings blackened it too, not just from sadness but guilt. All of them had stressed their support for what they were doing, confessing they would miss them of course, but totally agreeing with all their reasons to seek a new life. The opportunities were still limited in Northern Ireland/North of Ireland, terrorism still continued, hardened hearts and bitterness still prevailed. Despite this Joe still felt he was betraying loved-ones, especially his ma. They had reared him, advised him, shaped him and made him the boy, youth and man he now was. Joe sighed deeply as that too was now all in the past. Once they were on that plane, they would leave everything behind, the good and the bad. His ma, siblings, their kids and their partners, were the good. Despite the heavy burden this placed on Joe's conscience, it was still rationally outweighed by everything else that was bad. After these minutes of repeating the same circling arguments, Joe felt enlightened. Finally, he had put to bed that he was not a traitor to either his country, his people or his family. He could sleep easier now that inner debate would not bate him any longer.

Joe actually laughed out loud in relief. He was in many ways like Lundy, falsely being labelled, mostly by himself, as a traitor. The truth was far more than that. Like Lundy, he was doing the very best he could for those he cared about. Joe sniggered as he was unable to picture himself being burned in effigy. He and his family were just four people of thousands over past decades, millions over the centuries that had left for promised lands when the only promises at home were broken ones.

Gathering his thoughts, which took longer than he thought, Joe looked around. The group had moved further ahead, He half jogged to catch up. Dee hearing his boots on the cobbles, turned and moved towards him. As he neared, she asked, "And where did you wander off to in your head?"

He only smiled and replied rather cryptically, "A treacherous place, but we will be leaving it soon." They walked along hand in hand, thinking Ava and Bella were only joking about having their heads stuck in railings but not entirely sure. Ava especially was acting very convincingly, Bella playing a superb supporting role. Then their giggles betrayed them as they squeezed and squirmed their heads out. Joe was glad they had kept their head, just as he had kept his with his traitor conundrum he had now beaten.

Long-term

This was it! This was the necessary and long-awaited sitting around the table, to tell all four-and-a-bit family members that they were going. They were actually going! There had been months and months of planning gone into this. There had been a lot of job applications and, almost the same number of rejections. Except for this one! It had been a roller-coaster ride of emotions causing the towel to be held aloft several times, sometimes amid tears and tantrums, but it was never thrown in and perseverance persevered. Now! Now it had become a reality. That long, long awaited final major piece could now be slotted into place and the green light would flash. With one email in the wee hours of the morning this Average family's life was turned upside down quite literally. The words 'we would be delighted to offer you...' from the Canberra company meant Joe and his family were all going to the other end of the world. This meant the start a new, far-from-average, life.

As Joe sat alone at the kitchen table waiting on the others, his body had gone hyper. Maybe it was from having only eight and a half minutes of sleep since he read that e-mail in the wee hours. How could he have slept anyway! This was a world away he and Dee had only dreamt about so far. There had been nightmarish forms after forms to be completed that put none of them in good form. Details that required serious attic paperwork rummaging had been needed. All of their previous addresses were asked for, which was expected but still tedious. Recalling previous houses and their postcodes, especially for their student and rented digs, had required some major brain and ancient filing systems digging. The visa bill for their visas they had credited themselves for being able to pay off surprisingly quickly. Despite stretching their financial flexibility, they were able to bounce back, eventually after some dark worries, into the black a few months afterwards. Both of them had been slightly apprehensive regarding the politely requested, but nonetheless privacy invasion, of intimate information about Joe and Dees' relationship. They had to divulge about how they met and how long they had been together.

Even if previous relationships had ended in divorce or children. Although the 'no' box was ticked for these, Joe's joking about had still caused a slightly strained atmosphere between them, as old flames burned brightly again briefly in their thoughts. Security checks had left them both feeling insecure. Joe's taking a lot longer to play out than Dee's meant he felt singled out. His relief at eventually having no criminal record was a hit greater than hers. Both of them had a new release after that number one on their emigration worry list. The supporting letters from friends and family had churned up some serious emotions too. No amount of buttering up, explaining the purpose of these to those they had selected to ask, helped spread the separation pain this emotive knife inflicted. Every time Joe reread these written from the heart letters, his heart swole to breaking point.

He had gone to bed eventually at two thirty a.m., but just lay there rocking and rolling in mind and body, failing to contain his excitement and additional worries. He felt he could no longer stay fidgeting in bed disturbing Dee. She had grunted and groaned in her sleep every time he moved. Joe was sure that was his beloved wife telling him off in her dreams. He had debated wakening her up, but she was so sound asleep. So, he had risen from bed ever so carefully at around four a.m. Since then, he had sat in turn at the computer, on the sofa, on a kitchen chair, constantly restless and wanting to be on the move. He had been slurping more coffee, which he certainly did not need to stimulate or keep him awake. His own body was proving adrenaline was a much more powerful analeptic than caffeine ever would be. Certainly in the gallons he was creating and consuming.

With only an hour or two until dawn anyway, he thought it was better to wait. Waiting only made it harder to contain the news. His continual rehearsing of how and what he was going to say to them did not kill time any easier. Rummaging through the file marked 'New Life' on the computer again and again did not provide any more hope for structure or content to the speech to his family he was preparing. In the end, all he needed to tell them was he had got a job in Australia which meant they could go. As simple, yet so complex, as that!

No doubt she would tell him off for not letting her know as soon as he did. Dee was certainly not a morning person, even when her alarm went at seven a.m.! He needed to sort his own head out first before he spoke to Dee, his daughters and bump. It had taken some time to achieve. Only weeks and months, thankfully, instead of years, for this huge change to move from fantasy, to 'let's try', to possibility. And now? Now, with that one email it was real! It still seemed like he was in a dreamlike state as he went silently on walkabout from room to room, boomeranging back and forth. He needed to calm down before he told them. It was five a.m., and he could wait no longer. He had to tell them.

He deliberately made noise going up the stairs, treading for an extended period on that one squeaky stair that everyone has in their house. It was an attempt to break them out of their sleep gently but it made no difference. No change in breathing or signs of movement could he hear. He coughed a little as he reached the top step, but this tactic caused no bedclothes rustling or stirring either. He flicked on the landing light. Still nothing. Standing there for a moment to plan, he decided getting Dee up first would be best. Sucking up as much bravado as possible he entered their bedroom and gently whispered her name close to her ear. He ever so gently rocked her uncovered shoulder. She lay there completely zonked out. Repeating her name a little louder, rocking her shoulder a little harder still had no effect. It was almost as if his voice was a lullaby and his generated movement rocking her to sleep rather than achieving the desired complete opposite. After raising his voice a few more decibels, he rocked her shoulder so consistently he started to worry if he would make her sea-sick, but carried on. Changing tack, he went for several sharp shouts of, "Dee! Dee! Wake up, Dee! I've something to tell you!" Still no response. Although he could hear her steady breathing, he actually started to wonder if she had gone into hedgehog hibernation mode. Looking at her frizzed hair strewn across the pillow made that theory even more possible.

Frustrated, he scanned around the darkened room looking for more drastic options. With a guilty grin, he flicked on his bedside lamp. Dee snorted and shuffled, groaning loudly and muttering, "Wha! Off! Turn off!" She muttered something that could have been one of several swearword options, or maybe all of them jumbled together. She pulled the duvet over her head. Joe grabbed it and gently pulled it back down to uncover a one-eyed death stare.

"Sorry, Dee, but it is really important. Please get up. I am going to wake the girls now." She flicked the duvet back over her face. Joe stepped back a little annoyed, before stepping forward and flicking her bedside light on.

There was a repeat performance of 'Wha-! Off! Turn it off!' However, this time she sat up in bed and Joe knew he had won. Quickly, he darted out of their room to escape any potential feedback on his sleep awakening performance.

The same routine of an increasingly louder volume whisper of 'Bella!' accompanied by shoulder rocking incessantly proved a lot more successful and faster. Bella sat up in bed after enduring only a few seconds of disturbance. Rubbing eyes, she stuck out her tongue to wet her dry lips, her eyelids still drooped. "Great! You're awake. Come on downstairs. I have something important I really need to tell you." Joe spoke excitedly, clapping his hands together, interpreting her bleary 'huh' as 'yes, Daddy. I'm awake and I will come downstairs now!' Joe left her room and almost barged into Ava's. Tripping over a pile of clothes, then a couple of pairs of trainers, followed by a tennis racket, all left just at the doorway, catapulted him across her room into the cluttered desk beside her bed. Books and all sorts clattered off it as Joe swore loudly at the pain the pointed corner inflicted on his left kneecap. Ava sat up, her eyes wide and alert in the semi-darkness. In pain, Joe lost his politeness. Feverishly rubbing his kneecap, he said, through gritted teeth, "Right, AVA. Downstairs. I have something I need to tell you." As he left the room, unaware of Ava's bewildered stares, he shouted back, "It's really good news."

All that was at least fifteen minutes ago, he thought. He checked his watch, sitting on the kitchen chair, with all the lights on. It was in fact only five minutes. They were taking their time, he thought. He was about to go back upstairs when he heard footsteps moving across the bedroom floorboards. The toilet flushed, meaning at least two of them were up. He heard footsteps on the stairs, smiled broadly, straightened his back, clasped his hands on the table in front of him and waited. Both his daughters slouched through the kitchen door, their bare feet slapping on the tiles as they slumped into their seats at the table. Both instantly folded their arms on the table top and slumped their heads down on their improvised pillows. Joe reached over and poked Bella, who was closest, on the elbow. "Come on! Come on! I need to tell you. I need to tell you something really important."

She cocked her head to the side and mumbled, "Well, just tell us then!"

"I have to wait for all of us. I have to tell you all at the same time," Joe replied with agitation.

"You could do it at breakfast!" Ava mumbled, not even lifting her head.

"It can't wait until then," Joe rebuked her. "Where is your mother?" he added.

The girls returned to their slumped head on arms position and, in perfect harmony, yelled, "Mum!"

Joe heard a muffled and distant 'Wha-?' from upstairs, followed by, 'Lights! Off! Turn off!' This did not fill him with optimism. This changed as he heard their bedroom door creak and her shuffling footsteps on the landing. One slow thud at a time signalled Dee was coming downstairs. Slowly, very slowly. It took an age, Joe almost bouncing on his seat, but eventually Dee materialised, in body, anyway, at the kitchen door.

"Wha time's it?" she mumbled.

"Five thirty but that doesn't matter. Sit down. Sit down please!" he replied with urgency she did not sense.

She only responded by stopping exactly where she was, leaning against the doorframe, repeating, "Half five? Half five in the morning? Wha the…"

Joe interrupted her before she finished her last question with, "Please! Please sit down. I need to tell you all." Dee would have given him a dagger stare and a sharp-tongued comment, but she was too tired to see the point of doing that. So, she meandered over and flopped slowly into her seat at the other end of the table from Joe, leaving enough space for bump. Sitting as upright as her not-fully-functioning, sleep-demanding body would allow, she placed her hands on the tabletop and stared at him expectantly.

"Are you all awake enough to hear me?" Joe asked optimistically. His daughters groaned something resembling 'yes!' from amongst their head and hair-covered forearms. Dee's head wavered a little sideways as she nodded. Or at least Joe thought that was her nodding and not her head just making a complete circular movement.

"I… got… the… job… in… Australia!" he slowly uttered to add what he hoped was dramatic effect. It may not have been dramatic but it did have an effect. He repeated it again at his normal speech speed this time. Both his daughters raised their heads together.

Bella asked, "Does that mean…?"

"Yes! Yes, it does!" Joe almost squealed at her with happiness.

Ava blinked hard before she too asked, "That means…"

"Yes! Yes, it does!" Joe repeated, more enthusiastically.

"The Canberra company one…?" Dee asked, before adding, "The really good paying one that you really wanted?"

"Yes! And Yes!" Joe answered his face lighting up like a one hundred-watt bulb.

Dee added, "That means…"

"Yes! Yes, it does!" Joe repeated yet again, almost at bursting point.

The silence was deafening. Joe just looked from brightening awake face to brightening awake face. As he beamed smiles, he could not have shone more light on his sleepy family. "When did you find out?" Dee asked after swallowing hard to wet her dry throat.

"At two thirty this morning by email." Joe answered.

"Why did you not wake me?" Dee asked with a hint of cold scold. "It was too early, I thought!" Joe answered honestly.

"And five thirty a.m. isn't!" Ava and Bella uttered sarcastically in unison.

As the news sank in through the dissolving layers of sleepiness, all three of them suddenly became alert. Dee was speechless and motionless but he could tell from her face she was ecstatic. Bella and Ava sat up straight, looked over at each other with fear and happiness combining on their faces. Together they rose from their seats, and each was embraced by one of their da's outstretched arms. He pulled them close and they kissed him on each cheek. "Well done, Daddy!" they both said in turn. "That's brilliant!" Then ominous fear seemed to creep over them. They both stepped back slightly, their daddy's arms still holding them around their waists. Nervously, Bella began to stutter out, "When… When do we go?"

"In a month or two's time!" Joe replied. "I will need to work my notice and it will take a week or two to sort all the final paperwork out. So, by the time you finish school for the summer, we will be on our way!"

"Wow!" was all Bella could say. Ava went very quiet, and a little pale. "So, by the end of term we will be going to Australia!" Ava spoke gingerly through the blonde hair draping her face like curtains.

"Yup!" Joe said extremely cheerily, jutting his jaw to add a bit of extra oomph, as if any more oomph of any sort was needed for this life changing meeting.

"It's going to be a very long-term!" was all Bella muttered, leaving Joe unsure if that was in a good way or not.

Last

It was a nice restaurant. Not a really nice restaurant where Joe would feel his table manners and etiquette simultaneously and constantly under a spotlight and microscope. Such pricey places were like tiger compounds at the zoo to Joe, where he always felt so removed from his more natural jungle habitat of cafes and pub meals. This eatery, where they had not been before, was a step up from those, meaning Joe felt only a little more apprehensive than usual. He scanned the menu again, sniggering again that he still would not be ordering spaghetti bolognaise. That was a meal he believed should consistently be consigned to the dinner table at home, where the slurping and splattering had only a family audience. Joe remembered watching in absolute awe, on a previous restaurant visit, a couple deftly using the spoon and fork combination to swirl pasta and tomatoey mince from plate to mouth effortlessly. Proficient chopstick use likewise made him admire and salute the users, his own attempts with such thin sticks he could not have made a bigger hash of it he had been wearing boxing gloves.

He sipped his beer and looked a little longingly towards the small bar, stuck in the corner to maximise the floor area for dining tables. Dee was still there, having been well and truly cornered, despite her edging away and protests, by a pincer movement from a former work colleague on her way back from the ladies'. He caught Dee's eye and she smiled awkwardly, mouthing two minutes as she discreetly raised two fingers, palm outwards, behind the back of the woman totally immersed in talking one-way to, or rather at, her. It was Bronagh who both Joe and Dee had seen as soon as they had walked in and had, with guilty relief, managed to stealthily reach their table without her having seen them. Despite some elaborate successful manoeuvring, using waiters and pillars for cover, on the outward journey to the toilets, Dee had been left exposed behind a slow-moving elderly couple when returning. Bronagh had spotted her, jumped up from her seat and pounced with a long hug to capture her prey. Joe had seen Dee's eyes pray when that happened, but had kept his head down not wishing to share in the experience and silently blasphemed. His mind was forced to accept this hoped to have been avoided delay, although his now rumbling stomach was voicing its disapproval.

As with many pre-planned special events, fate, destiny, divine will or whatever seem to have a knack of chucking a few spanners in. Joe had even experienced entire turbulent toolboxes causing big ados at big dos. Bronagh's presence now was just such a tool which, although not wrecking the works, was not exactly repairing them either. Joe froze as he saw Dee nod over to him. Bronagh turned, smiled and waved, her eyes gleaming at another target to hunt down. Joe felt himself raisin in this current situation as she waved over, meekly moving his hand in response. After a few moments he realised neither Dee nor Bronagh, wanted and unwanted respectively, were moving towards him. He dared to hope he had been saved by Dee's firmly grabbing Bronagh's upper arm and rapidly mouthing 'No! No!' to her, possibly guessing at lip reading Dee saying 'don't want to hold you back from your meal.' Joe's only qualification in lip reading was watching telly on mute without subtitles. So, Dee could have been saying 'Donna can't get told to sack some fur seal' or anything at all, really. Though he could not hear, he was delighted with this result, as they stood where they were, returning to their previous Bronagh talking and Dee listening.

This was Joe and Dee's last meal out in Northern Ireland/North of Ireland. In five days' time, they both, with their daughters and a few-months-away family addition, would be on a plane for Australia. It was to be a special night, just the two of them. He sniggered guiltily at his bitchy thought that Bronagh could be considered as reason enough to jet off to the other side of the world to avoid her! His regret at being so nasty increased and he tried to think of nice things about Bronagh. He had only met her a few times, at Dee's work dos and other places. Those longer-than-wanted interactions had been far more than enough to assess her character, therefore supposedly justifying his assassination of it. He persevered as he waited, and scared himself a little that he could not think of anything praise-worthy about Bronagh at all! *Surely, she could not be that bad*, he thought, before he deliberately stuck another thought into his head as he shook it in disbelief.

Goodbyes was what he focused on. Such a big topic he felt deserved a large slug of his beer, so he imbibed that resolution. His glass was half empty, which he hoped was not prophetic. He glanced around hoping a waiter or waitress would pass by soon to order another pint to remove any potential ill omens. None were anywhere near his table, something he hoped was not in itself a bad sign. Another beer was required, whether he was a seer or not, he assured himself. It was a celebration, after all! He and his family had done the rounds in the past two weeks, telling those close friends and extended family the same looping Australia story. Joe joked they should have just made a recording and played it when they visited. It was mostly the same follow-up questions that were asked each time, to which they gave, almost word for word, similar answers. They only told those that they wanted to tell. They had carefully selected their targets, so that the news would spread to the others they felt should know but had neither the time, or in some cases the inclination, to inform of their big life change in person.

As he sipped from his glass again, he scanned with a furrowed brow over at Dee again. She gave him the same two-minute mouthing. This was followed by the same behind back two-minute finger gesture, which then briefly morphed into a stabbing motion! Her face was twice as scunnered as it had been those two, or was it ten, minutes previous. Realising she would be a while yet, he tried to think how best to describe those emigration visits they had made so far. There were still a couple more they would have liked to have done, but were not what they considered essential and they were out of time anyway. Obviously, they had informed their widowed mothers first. This was not only purely out of respect for family hierarchies and seniority, but was a way of clearing the largest emotional hurdle first. Joe told his ma individually, face to face, Dee hers individually by phone, that lasted way longer than they would have expected.

Both Joe and Dee took a considerable amount of time to warm up before tackling their respective jumps. Once they felt they were ready, they had lined themselves up for a long run-up. Both of them had a couple of false starts. Dee had lifted the phone to ring her mum but had pressed the red button rather than the last phone number digit on three occasions. Then when she had gone through the entire process and achieved a ringing at the end of the line. Dee's heart had been palpitating in time to the multiple dial tones before she had to hang up! Her mum had, unbeknown to her, very irresponsibly and inconveniently gone out! Dee had sworn rather loudly immediately afterwards, angry at having used up so much energy to climb this emotional mountain, only to have had to scale back down it again. When Dee's mum picked up the missed call two hours later, Dee had answered without checking the caller number. Although stunned when she answered, this helped take a lot of the drama out of the situation. It meant Dee did not need to act or gather her courage. Instead, she just flung herself straight into the lead role and performed her very well-rehearsed lines almost word perfect. Although her mum knew their plans, it was still a very long, tearful with joy and sadness, conversation worthy of an Oscar for Dee if it had been acted instead of so heart wrenchingly real.

Joe had fared little better. He could not have helped feeling a little envious of Dee being able to pass on such information by phone. That was an easier option, he had thought, which took some of the sting out of the nettle they were both grasping. When, midst his frustration he had mentioned it, Dee had strongly assured him that it was in fact harder by phone than face-to- face. "At least you will be able to hug your ma and hold her hand!" she had sharply explained, apologising to him afterwards for her snappiness. He had totally understood and held no malice, as he very rarely did with her. However, the realised guilt that induced in him had caused a labour of guilt. This, in turn, had birthed all sorts of second and third thoughts, not about emigrating, but about how he should have approached this necessary task. He had even thought about writing a letter to his ma, but knew that was far too cowardly. He had stirred himself mentally so much he could have made meringues with the results.

There was no sugar in that recipe, however, to make this medicine sweeter for his ma to swallow, apart from the sugar-coated better life Australia promised. He had worried himself into a mental lather before having that conversation, knowing there was no way he could soft soap his ma. He had kept remembering her reactions when he went over to England those many years ago. He worried about her high emotions back when he took that ferry. If these were anything to go by, they would be multiplied by the thousands of extra miles he was travelling this time. AND it was not just him going this time. The fact he was taking Dee and two and a growing bit of her grandkids with him too was leaving an even bigger hole in his ma's life to fill! This troubled him greatly, as it had Dee telling her mum in England.

The mental pain trauma Joe created meant that the first time he went to tell his ma, he was reduced to feeling like he was eight years old again, having put the knee out of his school trousers falling off his, not designed for stunt riding, bike. Again! Feeling so childlike he had driven right past

362

her house and parked up a mile or two away to compose himself. There he had sat in a field gateway, frustratedly berating himself at such a zero-rated performance that only a chicken would have been proud of. Breathing hard, he had inflated his courage using the facts that she already knew it was going to happen at some stage. That stage was now set, but he had feared his ma was either going be blown away by the news or blown up by such a blow he was about to deliver. Like Dee, Joe felt, despite his rehearsals, ill-prepared for that lead role that felt as heavy as lead. He had known before it happened it would not be a star performance and so, not surprisingly, it proved to be. Shades were not needed as his star had not shone brightly.

He sunk deep into reminiscing that conversation with her. She had been upset, but, to his relief, not as much as he had thought. He had realised he actually would have been upset if she had not been. She had been preparing herself for this conversation, she confessed, which eased and guilted Joe equally. In the end it was easier than what he had ballooned it up to be, probably more to do with his own coping with this situation than his ma. He drove away from his former home, tearful with pride at the inner strength his ma had shown she had, hoping he had inherited some of it. Hoping he had inherited a lot of it, in fact, as he was going to need it for the big Average Australian adventure ahead.

Dee sat down in front of him suddenly. It awoke him from the self-imposed suspended animation he had created without any cartoon characters or jokes. She sighed loudly and snorted out a tirade. "That woman's good a reason to get to the other side of the world as any! I literally had to tell her to 'fuck off' in the end, as my patience just snapped! Then she started a full-blown argument. Did you not hear it?" Joe just shook his head robotically, having not registered raised voices outside of the depths of his thoughts where he had climbed down into. "I cut her short and let her stomp away off to her table. I did not give her our Australian address. Not that I would have! I doubt she will be sending us a Christmas card, anyway!" She laughed sarcastically.

"Okay! I'm here now. This is our special night. Our last night out in this land. It's exciting, isn't it?" Joe robotically nodded his head and muttered agreement. Caringly, she asked, "What's up with you?" before teasingly adding, "Have you missed me so much while I was over there with that Bronagh..." She stopped speaking, probably unable to describe the complexity and extent of Bronagh's annoyance in a single insulting name. Her inability said lots, leaving the long-standing question of why Dee had not told Bronagh to 'f off' a lot sooner now answered. Joe added another item to the, now redundant, 'Reasons for Emigrating' list, and ticked that box, as it had equipped Dee with that additional courage and opportunity.

"I was just thinking..." Joe began.

"That's not like you!" Dee interrupted, poking fun at it, but with a sarcastic sharp point that dug into him.

He grimaced mockingly in response before continuing. "I was just thinking how to describe telling people we were emigrating. I know it was really hard telling our mas especially. It was not so bad with our brothers and my sister, but hard with our mates. Don't know about you, but I actually found it joyful telling my boss?" Dee nodded enthusiastically to agree with that. "But all the other friends and neighbours... How did you feel about that?"

"Relieved!" was all Dee said, sipping from her now long flat, sparkling water. Joe paused and threw a question at her with his eyes. Dee shrugged her shoulders and repeated, "Relieved!" Joe probed again with the eyes under his raised eyebrows. "Well – it would have been far worse if all these people knew we were planning to do it and it had all fell to an arse. It feels good to have accomplished what we set out to do. I would have felt a bit embarrassed if we had gone to all this effort and it had not happened. Wouldn't you have?"

"Yeah! Sure, I would. And yeah! Relieved is the best way to describe telling people. Especially my mates! They genuinely believed it would not happen for us. Would you believe that? I know I have not the best track record in... Anyway. It does feel good! It feels like a weight has been lifted and we are lighter somehow. That will make it a lot easier to travel, with all that baggage left behind." He went quiet thinking his ma, family and mates were not baggage on his back but ingrained inside him. They would always be carried with him in his heart and head. Dee saw his eyes sadden and instinctively knew where his erratic thoughts had gone. Hers were in that same place.

The waiter arrived, asking politely for their order. His accent was obviously put on, mixing a strange blend of English/Northern Irish. "A pint of stout and a glass of sparkling white wine for a start, please," Joe began, sinking the last of the dregs of his now empty glass and actually excited for the new full one he was about to have.

"Which wine?" the waiter asked politely, directing his question to Dee with a smile.

"Australian, obviously!" she answered, exchanging a beaming smile which Joe reciprocated. It left the waiter bemused and unaware of the significance.

Nevertheless, he entered into the spirit of it by saying, in his now clearly original Australian accent, "Fair go, mate! You will be wrapping your laughing gear around those quick as I can!" Joe and Dee laughed loudly, taking it as yet another sign they were meant to go.